GOD'S KNOTTY LOG: *Selected Writings of John Bunyan*

A LIVING AGE BOOK

GOD'S KNOTTY LOG

Selected Writings of John Bunyan

Edited and Introduced by Henri A. Talon

He can take a rude and knotty log—such as John Bunyan was—and plane him away until He gets a smooth surface to write His will upon, yet is able to leave the hard knots below, for He was never one to spoil by Art the rough matter of Nature. God knows how to use a jack-plane. T. F. POWYS, *Kindness in a Corner*

Meridian Books
THE WORLD PUBLISHING COMPANY
Cleveland and New York

JOHN BUNYAN

John Bunyan was born in 1628 and became, after a rudimentary education, a tinker like his father. After three years in Cromwell's army, Bunyan returned to his village in Bedfordshire, married, resumed his occupation as a tinker, and was—under the influence of a Baptist minister—baptized in 1653. The restoration of the Stuarts brought about Bunyan's imprisonment for twelve years. During this period of his life he wrote *Grace Abounding,* his spiritual autobiography, and *The Pilgrim's Progress.* Among his other works are *The Heavenly Footman* and *The Holy War.* Bunyan died in 1688.

HENRI A. TALON

One of the most learned and sensitive of Bunyan scholars, Henri A. Talon is Professor of English Literature at the University of Dijon, France. He is the author of, among other works, *John Bunyan: The Man and His Works.*

CONSULTING EDITOR, LIVING AGE BOOKS:
MARVIN P. HALVERSON

AN ORIGINAL LIVING AGE BOOK (MERIDIAN)
Published by The World Publishing Company
2231 West 110 Street, Cleveland 2, Ohio
First printing April 1961

Library of Congress Catalog Card Number: 61-12373
Typography and design by Jack Reich
Printed in the United States of America

Contents

Editor's Introduction

1

By imposing limits, the relatively narrow frame of an introduction makes a choice necessary. I shall treat the details of Bunyan's life and his work as a whole as briefly as possible, referring readers who want more information to the books I recommend in the Bibliography. By way of presentation for *The Pilgrim's Progress* I aim at throwing light only on certain of its aspects, above all on one that seems to me to have received far too little attention: the relation between the hero and the road he follows, endowing the ground he covers with features and a meaning of its own. All the rest of this essay is directed more or less toward this end.

The Pilgrim's Progress is the work of a plain man who received most of his teaching from life itself. He was born in 1628 in a Bedfordshire village where he was given only a rudimentary education by ignorant and careless masters. At an early age he became a "brazier," or tinker, like his father, following a humble trade among humble people, and what is more, a trade that bore a very bad reputation. "If any would raise an army to extirpate knowledge and religion," has written an eminent Puritan, Richard Baxter, he can call on the "tinkers and sowgaters and crate-carriers and beggars and bargemen and all the rabble that cannot reade, nor ever use the Bible. . . ."[1] Certainly young John did not use the Bible yet. He was a lad who was fond of games and dancing, and was lavish with oaths: by no means a paragon of virtue! But everything leads us to believe that his description of himself as "the very ringleader of all the youth that kept me company in all manner of vice and ungodliness"[2] is a pious exaggeration. On the contrary, he early showed a strong religious sense.

At the age of sixteen, in 1644, he was taking an active part in the struggle between King and Parliament, but he had not joined the parliamentary army of his own free will: he had simply been called up and had had to obey. Three years in Cromwell's army could not but leave its mark on a man, especially a highly strung and intelligent young fellow like Bunyan. The whole of his intellectual and spiritual development shows the religious, and in a lesser measure, the political and social impression made on him by the time he spent with these officers and soldiers, men whose actions were ruled by their faith.

On his return home in 1647 he took up his old occupations again, and in the following year he married a young woman whose piety called him to deeper meditation and integrity of life. His marriage marks the beginning of a long period of intellectual and emotional tension, of storm and strife, like that through which thousands of other Puritans went. Bunyan's experience was not exceptional, but in his case it strengthened his genius and bore fruit.

Led by a remarkable Baptist minister, John Gifford, and encouraged by his example, and even more, by a conversation that showed him the road for his own soul, Bunyan was baptized in 1653 in the river at Bedford. Soon he was invited not only to speak to the brethren, but also to try to convert unbelievers as he himself had been converted. This he did with a passion sometimes amounting to violence which bore witness to his sincerity and to his effort to establish a genuine communication between one person and another. In these meetings and clashes and by these sermons and arguments he increased his natural fluency and hammered out his style, a style always swift and sinewy, tinged according to the demands of the moment with Biblical gravity or with familiarity: the vigorous style of a strong man who is master of his strength.

The restoration of the Stuarts marked for the Puritans the beginning of their trials. When Bunyan was arrested in 1660 he would have been able to buy his liberty by one concession. It would have been enough for him to have given up preaching his faith. But he might as well have been asked to give up his life, for life was to him a matter of ordering his existence by the demands of his faith. He refused this traffic. Tormented as he was at the thought of leaving his wife and children, he was still ready to risk the scaffold.

But the authorities were content to throw him into the county jail. He stayed there for twelve years. The prison is the symbol of his fourfold sense of his responsibilities: responsibility first toward God and toward himself; then responsibility toward his family, for, says a witness, he had no wish to pass his time "in a supine and careless manner or eat the bread of idleness." He provided for the needs of his family "by making many hundred grosse of long-tagged thread laces." [3] Finally there was his responsibility toward the brethren, for whom he wrote several works, including, among others, *Grace Abounding*, his spiritual autobiography, and *The Pilgrim's Progress*.

He was set free in 1672. As Baptist minister for Bedford, and as a now famous preacher, from 1672 until his death in 1688 Bunyan took upon himself a very heavy burden, which was only lightened a little by a fresh term of imprisonment in 1677.

2

A French painter (Rouault), regretting that in an early picture he had betrayed the influences under which he was working, provoked this reply from a friend (Degas): "Can a man be born alone?" For a long time Bunyan's assertion concerning his allegory, that "Manner and matter too was all mine own," [4] has been taken with a grain of salt. Bunyan had hardly been to school, but he had nonetheless read a great deal, and he needed no masters to teach him what school should teach, the art of listening. Oral tradition played a large part in his intellectual formation. And we did not even need the labor of James Blanton Wharey, Harold Golder, and other scholars to destroy the legend of Bunyan's spiritual virginity.[5] A little common sense was all that was needed. But, nonetheless, our gratitude to the detectives of literature is very deep. The borrowings have no interest in themselves: the interest lies in seeing what the writer does with them. Then we can better measure the part played by talent or genius.

There can be no question of showing here all the sources by which Bunyan was more or less unconsciously influenced—folk tales; "emblem" books; "books of characters"; homilies in dialogue form, an allegorical tradition that had been honored since the Middle Ages, and of which Bunyan is one of the last exponents; and above all, the Bible, whose influence was at once so profound and so subtle that no one has yet attempted to study it exhaustively. I only aim at recalling, in a swift and, perforce, incomplete sketch, what Bunyan's work owes to his environment. For more than half a century, from the 1570's until its brief triumph, English Puritanism, prevented by royal authority from "purifying" the Established Church, displayed its proselytizing zeal and its superb vitality in preaching and in the publication of innumerable sermons and treatises. For, as one Puritan has said, the Puritan "was a man of good spiritual appetite, and could not be contented with one meal a day. An afternoon sermon did relish as well to him as one in the morning." [6] Bunyan's debt to this religious literature is immense. The curious reader may quickly feel it, though of course he cannot measure it exactly, if among other historical studies he reads William Haller's *The Rise of Puritanism,* a book whose learning banishes pedantry but finds room for humor.

Bunyan doubtless had less occasion to read the learned Puritan theologians and churchmen than to hear lay preachers, who were often craftsmen like himself. They used the well-tried methods of oratory which they had inherited from the Elizabethan preachers, who themselves in their turn drew on a medieval tradition beyond the Reformation.[7]

All Bunyan's predecessors and contemporaries show a taste for the concrete, a close knowledge of the difficulties and torments of the life of the spirit, and a persuasive art addressed to both heart and imagination, embodying ideas in images borrowed now from the Bible, and now from the realities of daily life. Their sermons are woven from a poetic tissue of similes and metaphors; familiar proverbs and maxims add a tang of popular wisdom to their dialectic. These preachers often resort to portraits or anecdotes, and their practice of illuminating the moral with a tale led directly, more happily with Bunyan than with the others, to the unashamed pleasure of pointing the tale with a moral.[8] Their sternness did not prevent them from stopping to please "carnal minds," which it was their duty to enlighten as best they could. Bunyan openly avows: "I seek to please."

Finally, in their hands the ancient allegory that sees the life of the spirit as a journey[9] takes on a new lease of life and a new accent. The Puritan sees life as at once a pilgrimage and a perpetual battle. "His whole life hee accounted a warfare, wherein Christ was his Captaine, his armes, prayers and tears. The Crosse his Banner and his word *vincit qui patitur.*"[10]

These are the men and the books that molded Bunyan, these are the views of life and the rhetorical art that fed his genius. Mrs. Q. D. Leavis exaggerates just enough to emphasize one side of the truth when she writes: "It is not fantastic to assert that it was the Puritan culture as much as Bunyan that produced *The Pilgrim's Progress.*"[11]

3

But this culture could only produce a work of literature after it had formed a life. The direct source of *The Pilgrim's Progress* is Bunyan's own experience. The hero of the book is fashioned in his author's image. The spiritual development found in the autobiography, *Grace Abounding*, appears again in the allegory: but the growth of a conscience has become a pilgrimage, the inward action has taken a concrete form, and the invisible ways of the understanding have built a road and paths like those of seventeenth-century England. So the incidents in Christian's tale are symbols of his inward life, and the author's imagination was not so free that it could evade the dictates of a peremptory spiritual compulsion: the general movement and the particular incidents of the story as they are set before the reader serve an action that goes beyond them.

The story gives to the action a peopled setting, fields that are sometimes like those of Bedfordshire, hills that bring the

Chilterns vaguely to mind, houses that bear a certain resemblance to English country mansions, and travelers whose remarks, habits, and very prejudices belong to a particular epoch. The story gives the action a live historical reality.[12]

The action deals primarily with a man's relationship with God, but it also involves his relationship with other people. It may be said therefore that this already dates the action and that there is no need of the story to place it historically. The religious and moral outlook of the hero are enough to determine the historical period.

Is not Puritanism "a closed account," as Roger Sharrock puts it?[13] For my own part, I once wrote that Bunyan had lived in the theological age of Auguste Comte, and another Bunyan scholar, Maurice Hussey, has remarked that "Christian was not Everyman, but one of the Lord's chosen souls."[14]

Mr. Hussey wants by this to register a protest against those who read into the seventeenth century, ideas which belong to other periods of history and particularly to the present age, and who in so doing are guilty of an anachronistic way of thinking which modern scholarship was supposed to have rendered impossible.[15] I believe however that we may apply to Mr. Hussey's remark Leibniz's verdict on the sects: True in what they affirm, but false in what they deny.[16] Indeed, although the contemporary *ethos* is different from that of the seventeenth century, and although the Protestant faith is no longer confined within the bounds of a narrow Calvinism, yet, among the religious, moral, and metaphysical preoccupations of every man there is something independent of all dogmatism, and independent of the particular forms of this belief or that ethical system. A man is never wholly prisoner of his age. Everyman is seen in Christian as in every truthfully imagined character.

So the universal in the hero's inward life can still waken a response in us. And so we can in a large measure share in the action that is the inner life of the book, while we can only watch from a distance the incidents of the story, with its fights, its giants, and its monsters. The action transcends the story. Besides, many details of the book were only prompted by Bunyan's responsibilities as a minister, and bear witness to his homiletic talent alone; but the topography of the road and the chief incidents of the pilgrimage were dictated by his concern for psychological realism in the hero, the only kind of realism that is really important in this work. It even seems to me that formerly, following Sir Charles Firth, I laid too much stress on the realism of the background and of certain secondary characters.[17] A hundred or even a thousand realistic features are not enough to give the appearance of reality to the wonderful land where Christian knew suffering and joy.

It is a dreamland which rises from the very first sentence of the book. Mingled and blending into one another, we find, making a new and individual landscape, the worlds of the Bible and of the folk tales dear to the author,[18] pictures of his native country and of the Holy Land, all dominated by the features of that inner landscape[19] where his conversion takes place, where his salvation is decided, and where, in short, the lot for his whole life is cast. And in this sense we may say that the real country is just precisely this dreamland which Bunyan created with that energy of vision and of faith which is one of the characteristics of genius. Thus, as soon as we have understood the spiritual meaning of the setting, we no longer find, as Coleridge did,[20] that "the wide field full of dark mountains" where one of the false pilgrims is lost, is ridiculous. The mountain chain does not only represent a landscape, but brings to mind Jeremiah, and through him, the word of God: "Give glory to the Lord your God, before he cause darkness, and before your feet stumble upon the dark mountains."[21]

The country through which Christian travels is at once distant and immeasurably close. It transcends the pragmatic distinction between "here" and "there." The reader quickly sees that this is a country of the soul, where Biblical heroes and the Pilgrim may meet, and where past and present are fused.

The hero's meeting with God gains a remarkable concrete quality because the signs of God's will and of the conflict with Satan can be read in the very landscape. Christian's encounters with objects are no more accidental than his encounters with people. It is not by chance that he passes a mountain spitting fire, or comes "to a place somewhat ascending," surmounted with a cross. In the universe of the allegory the circumstantial *data* are not fortuitous, any more, for that matter, than, for Bunyan, they were in early life. He tells us, in *Grace Abounding*, that he fell in the river at Bedford but was not drowned, that he put his hand between the jaws of a snake without being bitten, and that he escaped death during the siege of a town because another soldier asked to take his place at the last minute. All these seemed to be signs from the Lord designed to waken his spirit (§§ 12-14). The world is a significant whole to which Bunyan, like his hero, responded with that intensity of all his being which characterized him.

Thus out of the symbolic vision natural to a Puritan there grew with Bunyan a literary vision,[22] just as the dreamer of *The Pilgrim's Progress* grew out of the dreams on which he had fed daily for years. Viewed in this light the dreamer no longer seems to be an artificial device or merely a figure of allegory.

God speaks throughout to Christian as he had spoken to Bunyan. *Grace Abounding* shows this constant interchange of words between God and the tinker, now in a wholly personal form—"A voice did suddenly dart from Heaven into my soul, which said, wilt thou leave thy sins and go to Heaven, or have thy sins and go to Hell?" (§ 22)—and now making Biblical words resound so loudly that he turned his head to find out where the voice was coming from (§ 93). The Puritan faith does not lead to mystical union but to speech with God.[23] It is no paradox to say that Bunyan did not so much *read* the Gospel as *hear* it from his Master's lips, and that by his fervor and imagination he realized that "contemporaneousness" with Christ that Kierkegaard deemed essential for a true Christian.

Part of himself lived always in the far depths of history. When doubts attacked him, his comforters rose immediately before him from the Bible, not like mighty shadows, but like living beings. For him, as for so many other Puritans, "the whole of Jewish history became," in Emerson's words, "flesh and blood." [24] And he saw the world through innumerable Biblical texts, like those marked for reference in the margin of *The Pilgrim's Progress,* texts that had entered so deeply into his life and his language that he came to quote them, as Louis L. Martz has remarked, "in his own way, binding [them] to his own particular style." [25] Language and vision are therefore naturally linked, since the style, and indeed the whole conception of the allegory, are determined by his vision and also by his way of judging the world. Christian's flight from the City of Destruction, his refusal to listen to the advice of Mr. Worldly Wiseman and other prosperous men, established solidly and comfortably in this world, his horror at the habits, customs, and profits of *Vanity Fair,* where men sell themselves like objects, the fight with Apollyon, the conjuring up of the Palace Beautiful and many other aspects and events of the story form a real Christian Utopia, seen in a Puritan light. In *The Pilgrim's Progress,* as in so many other allegories, we find, of course, a critical view of reality and, as Edwin Honig puts it, "a re-examination of the objective norms of experience in the light of human ideality. It includes the making of a new version of reality by means of an ideal which the reality of the fiction proves." [26] And this brings me back once more to the highly individual character of the Pilgrim's native land, where contradictory elements are found in harmony, a land ideal and concrete at once, a dreamland that is nevertheless real, a land whose horizons are often familiar, and yet one of which it can be said, in the words with which Bacon concludes his *New Atlantis,* "for we are here in God's bosom, a land unknown."

In the end, the Pilgrim must not therefore be considered apart from the country that is a projection of his inward landscape and the manifestation in space of his sense of values. Mountains, plains, and sloughs have a meaning at once psychological, religious, and axiological. We must look at the man.

What first marks him out is his single-mindedness. In him, feeling and thought unite to dictate an irrevocable decision: he will live according to the demands of his faith, as the first scene illustrates in dramatic fashion. Throughout his pilgrimage Christian continually recalls this moment in his past, a moment that he has singled out from all others, for he feels that he has never come nearer to realizing fullness of being than in that moment, when he was so ardently straining toward his goal. By leaving his family he puts into practice the most terrible of Christ's commands: "If any man come to me, and hate not his father, and mother, and wife, and children, and brethren, and sisters, yea, and his own life also, he cannot be my disciple." [27] And the cry he utters repeats the gaoler's question to Paul and Silas: "Sirs, what must I do to be saved?"

This traditional question and the man's appearance are alone enough to reveal the Puritan: he is "cloathed with raggs," rags which are the symbol of the worthlessness of our works, as they had been for Isaiah: "But we are all as an unclean thing, and all our righteousnesses are as filthy rags." [28]

To begin with, Bunyan does not give his character a name.[29] He is "a man" or "he." We do not know *who* he is but only *what* he is. For the seventeenth-century Puritan, he is a "brother" who has not yet received personal evidence of grace and election, and the load he carries on his back immediately recalls the words of the Psalmist: "For mine iniquities are gone over mine head; as an heavy burden they are too heavy for me." [30] For the modern reader the burden has a more general meaning. The stranger appears to be a tormented man. Everyman casts his shadow behind the silhouette of the Puritan. A universal symbol is superimposed upon the national symbol, the man "cloathed with raggs," who had been a familiar figure in Protestant England since the time of Wycliffe.[31] The original meaning, which the reader must never forget, is enriched by a new meaning, for like all works of genius, the book continues to lead an independent life.

This man's decision and effort, by granting him his first meeting with the Evangelist who becomes his guide, wrench him from his anonymity—he becomes Christian. In one respect *The Pilgrim's Progress* is really the account of all the meetings and dialogues that have directed the hero in the way he has taken, Bible in hand.

This man of decision is also a genuine man. The way in which he tackles obstacles reveals the completeness of his response. With him, there is no distinction between reality and appearance, no duality between his being and his existence, and no divorce between the "ought" of his conscience and the way he leads his life. Bunyan offers us more than the adequate picture of Puritanism for which Perry Miller has so justly praised him; he has portrayed "the religious man" whom we have come to recognize through Sören Kierkegaard, Martin Buber, and many others before them.

Christian shows his authenticity not only by decision but by the courage with which he recognizes his weaknesses, just as Bunyan had the courage to see the evil in his own nature. *Grace Abounding* shows clearly that if, for Bunyan, sin is often the transgression of the moral law, it is also a change in his relationship to God, a breach of faith with His love.

We see this, for example, in his fear that he had "sold" Christ.[32] There is a Hebrew streak in the spirit of this Puritan. "The Biblical view of sin," writes the French philosopher, Paul Ricoeur, "concerns itself first and foremost with the sinner's position *before God*. Sin has above all a religious significance, not a moral one; it is not the infringement of an abstract command, not the violation of moral values, but the appearance of a flaw in the sinner's relationship with God." [33]

For this true pilgrim, hypocrisy is perhaps the most insidious form evil can take. He is continually unmasking hypocrites, Talkative, By-ends, and others, whom he regards as hollow men. Indeed, scattered along the road are "men of straw," whom he names Mistrust, Formalist, etc., names that are no more than descriptive labels, whereas others such as Christian, Faithful, Great-heart have a deep significance. It is clear that, for Bunyan, to be significant a man must live to the full in mind, emotion, and deed. This is what he calls "that harmony and oneness of body and soul" [34] which leads the Christian "to have [his] life squared according to the Scriptures, both in word and practice." [35]

Bunyan shares this concern for sincerity with all genuine Puritans. Like them all, he recognizes true faith by its deeds alone, and only sets a value on words if the bitter experience of battle and sacrifice has, if I may be permitted the expression, scored their flesh. This is the source of his scorn for Two-tongues, Say-well, and all the other inhabitants of Prating Row or of the City of Fair Speech, whose language and lives alike are, Bunyan would say, as empty of substance as the white of an egg is of savor.

But Christian, the true pilgrim, the knight of the faith, gains in vigor and confidence as he moves forward, despite the anxiety inherent in both Puritanism and the human condition. By the heights he scales, from which he discovers ever more distant horizons, the country symbolizes the growth of his moral force and the deepening of his spiritual vision. The bypaths tempt him, but do not lead him to his ruin, for he is always able to tear himself away from them. The upward path is his destiny. And, as belief in predestination never weakens this pilgrim's sense that he must strive, and as Calvinistic determinism never sapped the Puritan's will, so Bunyan shows unconsciously how free will and fate may be reconciled. The hero's story (like the autobiography) leads to a conclusion foreign to its design, one which may be expressed in Martin Buber's words: "Only the man who makes freedom real to himself meets destiny. In my discovery of the deed that aims at me—in this movement of my freedom the mystery is revealed to me." [36]

In order to understand the complete development of religious man, and to see the whole expansion of the Puritan landscape, we must always consider the hero of the Second Part, Great-heart, as Christian under another name and at another stage of his growth. He is the fully mature Pilgrim. The time of uneasy seeking and perpetual worry about election has passed. Such consciousness of his inadequacy and shortcomings as still exists, far from disturbing the stability of his mind, acts as a stimulant. Because he is whole, Great-heart is less reserved toward others than is Christian. He shows his strength by being freely accessible: he is at the service of all who call upon him.

Once he has become guide to the weak and undecided he fits his step to theirs. The urgency of the first pilgrim's pace has given place to the slow speed made necessary, if not by the women, at least by the children. The dialogue has changed key. Its solemnity is relieved by a smile. To the irony and the slightly caustic humor which were not lacking in the First Part is added a sense of fun. The road is the same, but because the spiritual temperature and the inward climate of the pilgrims have changed, the landscape appears in a new light. The life of the spirit is no longer a lonely struggle, one continuous tension between fear of God's anger and trust in his love, but is led in the innocence of each successive hour. A valley which was threatening before is now "as fruitful a place as the crow flies over," the air the pilgrims breathe is "pleasant," and how cheerful is the light on the "sun-shine morning" when Mercy decides to travel with Christiana!

Without the Second Part of *The Pilgrim's Progress* we would only have an unfinished portrait of the Puritan and of Man as a religious being.[37] Here he does not pass his whole life with his gaze riveted on a list of prohibitions. He does not abjure the world; on the contrary, he accepts it in order to sanctify it, and in particular, as we must stress because

Bunyan himself does, to sanctify it by marriage and family life.

After sacrifice and despair, Christian, Faithful, and Hopeful know a joy that is not of this world. Christiana, Mercy, Greatheart, Father Honest and their companions experience also a fully human joy. *Laetitia* before *Beatitudo.*

HENRI A. TALON

Editor's Note

The date when the First Part of *The Pilgrim's Progress* was written is still unknown. However, as Roger Sharrock contends (his argumentation is not peremptory, but it is certainly persuasive), it seems that Bunyan wrote the greater part of the book during his first imprisonment, before he was set at liberty in 1672, and that he finished it a few years later, in the course of the six months he again spent in the prison at Bedford. (See Roger Sharrock, Introduction, *The Pilgrim's Progress,* Clarendon Press, Oxford, 1960; cf. Henri Talon, *John Bunyan: The Man and His Works,* London, and Harvard Univ. Press, 1951, and *John Bunyan,* in the pamphlet series Writers and Their Work, Longmans, London, 1956.)

In the apology in verse that serves as a preface to the First Part of *The Pilgrim's Progress,* Bunyan says that the idea of the book occurred to him suddenly, while he was engaged in writing another book about "the Way and Race of Saints." The very subject of this book, the thought of a road and runners, gave birth to the allegory of the pilgrimage. He was enthralled and started jotting down the ideas that poured into his mind "like sparks that from the coals of fire do fly," in order to elaborate them separately in another book that was to become the now-famous allegory.

The only work of Bunyan's that could thus have begotten *The Pilgrim's Progress* is *The Heavenly Footman*. This is a short treatise in which the author's meditation on Saint Paul's words, "So run, that ye may obtain" (I Cor. 9:24), made him conjure up a picture of a road with "many a dirty step, many a high hill," and of a Christian who "must run a long and tedious journey, through the vast howling wilderness." The vision was so precise that one can well understand the inner necessity and creative joy which urged him irresistibly to write the heroic adventures of Christian.

As it is almost impossible now to buy a copy of *The Heavenly Footman*, the whole book is reprinted here, so great is its importance for Bunyan scholars, and indeed for all who are interested in the genesis of a masterpiece like *The Pilgrim's Progress*.

The First Part of *The Pilgrim's Progress* is here reprinted almost completely, as is all that is best in the Second Part, and in fact, all that is necessary for anyone to appreciate the important aspects of the work on which I have attempted to shed light in my introduction.

Bunyan published the Second Part in 1685, yielding as it were to the pressure of the readers of the First Part, who clamored for a sequel. For the success of the first book had been very great. Two editions were sold out in the first year. The third edition, which appeared in 1679, contained notable additions; it was virtually the first complete edition.

In 1680 was published *The Life and Death of Mr. Badman*, a major work, particularly interesting for anyone who wishes to study the development of the English novel; and in 1682 there came out *The Holy War*, an ambitious work, which testifies to Bunyan's intellectual agility, but which has never won universal applause. Some agree with Edward Dowden that it is "an allegory rather manufactured than inspired"; others contend with E. M. W. Tillyard that "no other work has so good a claim to be called England's puritan epic." I recommend Tillyard's excellent essay all the more warmly as he disagrees with me.

The present edition retains Bunyan's Biblical references, for they reveal the extent of his indebtedness to the Bible, and they enable the modern reader to understand the author's allusions. However, his comments on both the characters and the progress of the story have been left out, except when they are more than mere résumés. I have also done away with his superabundant italics.

In brief, I have endeavored to provide the modern reader with a useful edition, and I have given all the explanatory notes that I thought he might need.

In several places I have corrected the generally received text of *The Pilgrim's Progress* by reference to Roger Sharrock's edition.

A SHORT BIBLIOGRAPHY

There is no complete recent edition of Bunyan's works; but George Offor's edition in 3 volumes (Glasgow, 1853, and London, 1862) is still fairly easy to obtain.

Roger Sharrock's superb edition of *The Pilgrim's Progress,* Clarendon Press, Oxford, 1960, is likely to be the definitive edition. Mr. Sharrock has also prepared an edition of *Grace Abounding,* which will be published shortly by the Clarendon Press.

The Life and Death of Mr. Badman, with an introduction by Bonamy Dobrée, is available in the Oxford World's Classics.

The Holy War and Mr. Badman, edited by John Brown, was published by Cambridge, 1905.

The Holy War and The Heavenly Footman, with introduction and notes by Mabel Peacock, Clarendon Press, Oxford, 1892, is now almost impossible to obtain.

BOOKS ON BUNYAN

The only complete, factual biography is that by John Brown of Bedford (1885). This *John Bunyan* was revised by F. M. Harrison, 1928.

Several biographical and critical books have been published in recent years. The following should be mentioned:

G. B. Harrison, *John Bunyan: A Study in Personality,* Doubleday, Doran & Co., 1928.

W. Y. Tindall, *John Bunyan, Mechanick Preacher,* Columbia Univ. Press, 1934. (A very important study, but one whose tone is sometimes irritating.)

H. A. Talon, *John Bunyan, The Man and his Works,* London, and Harvard Univ. Press, 1951. (Contains an extensive bibliography.)

Roger Sharrock, *John Bunyan,* Longmans, 1954.

F. R. Leavis in *The Common Pursuit,* Stewart, 1952.

Dorothy Van Ghent in *The English Novel: Form and Function,* Rinehart, 1953. (A book designed for the general reader and the student, who will find it very useful indeed.)

E. M. W. Tillyard, in *The English Epic and Its Background,* Oxford Univ. Press, 1954.

Maurice Hussey in *From Donne to Marvell.* Pelican Guide to English Literature, Penguin Books, 1956.

Wolfgang Isser, "Bunyan's Pilgrim's Progress: Die kalvinistische Heilsgewissheit und die Form des Romans," in *Festschrift für Walther Bulst,* Heidelberg, 1960. (A remarkable essay that no Bunyan scholar should miss.)

THE HEAVENLY FOOTMAN;[1]

or a Description of the Man that Gets to Heaven;
Together with the Way He Runs In,
the Marks He Goes by;
also Some Directions How to Run so as to Obtain.

And it came to pass, when they had brought them forth abroad, that he said Escape for thy life; look not behind thee, neither stay thou in all the plain: escape to the mountain, lest thou be consumed.—Gen. 19:17.

SO RUN, THAT YE MAY OBTAIN.—I COR. 9:24

The Heavenly Footman

Heaven and happiness is that which every one desireth, insomuch that wicked Balaam could say, "Let me die the death of the righteous, and let my last end be like his" (Num. 23:10). Yet for all this, there are but very few that do obtain that ever-to-be-desired glory, insomuch that many eminent professors drop short of a welcome from God into his pleasant place.

The apostle, therefore, because he did desire the salvation of the souls of the Corinthians, to whom he writes this epistle, layeth them down in these words, such counsel, which if taken, would be for their help and advantage. *First,* Not to be wicked, and sit still, and wish for heaven; but TO RUN for it. *Second,* Not to content themselves with every kind of running; but, saith he, "So RUN, that ye may obtain." As if he should say, Some, because they would not lose their souls, they begin to run betimes (Eccles. 12:1), they run apace, they run with patience (Heb. 12:1), they run the right way (Matt. 14:26). Do you so run? Some run from both father and mother, friends and companions, and this that they may have the crown. Do you so run? Some run through temptations, afflictions, good report, evil report, that they may win the pearl (I Cor. 4:13; II Cor. 6). Do you so run? "So run that ye may obtain."

These words, they are taken from men's running for a wager: a very apt similitude to set before the eyes of the saints of the Lord. "Know ye not that they which run in a race run all, but one receiveth the prize? So run, that ye may obtain." That is, do not only run, but be sure you win as well as run. "So run, that ye may obtain."

I shall not need to make any great ado in opening the words at this time, but shall rather lay down one doctrine that I do find in them; and in prosecuting that, I shall show you, in some measure, the scope of the words.

The doctrine is this: THEY THAT WILL HAVE HEAVEN, MUST RUN FOR IT; I say, they that will have heaven, they must run for it. I beseech you to heed it well. "Know ye not that they which run in a race run all, but one receiveth the prize? So run ye." The prize is heaven, and if you will have it, you must run for it. You have another scripture for this in the 12th of the Hebrews, the 1st, 2d, and 3rd verses: "Wherefore seeing we also," saith the apostle, "are compassed about with so great a cloud of witnesses, let us lay aside every weight, and the sin which doth so easily beset us, and let us run with patience the race that is set before us." And LET US RUN, saith he. Again, saith Paul, "I therefore so run, not as uncertainly, so fight I," &c.

But before I go any further, observe,

First—FLYING—That this running is not an ordinary, or any sort of running, but it is to be understood of the swiftest sort of running; and therefore in the 6th of the Hebrews it is called "a fleeing"; that "we might have a strong consolation, who have fled for refuge, to lay hold upon the hope set before us." Mark, "who have fled." It is taken from that 20th of Joshua, concerning the man that was to flee to the city of refuge, when the avenger of blood was hard at his heels, to take vengeance on him for the offence he had committed; therefore it is a RUNNING OF FLYING for one's life. A running with all might and main, as we use to say. So run!

Second—PRESSING—This running in another place is called a pressing. "I press toward the mark" (Phil. 3:14); which signifieth, that they that will have heaven, they must not stick at any difficulties they meet with; but press, crowd and thrust through all that may stand between heaven and their souls. So run!

Third—CONTINUING—This running is called in another place, "a continuing in the way of life." "If ye continue in the faith grounded, and settled, and be not moved away from the hope of the gospel" of Christ (Col. 1:23). Not to run a little now and then, by fits and starts, or half-way, or almost thither; but to run for my life, to run through all difficulties, and to continue therein to the end of the race, which must be to the end of my life. "So run, that ye may obtain."

And the reasons for this point are these,

First, Because all or every one that runneth doth not obtain the prize; there be many that do run, yea, and run far too, who yet miss of the crown that standeth at the end of the race. You know that all that run in a race do not obtain the victory; they all run, but one wins. And so it is here; it is not every one that runneth, nor every one that seeketh, nor every one that striveth for the mastery, that hath it (Luke 13). Though a man do strive for the mastery, saith Paul, "yet he is not crowned, except he strive lawfully"; that is, unless he so run, and so strive, as to have God's approbation (II Tim. 2:5). What, do you think that every heavy-heeled professor will have heaven? What, every lazy one; every wanton and foolish professor, that will be stopped by anything, kept back by anything, that scarce runneth so fast heavenward as a snail creepeth on the ground? Nay, there are some professors do not go on so fast in the way of God as a snail doth go on the wall; and yet these think, that heaven and happiness is for them. But stay, there are many more that run than there be that obtain; therefore he that will have heaven must RUN for it.

Second, Because you know that though a man do run, yet if he do not overcome, or win, as well as run, what will he be the better for his running? He will get nothing. You know the man that runneth, he doth do it that he may win the prize; but if he doth not obtain, he doth lose his labour, spend his pains and time, and that to no purpose; I say, he getteth nothing. And ah! how many such runners will there be found at the day of judgment! Even multitudes, multitudes that have run, yea, run so far as to come to heaven gates, and not able to get any further, but there stand knocking, when it is too late, crying, Lord, Lord, when they have nothing but rebukes for their pains. Depart from me, you come not here, you come too late, you run too lazily; the door is shut. "When once the master of the house is risen up," saith Christ, "and hath shut to the door, and ye begin to stand without, and to knock at the door, saying, Lord, Lord, open unto us, I will say, I know ye not, Depart," &c. (Luke 13:25). O sad will the estate of those be that run and miss; therefore, if you will have heaven, you must run for it; and "so run that ye may obtain."

Third, Because the way is long (I speak metaphorically), and there is many a dirty step, many a high hill, much work to do, a wicked heart, world, and devil, to overcome; I say, there are many steps to be taken by those that intend to be saved, by running or walking, in the steps of that faith of our father Abraham. Out of Egypt thou must go through the Red Sea; thou must run a long and tedious journey, through the vast howling wilderness, before thou come to the land of promise.

Fourth, They that will go to heaven they must run for it; because, as the way is long, so the time in which they are to get to the end of it is very uncertain; the time present is the only time; thou hast no more time allotted thee than that thou now enjoyest. "Boast not thyself of tomorrow, for thou knowest not what a day may bring forth" (Prov. 27:1). Do not say, I have time enough to get to heaven seven years hence; for I tell thee, the bell may toll for thee before seven days more be ended; and when death comes, away thou must go, whether thou art provided or not; and therefore look to it; make no delays; it is not good dallying with things of so great concernment as the salvation or damnation of thy soul. You know he that hath a great way to go in a little time, and less by half than he thinks of, he had need RUN for it.

Fifth, They that will have heaven they must run for it; because the devil, the law, sin, death, and hell, follow them. There is never a poor soul that is going to heaven, but the devil, the law, sin, death, and hell, make after that soul. "Your adversary, the devil, as a roaring lion, walketh about, seeking whom he may devour" (I Pet. 5:8). And I will assure you, the devil is nimble, he can run apace, he is light of foot, he hath overtaken many, he hath turned up their heels,[2] and hath given them an everlasting fall. Also the law, that can shoot a great way, have a care thou keep out of the reach of those great guns, the ten commandments. Hell also hath a wide mouth; it can stretch itself further than you are aware of. And as the angel said to Lot, Take heed, "look not behind thee, neither tarry thou in all the plain," that is, anywhere between this and heaven, "lest thou be consumed" (Gen. 19:17). So I say to thee, Take heed, tarry not, lest either the devil, hell, death, or the fearful curses of the law of God, do overtake thee, and throw thee down in the midst of thy sins, so as never to rise and recover again. If this were well considered, then thou, as well as I, wouldst say, They that will have heaven must run for it.

Sixth, They that will go to heaven must run for it; because perchance the gates of heaven may be shut shortly. Sometimes sinners have not heaven-gates open to them so long as they suppose; and if they be once shut against a man, they are so heavy, that all the men in the world, nor all the angels in heaven, are not able to open them. I shut, "and no man openeth," saith Christ. And how if thou shouldst come but one quarter of an hour too late? I tell thee, it will cost thee an eternity to bewail thy misery in. Francis Spira[3] can tell thee what it is to stay till the gate of mercy be quite shut; or to run so lazily, that they be shut before thou get within them. What, to be shut out! what, out of heaven! Sinner, rather than lose it, run for it; yea, and "so run that thou mayst obtain."

Seventh, Lastly, Because if thou lose, thou losest all, thou losest soul, God, Christ, heaven, ease, peace, &c. Besides, thou layest thyself open to all the shame, contempt, and reproach, that either God, Christ, saints, the world, sin, the devil, and all, can lay upon thee. As Christ saith of the foolish builder, so will I say of thee, if thou be such a one who runs and missest; I say, even all that go by will begin to mock at thee, saying, This man began to run well, but was not able to finish (Luke 14:28-30). But more of this anon.

Quest. But how should a poor soul do to run? For this very thing is that which afflicteth me sore, as you say, to think that

I may run, and yet fall short. Methinks to fall short at last, O, it fears me greatly. Pray tell me, therefore, how I should run.

Answ. That thou mightest indeed be satisfied in this particular, consider these following things.

Nine Directions how to run.

The First Direction. If thou wouldst so run as to obtain the kingdom of heaven, then be sure that thou get into the way that leadeth thither. For it is a vain thing to think that ever thou shalt have the prize, though thou runnest never so fast, unless thou art in the way that leads to it. Set the case, that there should be a man in London that was to run to York for a wager; now, though he run never so swiftly, yet if he run full south, he might run himself quickly out of breath, and be never the nearer the prize, but rather the further off. Just so is it here; it is not simply the runner, nor yet the hasty runner, that winneth the crown, unless he be in the way that leadeth thereto. I have observed, that little time which I have been a professor,[4] that there is a great running to and fro, some this way, and some that way, yet it is to be feared most of them are out of the way, and then, though they run as swift as the eagle can fly, they are benefitted nothing at all.

Here is one runs a-quaking, another a-ranting;[5] one again runs after the Baptism,[6] and another after the Independency. Here is one for free-will, and another for Presbytery; and yet possibly most of all these sects run quite the wrong way, and yet every one is for his life, his soul, either for heaven or hell.

If thou now say, Which is the way? I tell thee it is CHRIST, THE SON OF MARY, THE SON OF GOD. Jesus saith, "I am the way, and the truth, and the life; no man cometh unto the Father but by me" (John 14:6). So then thy business is, if thou wouldst have salvation, to see if Christ be thine, with all his benefits; whether he hath covered thee with his righteousness, whether he hath showed thee that thy sins are washed away with his heart-blood, whether thou art planted into him, and whether thou have faith in him, so as to make a life out of him, and to conform thee to him. That is, such faith as to conclude that thou art righteous, because Christ is thy righteousness, and so constrained to walk with him as the joy of thy heart, because he saveth thy soul. And for the Lord's sake take heed, and do not deceive thyself, and think thou art in the way upon too slight grounds; for if thou miss of the way, thou wilt miss of the prize; and if thou miss of that, I am sure thou wilt lose thy soul, even that soul which is worth more than the whole world.

But I have treated more largely on this in my book of the two covenants, and therefore shall pass it now; only I beseech thee to have a care of thy soul, and that thou mayest so do, take this counsel: Mistrust thy own strength, and throw it away; down on thy knees in prayer to the Lord for the spirit of truth; search his word for direction; fly seducers' company; keep company with the soundest Christians, that have most experience of Christ; and be sure thou have a care of Quakers, Ranters, Freewillers; also do not have too much company with some Anabaptists, though I go under that name myself. I tell thee this is such a serious matter, and I fear thou wilt so little regard it, that the thoughts of the worth of the thing, and of thy too light regarding of it, doth even make my heart ache whilst I am writing to thee. The Lord teach thee the way by his Spirit, and then I am sure thou wilt know it. So RUN.

Only by the way, let me bid thee have a care of two things, and so I shall pass to the next thing.

1. Have a care of relying on the outward obedience to any of God's commands, or thinking thyself ever the better in the sight of God for that.

2. Take heed of fetching peace for thy soul from any inherent righteousness; but if thou canst believe that as thou art a sinner, so thou art justified freely by the love of God, through the redemption that is in Christ; and that God for Christ's sake hath forgiven thee, not because he saw any thing done, or to be done, in or by thee, to move him thereunto to do it; for that is the right way; the Lord put thee into it, and keep thee in it.

The Second Direction. As thou shouldst get into the way so thou shouldst also be much in studying and musing on the way. You know men that would be expert in any thing, they are usually much in studying of[7] that thing, and so likewise is it with those that quickly grow expert in any way. This therefore thou shouldst do; let thy study be much exercised about Christ, which is the way; what he is, what he hath done, and why he is what he is, and why he hath done what is done; as, why "He took upon him the form of a servant," why he "was made in the likeness of men" (Phil. 2:7). Why he cried; why he died; why he bare the sin of the world; why he was made sin, and why he was made righteousness; why he is in heaven in the nature of man, and what he doth there? (II Cor. 5:21.) Be much in musing and considering of these things; be thinking also enough of those places which thou must not come near, but leave some on this hand, and some on that hand; as it is with those that travel into other countries, they must leave such a gate on this hand, and such a bush on that hand, and go by such a place, where standeth such a thing. Thus, therefore, thou must do: Avoid such things which are expressly forbidden in the Word of God. "Withdraw thy foot far from her, and come not nigh the door of her house, for her steps take hold on hell, going down to the chambers of death" (Prov. 5, 7). And so of every thing that is not in the way, have a care of it, that thou go not by it; come not near it, have nothing to do with it. So RUN.

The Third Direction. Not only thus, but, in the next place, thou must strip thyself of those things that may hang upon thee to the hindering of thee in the way to the kingdom of heaven, as covetousness, pride, lust, or whatever else thy heart may be inclining unto, which may hinder thee in this heavenly race. Men that run for a wager, if they intend to win as well as run, they do not use to encumber themselves, or carry those things about them that may be a hindrance to them in their running. "Every man that striveth for the mastery is temperate in all things" (I Cor. 9:25), that is, he layeth aside every thing that would be any ways a disadvantage to him; as saith the apostle, "Let us lay aside every weight, and the sin which doth so easily beset us, and let us run with patience the race that is set before us" (Heb. 12:1). It is but a vain thing to talk of going to heaven, if thou let thy heart be encumbered with those things that would hinder. Would you not say that such a man would be in danger of losing, though he run, if he fill his pockets with stones, hang heavy garments on his shoulders, and great lumpish shoes on his feet? So it is here; thou talkest of going to heaven, and yet fillest thy pocket with stones, i.e., fillest thy heart with this world, lettest that hang on thy shoulders, with its profits and pleasures. Alas, alas, thou art widely mistaken! I thou intendest to win, thou must strip, thou must lay aside every weight, thou must be temperate in all things. Thou must SO RUN.

The Fourth Direction. Beware of by-paths; take heed thou

dost not turn into those lanes which lead out of the way. There are crooked paths, paths in which men go astray, paths that lead to death and damnation, but take heed of all those (Isa. 59:8). Some of them are dangerous because of practice (Prov. 7:25); some because of opinion, but mind them not; mind the path before thee, turn neither to the right hand nor to the left, but let thine eyes look right on, even right before thee (Prov. 3:17). "Ponder the path of thy feet, and let all thy ways be established. Turn not to the right hand nor to the left. Remove thy foot far from evil" (Prov. 4:26, 27). This counsel being not so seriously taken as given, is the reason of that starting from opinion to opinion, reeling this way and that way, out of this lane into that lane, and so missing the way to the kingdom. Though the way to heaven be but one, yet there are many crooked lanes and by-paths shoot down upon it, as I may say. And again, notwithstanding the kingdom of heaven be the biggest city, yet usually those by-paths are most beaten, most travellers go those ways; and therefore the way to heaven is hard to be found, and as hard to be kept in, by reason of these. Yet, nevertheless, it is in this case as it was with the harlot of Jericho; she had one scarlet thread tied in her window, by which her house was known (Josh. 2:18). So it is here, the scarlet streams of Christ's blood run throughout the way to the kingdom of heaven; therefore mind that, see if thou do find the besprinkling of the blood of Christ in the way, and if thou do, be of good cheer, thou art in the right way; but have a care thou beguile not thyself with a fancy, for then thou mayst light into any lane[8] or way; but that thou mayst not be mistaken, consider, though it seem never so pleasant, yet if thou do not find that in the very middle of the road there is writing with the heart-blood of Christ, that he came into the world to save sinners, and that we are justified, though we are ungodly; shun that way; for this it is which the apostle meaneth when he saith, We have "boldness to enter into the holiest by the blood of Jesus, by a new and living way which he hath consecrated for us, through the veil, that is to say, his flesh" (Heb. 10:19, 20). How easy a matter is it in this our day, for the devil to be too cunning for poor souls, by calling his by-paths the way to the kingdom! If such an opinion or fancy be but cried up[9] by one or more, this inscription being set upon it by the devil, "This is the way of God," how speedily, greedily, and by heaps, do poor simple souls throw away themselves upon it; especially if it be daubed over with a few external acts of morality, if so good. But this is because men do not know painted [10] by-paths from the plain way to the kingdom of heaven. They have not yet learned the true Christ, and what his righteousness is, neither have they a sense of their own insufficiency; but are bold, proud, presumptuous, self-conceited. And therefore,

The Fifth Direction. Do not thou be too much in looking too high in thy journey heavenwards. You know men that run in a race do not use to stare and gaze this way and that, neither do they use to cast up their eyes too high, lest happily, through their too much gazing with their eyes after other things, they in the meantime stumble and catch a fall. The very same case is this; if thou gaze and stare after every opinion and way that comes into the world; also if thou be prying overmuch into God's secret decrees, or let thy heart too much entertain questions about some nice foolish curiosities, thou mayst stumble and fall, as many hundreds in England have done, both in Ranting and Quakery, to their own eternal overthrow; without the marvellous operation of God's grace be suddenly stretched forth to bring them back again. Take heed therefore, follow not that proud and lofty spirit, that, devil-like, cannot be content with his own station. David was of an excellent spirit where he saith, "Lord, my heart is not haughty, nor mine eyes lofty, neither do I exercise myself in great matters, or in things too high for me. Surely I have behaved and quieted myself as a child that is weaned of his mother; my soul is even as a weaned child" (Ps. 131:1, 2). Do thou SO RUN.

The Sixth Direction. Take heed that you have not an ear open to every one that calleth after you as you are in your journey. Men that run, you know, if any do call after them, saying, I would speak with you, or go not too fast, and you shall have my company with you, if they run for some great matter, they use to say, Alas, I cannot stay, I am in haste, pray talk not to me now; neither can I stay for you, I am running for a wager: if I win I am made, if I lose I am undone, and therefore hinder me not. Thus wise are men when they run for corruptible things, and thus should thou do, and thou hast more cause to do so than they, forasmuch as they run but for things that last not, but thou for an incorruptible glory. I give thee notice of this betimes, knowing that thou shalt have enough call after thee, even the devil, sin, this world, vain company, pleasures, profits, esteem among men, ease, pomp, pride, together with an innumerable company of such companions; one crying, Stay for me; the other saying, Do not leave me behind; a third saying, And take me along with you. What, will you go, saith the devil, without your sins, pleasures, and profits? Are you so hasty? Can you not stay and take these along with you? Will you leave your friends and companions behind you? Can you not do as your neighbours do, carry the world, sin, lust, pleasure, profit, esteem among men, along with you? Have a care thou do not let thine ear now be open to the tempting, enticing, alluring, and soul-entangling flatteries of such sink-souls[11] as these are. "My son," saith Solomon, "if sinners entice thee, consent thou not" (Prov. 1:10).

You know what it cost the young man which Solomon speaks of in the 7th of the Proverbs, that was enticed by a harlot, "With her much fair speech she" won him, and "caused him to yield, with the flattering of her lips she forced him," till he went after her "as an ox to the slaughter, or as a fool to the correction of the stocks"; even so far, "till the dart struck through his liver, and knew not that it was for his life. Hearken unto me now therefore," saith he, "O ye children, and attend to the words of my mouth, let not thine heart decline to her ways, go not astray in her paths, for she hath cast down many wounded, yea, many strong men have been slain by her," that is, kept out of heaven by her, "her house is the way to hell, going down to the chambers of death." Soul, take this counsel and say, Satan, sin, lust, pleasure, profit, pride, friends, companions, and everything else, let me alone, stand off, come not nigh me, for I am running for heaven, for my soul, for God, for Christ, from hell and everlasting damnation: if I win, I win all, and if I lose, I lose all; let me alone, for I will not hear. SO RUN.

The Seventh Direction. In the next place, be not daunted though thou meetest with never so many discouragements in thy journey thither. That man that is resolved for heaven, if Satan cannot win him by flatteries, he will endeavour to weaken him by discouragements; saying, thou art a sinner, thou hast broke God's law, thou art not elected, thou comest too late, the day of grace is past, God doth not care for thee, thy heart is naught, thou art lazy, with a hundred other discouraging suggestions. And thus it was with David, where he saith, "I had fainted, unless I had believed to see the goodness of the Lord in the land of the living" (Ps. 27:13, 14). As if he should say, the devil did so rage and my heart was so base, that had I judged according to my own sense and feeling, I had been absolutely distracted; but I trusted to Christ in the promise, and looked that God would be as good as his promise, in having mercy upon me, an unworthy sinner; and this is that which encouraged me, and kept me from fainting. And thus must thou do when Satan, or the law, or thy own conscience, do go about to dishearten thee, either by the greatness of thy sins, the wickedness of thy heart, the tediousness of the way, the loss of outward enjoyments, the hatred that thou wilt procure from the world, or the like; then thou must encourage thyself with the freeness of the promises, the tenderheartedness of Christ, the merits of his blood, the freeness of his invitations to come in, the greatness of the sin of others that have been pardoned, and that the same God, through the same Christ, holdeth forth the same grace free as ever. If these be not thy meditations, thou wilt draw very heavily in the way to heaven, if thou do not give up all for lost, and so knock off [12] from following any farther; therefore, I say, take heart in thy journey, and say to them that seek thy destruction, "Rejoice not against me, O mine enemy, when I fall I shall arise, when I sit in darkness the Lord shall be a light unto me" (Mic. 7:8). SO RUN.

The Eighth Direction. Take heed of being offended at the cross that thou must go by, before thou come to heaven. You must understand, as I have already touched, that there is no man that goeth to heaven but he must go by the cross. The cross is the standing way-mark[13] by which all that go to glory must pass by. "We must through much tribulation enter into the kingdom of God" (Acts 14:22). "Yea, and all that will live godly in Christ Jesus shall suffer persecution" (II Tim. 3:12). If thou art in the way of the kingdom, my life for thine thou wilt come at the cross shortly—the Lord grant thou dost not shrink at it, so as to turn thee back again. "If any man will come after me," saith Christ, "let him deny himself, and take up his cross daily, and follow me" (Luke 9:23). The cross it stands, and hath stood, from the beginning, as a way-mark to the kingdom of heaven. You know if one ask you the way to such and such a place, you, for the better direction, do not only say, this is the way, but then also say, you must go by such a gate, by such a style, such a bush, tree, bridge, or such like. Why, so it is here; art thou inquiring the way to heaven? Why, I tell thee, Christ is the way; into him thou must get, into his righteousness, to be justified; and if thou art in him, thou wilt presently see the cross, thou must go close by it, thou must touch it, nay, thou must take it up, or else thou wilt quickly go out of the way that leads to heaven, and turn up some of those crooked lanes that lead down to the chambers of death.

How thou mayest know the cross by these six things. 1. It is known in the doctrine of justification. 2. In the doctrine of mortification. 3. In the doctrine of perseverance. 4. In self-denial. 5. Patience. 6. Communion with poor saints.

1. In the doctrine of justification; there is a great deal of the cross in that: a man is forced to suffer the destruction of his own righteousness for the righteousness of another. This is no easy matter for a man to do; I assure to you it stretcheth every vein in his heart before he will be brought to yield to it. What, for a man to deny, reject, abhor, and throw away all his prayers, tears, alms, keeping of sabbaths, hearing, reading, with the rest, in the point of justification, and to count them accursed; and to be willing, in the very midst of the sense of his sins, to throw himself wholly upon the righteousness and obedience of another man, abhorring his own, counting it as deadly sin, as the open breach of the law; I say, to do this in deed and in truth, is the biggest piece of the cross; and therefore Paul calleth this very thing a suffering; where he saith, "And I have SUFFERED the loss of all things," which principally was his righteousness, "that I might win Christ, and be found in him, not having," but rejecting, "mine own righteousness" (Phil. 3:8, 9). That is the first.

2. In the doctrine of mortification is also much of the cross. Is it nothing for a man to lay hands on his vile opinions, on his vile sins, of his bosom sins, of his beloved, pleasant, darling sins, that stick as close to him, as the flesh sticketh to the bones? What, to lose all these brave things that my eyes behold, for that which I never saw with my eyes? What, to lose my pride, my covetousness, my vain company, sports, and pleasures, and the rest? I tell you this is no easy matter; if it were, what need all those prayers, sighs, watchings? What need we be so backward to it? Nay, do you not see, that some men, before they will set about this work, they will even venture the

loss of their souls, heaven, God, Christ, and all? What means else all those delays and put-offs, saying, Stay a little longer, I am loth to leave my sins while I am so young, and in health? Again, what is the reason else, that others do it so by the halves, coldly and seldom, notwithstanding they are convinced over and over; nay, and also promise to amend, and yet all's in vain? I will assure you, to cut off right hands, and to pluck out right eyes, is no pleasure to the flesh.

3. The doctrine of perseverance is also cross to the flesh; which is not only to begin, but for to hold out, not only to bid fair, and to say, Would I had heaven, but so to know Christ, to put on Christ, and walk with Christ as to come to heaven. Indeed, it is no great matter to begin to look for heaven, to begin to seek the Lord, to begin to shun sin. O but it is a very matter to continue with God's approbation! "My servant Caleb," saith God, is a man of "another spirit, he hath followed me," followed me always, he hath continually followed me, "fully, he shall possess the land" (Num. 14:24). Almost all the many thousands of the children of Israel in their generation, fell short of perseverance when they walked from Egypt towards the land of Canaan. Indeed they went to the work at first pretty willingly, but they were very short-winded, they were quickly out of breath, and in their hearts they turned back again into Egypt.

It is an easy matter for a man to run hard for a spurt,[14] for a furlong, for a mile or two; O, but to hold out for a hundred, for a thousand, for ten thousand miles: that man that doth this, he must look to meet with cross, pain, and wearisomeness to the flesh, especially if as he goeth he meeteth with briars and quagmires, and other incumbrances, that make his journey so much the more painfuller.

Nay, do you not see with your eyes daily, that perseverance is a very great part of the cross? why else do men so soon grow weary? I could point out a many, that after they have followed the ways of God about a twelve month, others it may be two, three, or four, some more, and some less years, they have been beat out of wind,[15] have taken up their lodging and rest before they have got half-way to heaven, some in this, and some in that sin; and have secretly, nay, sometimes openly said, that the way is too strait, the race too long, the religion too holy, and cannot hold out, I can go no farther.

4, 5, 6. And so likewise of the other three, to wit, patience, self-denial, communion, and communication with and to the poor saints. How hard are these things? It is an easy matter to deny another man, but it is not so easy a matter to deny one's self; to deny myself out of love to God, to his gospel, to his saints, of this advantage, and of that gain; nay, of that which otherwise I might lawfully do, were it not for offending them. That scripture is but seldom read, and seldomer put in practice, which saith, "I will eat no flesh while the world standeth, if it make my brother to offend" (I Cor. 8:13). Again, "We that are strong ought to bear the infirmities of the weak, and not to please ourselves" (Rom. 15:1). But how froward,[16] how hasty, how peevish,[17] and self-resolved are the generality of professors at this day! Also, how little considering the poor, unless it be to say, Be thou warmed and filled! But to give is a seldom work;[18] also especially to give to any poor (Gal. 6:10). I tell you all things are cross to flesh and blood; and that man that hath but a watchful eye over the flesh, and also some considerable measure of strength against it, he shall find his heart in these things like unto a starting horse, that is rid without a curbing bridle, ready to start at everything that is offensive to him; yea, and ready to run away too, do what the rider can.

It is the cross which keepeth those that are kept from heaven. I am persuaded, were it not for the cross, where we have one professor, we should have twenty; but this cross, that is it which spoileth all.

Some men, as I said before, when they come at the cross they can go no farther, but back again to their sins they must go. Others they stumble at it, and break their necks; others again, when they see the cross is approaching, they turn aside to the left hand, or to the right hand, and so think to get to heaven another way; but they will be deceived. "Yea, and all that will live godly in Christ Jesus SHALL," mark, shall be sure to "suffer persecution" (II Tim. 3:12). There are but few when they come at the cross, cry, "Welcome cross," as some of the martyrs did to the stake they were burned at. Therefore, if thou meet with the cross in thy journey, in what manner soever it be, be not daunted, and say, Alas, what shall I do now! But rather take courage, knowing, that by the cross is the way to the kingdom. Can a man believe in Christ and not be hated by the devil? Can he make a profession of this Christ, and that sweetly and convincingly, and the children of Satan hold their tongue? Can darkness agree with light? or the devil endure that Christ Jesus should be honoured both by faith and a heavenly conversation, and let that soul alone at quiet? Did you never read, that "the dragon persecuteth the woman"? (Rev. 12.) And that Christ saith, "In the world ye shall have tribulation" (John 16:33).

The Ninth Direction. Beg of God that he would do these two things for thee: *First,* Enlighten thine understanding. And, *Second,* Inflame thy will. If these two be but effectually done, there is no fear but thou will go safe to heaven.

(*First, Enlighten thine understanding.*) One of the great reasons why men and women do so little regard the other world, it is because they see so little of it. And the reason why they see so little of it is because they have their understandings darkened. And therefore, saith Paul, do not you believers "walk as do other Gentiles, even in the vanity of their minds, having the understanding darkened, being alienated from the life of God through the ignorance," or foolishness "that is in them, because of the blindness of their heart" (Eph. 4:17, 18). Walk not as those, run not with them; alas, poor souls, they have their understandings darkened, their hearts blinded, and that is the reason they have such undervaluing thoughts of the Lord Jesus Christ, and the salvation of their souls. For when men do come to see the things of another world, what a God, what a Christ, what a heaven, and what an eternal glory there is to be enjoyed; also when they see that it is possible for them to have a share in it, I tell you it will make them run through thick and thin to enjoy it. Moses, having a sight of this, because his understanding was enlightened, he feared not the wrath of the king, but chose "rather to suffer affliction with the people of God, than to enjoy the pleasures of sin for a season." He refused to be called the son of the king's daughter; accounting it wonderful riches to be counted worthy of so much as to suffer for Christ, with the poor despised saints; and that was because he saw him who was invisible, and "had respect unto the recompence of the reward" (Heb. 11:24-27). And this is that which the apostle usually prayeth for in his epistles for the saints, namely, "That they might know what is the hope of God's calling, and the riches of the glory of his inheritance in the saints" (Eph. 1:18). And that they might "be able to comprehend with all saints, what is the breadth, and length, and depth, and height, and to know the love of

Christ which passeth knowledge" (Eph. 3:18, 19). Pray therefore that God would enlighten thy understanding: that will be very great help unto thee. It will make thee endure many a hard brunt for Christ; as Paul saith, "After ye were illuminated, ye endured a great fight of afflictions. You took joyfully the spoiling of your goods, knowing in yourselves that ye have in heaven a better and an enduring substance" (Heb. 10:32-34). If there be never such a rare jewel lie just in a man's way, yet if he sees it not, he will rather trample upon it than stoop for it, and it is because he sees it not. Why, so it is here, though heaven be worth never so much, and thou hast never so much need of it, yet if thou see it not, that is, have not thy understanding opened or enlightened to see it, thou wilt not regard at all: therefore cry to the Lord for enlightening grace, and say, Lord, open my blind eyes: Lord, take the veil off my dark heart, show me the things of the other world, and let me see the sweetness, glory, and excellency of them for Christ his sake. This is the first.

(*Second, Inflame thy will.*) Cry to God that he would inflame thy will also with the things of the other world. For when a man's will is fully set to do such or such a thing, then it must be a very hard matter that shall hinder that man from bringing about his end. When Paul's will was set resolvedly to go up to Jerusalem, though it was signified to him before what he should there suffer, he was not daunted at all; nay, saith he, "I am ready," or willing, "not to be bound only, but also to die at Jerusalem for the name of the Lord Jesus" (Acts 21:13). His will was inflamed with love to Christ; and therefore all the persuasions that could be used wrought nothing at all. Your self-willed people nobody knows what to do with them; we used to say, He will have his own will, do all what you can. Indeed to have such a will for heaven, is an admirable advantage to a man that undertaketh the race thither; a man that is resolved, and hath his will fixed, saith he, I will do my best to advantage myself; I will do my worst to hinder my enemies; I will not give out as long as I can stand; I will have it or I will lose my life; "though he slay me yet will I trust in him" (Job 13:15). "I will not let thee go except thou bless me" (Gen. 32:26). I WILL, I WILL, I WILL, O this blessed inflamed will for heaven! What is like it? If a man be willing, then any argument shall be matter of encouragement; but if unwilling, then any argument shall give discouragement; this is seen both in saints and sinners; in them that are the children of God, and also those that are the children of the devil. As,

1. The saints of old, they being willing and resolved for heaven, what could stop them? Could fire or faggot, sword or halter, stinking dungeons, whips, bears, bulls, lions, cruel rackings, stoning, starving, nakedness, &c. (Heb. 11). "Nay, in all these things they were more than conquerors, through him that loved them" (Rom. 8:37); who had also made them "willing in the day of his power."

2. See again, on the other side, the children of the devil, because they are not willing (to run to heaven), how many shifts and starting-holes[19] they will have. I have married a wife, I have a farm, I shall offend my landlord, I shall offend my master, I shall lose my trading, I shall lose my pride, my pleasures, I shall be mocked and scoffed, therefore I dare not come. I, saith another, will stay till I am older, till my children are out of fit,[20] till I am got a little aforehand in the world, till I have done this and that, and the other business; but alas, the thing is, they are not willing; for were they but soundly willing, these, and a thousand such as these, would hold them no faster than the cords held Samson when he broke them like burned flax (Judg. 15:14). I tell you the will is all: that is one of the chief things which turns the wheel either backwards or forwards; and God knoweth that full well, and so likewise doth the devil; and therefore they both endeavour very much to strengthen the will of their servants. God, he is for making of his a willing people to serve him; and the devil, he doth what he can to possess the will and affection of those that are his, with love to sin; and therefore when Christ comes close to the matter, indeed, saith he, "Ye will not come to me" (John 5:40), "How often would I have gathered you as a hen doth her chickens, and ye would not" (Luke 13:34). The devil had possessed their wills, and so long he was sure enough of them. O therefore cry hard to God to inflame thy will for heaven and Christ: thy will, I say, if that be rightly set for heaven, thou wilt not be beat off with discouragements; and this was the reason that, when Jacob wrestled with the angel, though he lost a limb, as it were, and the hollow of his thigh was put out of joint, as he wrestled with him, yet, saith he, "I will not," mark, "I WILL NOT let thee go except thou bless me" (Gen. 32:24-26). Get thy will tipt with the heavenly grace,[21] and

resolution against all discouragements, and then thou goest full speed for heaven; but if thou falter in thy will, and be not found there, thou wilt run hobbling and halting all the way thou runnest, and also to be sure thou wilt fall short at the last. The Lord give thee a will and courage!

Thus have I done with directing thee how to run to the kingdom; be sure thou keep in memory what I have said unto thee, lest thou lose thy way. But because I would have thee think of them, take all in short in this little bit of paper.

1. Get into the way. 2. Then study on it. 3. Then strip, and lay aside everything that would hinder. 4. Beware of by-paths. 5. Do not gaze and stare too much about thee, and be sure to ponder the path of thy feet. 6. Do not stop for any that call after thee, whether it be the world, the flesh, or the devil; for all these will hinder thy journey, if possible. 7. Be not daunted with any discouragements thou meetest with as thou goest. 8. Take heed of stumbling at the cross. 9. Cry hard to God for an enlightened heart, and a willing mind, and God give thee a prosperous journey. Yet before I do quite take my leave of thee, let me give thee a few motives along with thee. It may be they will be as good as a pair of spurs to prick on thy lumpish heart in this rich voyage.

Nine Motives to urge us on in the way.

The First Motive. Consider there is no way but this, thou must either win or lose. If thou winnest, then heaven, God, Christ, glory, ease, peace, life, yea, life eternal, is thine; thou must be made equal to the angels in heaven; thou shalt sorrow no more, sigh no more, feel no more pain; thou shalt be out of reach of sin, hell, death, the devil, the grave, and whatever else may endeavour thy hurt. But contrariwise, and if thou lose, then thy loss is heaven, glory, God, Christ, ease, peace, and whatever else which tendeth to make eternity comfortable to the saints; besides, thou procurest eternal death, sorrow, pain, blackness, and darkness, fellowship with devils, together with the everlasting damnation of thy own soul.

The Second Motive. Consider that this devil, this hell, death and damnation, followeth after thee as hard as they can drive, and have their commission so to do by the law, against which thou hast sinned; and therefore for the Lord's sake make haste.

The Third Motive. If they seize upon thee before thou get

to the city of Refuge, they will put an everlasting stop to thy journey. This also cries, Run for it.

The Fourth Motive. Know also, that now heaven gates, the heart of Christ, with his arms, are wide open to receive thee. O methinks that this confederation,[22] that the devil followeth after to destroy, and that Christ standeth open-armed to receive, should make thee reach out and fly with all haste and speed! And therefore,

The Fifth Motive. Keep thine eye upon the prize; be sure that thy eyes be continually upon the profit thou art like to get. The reason why men are so apt to faint in their race for heaven, it lieth chiefly in either of these two things:

1. They do not seriously consider the worth of the prize; or else if they do, they are afraid it is too good for them; but most lose heaven for want of considering the price and the worth of it. And therefore, that thou mayst not do the like, keep thine eye much upon the excellency, the sweetness, the beauty, the comfort, the peace, that is to be had there by those that win the prize. This was that which made the apostle run through anything; good report, evil report, persecution, affliction, hunger, nakedness, peril by sea, and peril by land, bonds and imprisonments. Also it made others endure to be stoned, sawn asunder, to have their eyes bored out with augurs, their bodies broiled on gridirons, their tongues cut out of their mouths, boiled in cauldrons, thrown to the wild beasts, burned at the stakes, whipped at posts, and a thousand other fearful torments, "while they looked not at the things which are seen," as the things of this world, "but at the things which are not seen; for the things which are seen are temporal; but the things which are not seen are eternal" (II Cor. 4:18). O this word "eternal," that was it that made them, that when they might have had deliverance, they would not accept of it; for they knew in the world to come they should have a better resurrection (Heb. 11:35).

2. And do not let the thoughts of the rareness of the place make thee say in thy heart, This is too good for me; for I tell thee, heaven is prepared for whosoever will accept of it, and they shall be entertained with hearty good welcome. Consider, therefore, that as bad as thou have got thither; thither went scrubbed,[23] beggarly Lazarus, &c. Nay, it is prepared for the poor: "Hearken, my beloved brethren," saith James, take notice of it, "Hath not God chosen the poor of this world rich

in faith, and heirs of the kingdom?" (James 2:5). Therefore take heart and RUN, man. And,

The Sixth Motive. Think much of them that are gone before. First, How really they got into the kingdom. Secondly, How safe they are in the arms of Jesus; would they be here again for a thousand worlds? Or if they were, would they be afraid that God would not make them welcome? Thirdly, What would they judge of thee if they knew thy heart began to fail thee in thy journey, or thy sins began to allure thee, and to persuade thee to stop thy race? would they not call thee a thousand fools? and say, O, that he did but see what we see, feel what we feel, and taste of the dainties that we taste of! O, if he were here one quarter of an hour, to behold, to see, to feel, to taste and enjoy but the thousandth part of what we enjoy, what would he do? What would he leave undone? Would he favour sin? Would he love this world below? Would he be afraid of friends, or shrink at the most fearful threatenings that the greatest tyrants could invent to give him? Nay, those who have had but a sight of these things by faith, when they have been as far off from them as heaven from earth, yet they have been able to say with a comfortable and merry heart, as the bird that sings in the spring, that this and more shall not keep them from running to heaven. Sometimes, when my base heart hath been inclining to this world, and to loiter in my journey towards heaven, the very consideration of the glorious saints and angels in heaven, what they enjoy, and what low thoughts they have of the things of this world together, how they would befool [24] me if they did but know that my heart was drawing back; [this] hath caused me to rush forward, to disdain these poor, low, empty, beggarly things, and to say to my soul, Come, soul, let us not be weary; let us see what this heaven is; let us even venture all for it, and try if that will quit the cost. Surely Abraham, David, Paul, and the rest of the saints of God, were as wise as any are now, and yet they lost all for this glorious kingdom. O! therefore, throw away stinking lusts, follow after righteousness, love the Lord Jesus, devote thyself unto his fear, I'll warrant thee he will give thee a goodly recompense. Reader, what sayst thou to this? Nay, resolve if thou canst to get before me. "So run, that ye may obtain."

The Seventh Motive. To encourage thee a little farther, set to the work, and when thou hast run thyself down weary, then the Lord Jesus will take thee up, and carry thee. Is not this enough to make any poor soul begin his race? Thou, perhaps, criest, O but I am feeble, I am lame, &c.: well, but Christ hath a bosom; consider, therefore, when thou hast run thyself down weary, he will put thee in his bosom: "He shall gather the lambs with his arm, and carry them in his bosom, and shall gently lead those that are with young" (Isa. 40:11). This is the way that fathers take to encourage their children, saying: Run, sweet babe, while[25] thou art weary, and then I will take thee up and carry thee. "He will gather his lambs with his arm, and carry them in his bosom." When they are weary they shall ride.[26]

The Eighth Motive. Or else he will convey new strength from heaven into thy soul, which will be as well—"The youths shall faint and be weary, and the young men shall utterly fall; but they that wait upon the Lord shall renew their strength; they shall mount up with wings as eagles; they shall run and not be weary, they shall walk and not faint" (Isa. 40:30, 31). What shall I say besides what hath already been said? Thou shalt have good and easy lodging, good and wholesome diet, the bosom of Christ to lie in, the joys of heaven to feed on. Shall I speak of the satiety and of the duration of all these? Verily to describe them to the height it is a work too hard for me to do.

The Ninth Motive. Again methinks the very industry of the devil, and the industry of his servants, &c., should make you that have a desire to heaven and happiness to run apace. Why, the devil, he will lose no time, spare no pains, also neither will his servants, both to seek the destruction of themselves and others: and shall not we be as industrious for our own salvation? Shall the world venture the damnation of their souls for a poor corruptible crown; and shall not we venture the loss of a few trifles for an eternal crown? Shall they venture the loss of eternal friends, as God to love, Christ to redeem, the Holy Spirit to comfort, heaven for habitation, saints and angels for company, and all this to get and hold communion with sin, and this world, and a few base, drunken, swearing, lying, covetous wretches, like themselves? And shall not we labour as hard, run as fast, seek as diligently, nay, a hundred times more diligently, for the company of these glorious eternal friends, though with the loss of such as these, nay, with the loss of ten thousand times better than these poor, low, base, contemptible things? Shall it be said at the last day, that wicked men made more haste to hell than you did make to heaven? That they spent more hours, days, and that early and late, for hell, than you spent for that which is ten thousand thousand of thousands times better? O let it not be so, but run with all might and main.

Thus you see I have here spoken something, though but little. Now I shall come to make some use and application of what hath been said, and so conclude.

Nine uses of this subject.

The First Use. You see here, that he that will go to heaven, he must run for it; yea, and not only run, but so run, that is, as I have said, to run earnestly, to run continually, to strip off every thing that would hinder in his race with the rest. Well then, do you so run? And now let us examine a little.

1. Art thou got into the right way? Art thou in Christ's righteousness? Do not say yes in thy heart, when in truth there is no such matter. It is a dangerous thing, you know, for a man to think he is in the right way, when he is in the wrong. It is the next way for him to lose his way, and not only so, but if he run for heaven, as thou sayst thou dost, even to lose that too. O this is the misery of most men, to persuade themselves that they run right, when they never had one foot in the way! The Lord give thee understanding here, or else thou art undone for ever. Prithee, soul, search when was it thou turned out of thy sins and righteousness into the righteousness of Jesus Christ. I say, dost thou see thyself in him? and is he more precious to thee than the whole world? Is thy mind always musing on him? Dost thou love to be talking of him—and also to be walking with him? Dost thou count his company more precious than the whole world? Dost thou count all things but poor, lifeless, empty, vain things, without communion with him? Doth his company sweeten all things—and his absence imbitter all things? Soul, I beseech thee, be serious, and lay it to heart, and do not take things of such weighty concernment as the salvation or damnation of thy soul, without good ground.

2. Art thou unladen of the things of this world, as pride, pleasures, profits, lusts, vanities? What! dost thou think to run fast enough with the world, thy sins and lusts in thy heart? I tell thee, soul, they that have laid all aside, every

weight, every sin, and are got into the nimblest posture, they find work enough to run; so to run as to hold out. To run through all that opposition, all them jostles,[27] all them rubs, over all them stumbling-blocks, over all them snares from all these intanglements, that the devil, sin, the world, and their own hearts, lay before them; I tell thee, if thou art agoing heavenward, thou wilt find it no small or easy matter. Art thou therefore discharged and unladen of these things? Never talk of going to heaven if thou art not. It is to be feared thou wilt be found among the many that "will seek to enter in, and shall not be able" (Luke 13:24).

The Second Use. If so, then, in the next place, what will become of them that are grown weary before they are got half way thither? Why, man, it is he that holdeth out to the end that must be saved; it is he that overcometh that shall inherit all things; it is not every one that begins. Agrippa gave a fair step for a sudden, he steps almost into the bosom of Christ in less than half an hour. Thou, saith he to Paul, hast "almost persuaded me to be a Christian" (Acts 26:28). Ah! but it was but almost; and so he had as good have been never a whit; he stept fair indeed, but yet he stept short; he was hot while he was at it, but he was quickly out of wind. O this but almost! I tell you, this but almost, it lost his soul. Methinks I have seen sometimes how these poor wretches that get but almost to heaven, how fearfully their almost, and their but almost, will torment them in hell; when they shall cry out in the bitterness of their souls, saying, I was almost a Christian. I was almost got into the kingdom, almost out of the hands of the devil, almost out of my sins, almost from under the curse of God; almost, and that was all; almost, but not altogether. O that I should be almost at heaven, and should not go quite through! Friend, it is a sad thing to sit down before we are in heaven, and to grow weary before we come to the place of rest; and if it should be thy case, I am sure thou dost not so run as to obtain. But again,

The Third Use. In the next place, What then will become of them that some time since were running post-haste to heaven, insomuch that they seemed to outstrip many, but now are running as fast back again? Do you think those will ever come thither? What, to run back again, back again to sin, to the world, to the devil, back again to the lusts of the flesh? O! "It had been better for them not to have known the way of righteousness, than after they have known it, to turn," to turn back again, "from the holy commandment" (II Pet. 2:21). Those men shall not only be damned for sin, but for professing to all the world that sin is better than Christ; for the man that runs back again, he doth as good as say, "I have tried Christ, and I have tried sin, and I do not find so much profit in Christ as in sin." I say, this man declareth this, even by his running back again. O sad! what a doom they will have, who were almost at heaven-gates, and then run back again. "If any draw back," saith Christ (by his apostle), "my soul shall have no pleasure in him" (Heb. 10:38). Again, "No man having put his hand to the plough," that is, set forward, in the ways of God, "and looking back," turning back again, "is fit for the kingdom of God" (Luke 9:62). And if not fit for the kingdom of heaven, then for certain he must needs be fit for the fire of hell. And therefore, saith the apostle, those that "bring forth" these apostatizing fruits, as "briars and thorns, are rejected, and nigh unto cursing, whose end is to be burned" (Heb. 6:8). O there is never another Christ to save them by bleeding and dying for them! And if they shall not escape that neglect, then how shall they escape that reject and turn their back upon "so great a salvation"? (Heb. 2:3.) And if the righteous, that is, they that run for it, will find work enough to get to heaven, "then where will the ungodly" backsliding "sinner appear"? or if Judas the traitor, or Francis Spira, the backslider, were but now alive in the world to whisper these men in the ear a little, and tell them what it hath cost their souls for backsliding, surely it would stick by them and make them afraid of running back again, so long as they had one day to live in this world.

The Fourth Use. So again, fourthly, how unlike to these men's passions will those be that have all this while sat still, and have not so much as set one foot forward to the kingdom of heaven. Surely he that backslideth, and he that sitteth still in sin, they are both of one mind; the one he will not stir, because he loveth his sins, and the things of this world: is it not one and the same thing? They are all one here, and shall not one and the same hell hold them hereafter! He is an ungodly one that never looked after Christ, and he is an ungodly one that did once look after him and then ran quite back again; and therefore that word must certainly drop out of the mouth of Christ against them both, "Depart from me, ye cursed, into everlasting fire, prepared for the devil and his angels" (Matt. 15:41).

The Fifth Use. Again, here you may see, in the next place, that is, they that will have heaven must run for it; then this calls aloud to those who began but a while since to run, I say, for them to mend their pace if they intend to win; you know that they which come hindmost, had need run fastest. Friend, I tell thee, there be those that have run ten years to thy one, nay, twenty to thy five, and yet if thou talk with them, sometimes they will say they doubt they shall come late enough. How then will it be with thee? Look to it therefore that thou delay no time, not an hour's time, but speedily part with all, with everything that is an hindrance to thee in thy journey, and run; yea, and so run that thou mayest obtain.

The Sixth Use. Again, sixthly, You that are old professors, take you heed that the young striplings of Jesus, that began to strip but the other day,[28] do not outrun you, so as to have that scripture fulfilled on you, "The first shall be last, and the last first"; which will be a shame to you, and a credit for them. What, for a young soldier to be more courageous than he that hath been used to wars! To you that are hindmost, I say, strive to outrun them that are before you; and you that are foremost, I say, hold your ground, and keep before them in faith and love, if possible; for indeed that is the right running, for one to strive to outrun another; even for the hindmost to endeavour to overtake the foremost, and he that is before should be sure to lay out himself to keep his ground, even to the very utmost. But then,

The Seventh Use. Again, How basely do they behave themselves, how unlike are they to win, that think it enough to keep company with the hindmost? There are some men that profess themselves such as run for heaven as well as any; yet if there be but any lazy, slothful, cold, half-hearted professors in the country, they will be sure to take example by them; they think if they can but keep pace with them they shall do fair; but these do not consider that the hindmost lose the prize. You may know it, if you will, that it cost the foolish virgins dear for their coming too late—"They that were ready went in with him, and the door was shut. Afterward," mark, "afterward came the other," the foolish, "virgins, saying, Lord, Lord, open to us; but he answered, and said," Depart, "I know you not" (Matt. 25:10-12). Depart, lazy professors, cold professors, slothful professors. O! methinks the Word of God is so plain for the overthrow of your lazy professors, that it is to be wondered men do take no more notice of it. How was Lot's wife served for running lazily, and for giving but one look behind her, after the things she left in Sodom? How was Esau served for staying too long before he came for the blessing? And how were they served that are mentioned in the 13th of Luke, "for staying till the door was shut"? Also the foolish virgins; a heavy aftergroan will they give that have thus staid too long. It turned Lot's wife into a pillar of salt (Gen. 19:26). It made Esau weep with an exceeding loud and bitter cry (Heb. 12:17). It made Judas hang himself: yea, and it will make thee curse the day in which thou wast born, if thou miss of the kingdom, as thou wilt certainly do, if this be thy course. But,

The Eighth Use. Again, How, and if thou by thy lazy running shouldst not only destroy thyself, but also thereby be the cause of the damnation of some others, for thou being a professor thou must think that others will take notice of thee; and because thou art but a poor, cold, lazy runner, and one that seeks to drive the world and pleasure along with thee: why, thereby others will think of doing so too. Nay, say they, why may not we as well as he? He is a professor, and yet he seeks for pleasures, riches, profits; he loveth vain company, and he is proud, and he is so and so, and professeth that he is going for heaven; yea, and he saith also he doth not fear but he shall have entertainment; let us therefore keep pace with him, we shall fare no worse than he. O how fearful a thing will it be, if that thou shalt be instrumental of the ruin of others by thy halting in the way of righteousness! Look to it, thou wilt have strength little enough to appear before God, to give an account of the loss of thy own soul; thou needest not have to give an account for others; why, thou didst stop them from entering in. How wilt thou answer that saying, You would not enter in yourselves, and them that would you hinder; for that saying will be eminently fulfilled on them that through their own idleness do keep themselves out of heaven, and by giving of others the same example, hinder them also.

The Ninth Use. Therefore, now to speak a word to both of you, and so I shall conclude.

1. I beseech you, in the name of our Lord Jesus Christ, that none of you do run so lazily in the way to heaven as to hinder

either yourselves or others. I know that even he which runs laziest, if he should see a man running for a temporal life, if he should so much neglect his own well-being in this world as to venture, when he is a-running for his life, to pick up here and there a lock of wool that hangeth by the way-side,[29] or to step now and then aside out of the way for to gather up a straw or two, or any rotten stick, I say, if he should do this when he is a-running for his life, thou wouldst condemn him; and dost thou not condemn thyself that thou dost the very same in effect, nay worse, that loiterest in thy race, notwithstanding thy soul, heaven, glory, and all is at stake. Have a care, have a care, poor wretched sinner, have a care.

2. If yet there shall be any that, notwithstanding this advice, will still be flaggering[30] and loitering in the way to the kingdom of glory, be thou so wise as not to take example by them. Learn of no man further than he followeth Christ. But look unto Jesus, who is not only "the author and finisher of faith," but who did, "for the joy that was set before him, endured the cross, despising the shame, and is now set down at the right hand of God" (Heb. 12:2). I say, look to no man to learn of him no further than he followeth Christ. "Be ye followers of me," saith Paul, "even as I also am of Christ" (I Cor. 11:1). Though he was an eminent man, yet his exhortation was, that none should follow him any further than he followed Christ.

Now that you may be provoked to run with the foremost, take notice of this. When Lot and his wife were running from cursed Sodom to the mountains, to save their lives, it is said that his wife looked back from behind him, and she became a pillar of salt; and yet you see that neither her practice, nor the judgment of God that fell upon her for the same, would cause Lot to look behind him. I have sometimes wondered at Lot in this particular; his wife looked behind her, and died immediately, but let what would become of her, Lot would not so much as look behind him to see her. We do not read that he did so much as once look where she was, or what was become of her; his heart was indeed upon his journey, and well it might: there was the mountain before him, and the fire and brimstone behind him; his life lay at stake, and he had lost it if he had but looked behind him. Do thou so run: and in thy race remember Lot's wife, and remember her doom; and remember for what that doom did overtake her; and remember that God made her an example for all lazy runners, to the end of the world: and take heed thou fall not after the same example. But, if this will not provoke thee, consider thus,

1. Thy soul is thy own soul, that is either to be saved or lost; thou shalt not lose my soul by thy laziness. It is thy own soul, thy own ease, thy own peace, thy own advantage, or disadvantage. If it were my soul that thou art desired to be good unto, methinks reason should move thee somewhat to pity it. But alas, it is thy own, thy own soul. "What shall it profit a man if he shall gain the whole world, and lose his own soul?" (Mark 8:36.) God's people wish well to the souls of others, and wilt thou not wish well to thy own? And if this will not provoke thee, then think again,

2. If thou lose thy soul, it is thou also that must bear the blame. It made Cain stark mad to consider that he had not looked to his brother Abel's soul. How much more will it perplex thee to think, that thou hadst not a care of thy own? And if this will not provoke thee to bestir thyself, think again,

3. That if thou wilt not run, the people of God are resolved to deal with thee even as Lot dealt with his wife, that is, leave thee behind them. It may be thou hast a father, mother, brother, &c., going post-haste to heaven, wouldst thou be willing to be left behind them? Surely no. Again,

4. Will it not be a dishonour to thee to see the very boys and girls in the country to have more wit than thyself? It may be the servants of some men, as the horsekeeper, ploughman, scullion, &c., are more looking after heaven than their masters. I am apt to think sometimes, that more servants than masters, that more tenants than landlords, will inherit the kingdom of heaven. But is not this a shame for them that are such? I am persuaded you scorn, that your servants should say that they are wiser than you in the things of this world; and yet I am bold to say, that many of them are wiser than you in the things of the world to come, which are of greater concernment.

Well then, sinner, what sayest thou? Where is thy heart? Wilt thou run? Art thou resolved to strip? Or art thou not? Think quickly, man, it is no dallying in this matter. Confer not with flesh and blood; look up to heaven, and see how thou likest it;

also to hell—of which thou mayst understand something by my book, called, *A Few Sighs from Hell; or The Groans of a Damned Soul;* which I wish thee to read seriously over—and accordingly devote thyself. If thou dost not know the way, inquire at the Word of God. If thou wantest company, cry for God's Spirit. If thou wantest encouragement, entertain the promises. But be sure thou begin by times; get into the way; run apace and hold out to the end; and the Lord give thee a prosperous journey. Farewell.

THE PILGRIM'S PROGRESS

From This World to That Which is to Come

Delivered Under the Similitude of a Dream

Wherein Is Discovered
the Manner of His Setting Out, His Dangerous Journey
and Safe Arrival at the Desired Country

I have used similitudes.—Hos. 12:10

The Author's Apology for His Book

When at the first I took my Pen in hand
Thus for to write; I did not understand
That I at all should make a little Book
In such a mode; Nay, I had undertook
To make another, which when almost done,
Before I was aware I this begun.
  And thus it was: I writing of the Way
And Race of Saints, in this our Gospel-day,
Fell suddenly into an Allegory
About their Journey, and the way to Glory,
In more than twenty things which I set down:
This done, I twenty more had in my Crown,
And they again began to multiply,
Like sparks that from the coals of fire do fly.
Nay then, thought I, if that you breed so fast,
I'll put you by yourselves, lest you at last
Should prove *ad infinitum,* and eat out
The Book that I already am about.
  Well, so I did; but yet I did not think

To shew to all the World my Pen and Ink
In such a mode; I only thought to make
I knew not what: nor did I undertake
Thereby to please my Neighbour; no not I,
I did it mine own self to gratify.
  Neither did I but vacant seasons spend
In this my Scribble: nor did I intend
But to divert myself in doing this
From worser thoughts which make me do amiss.
  Thus I set Pen to Paper with delight,
And quickly had my thoughts in black and white.
For having now my Method by the end,
Still as I pull'd, it came;[1] and so I penn'd
It down, until it came at last to be
For length and breadth the bigness which you see.
  Well, when I had thus put mine ends together,
I shew'd them others, that I might see whether
They would condemn them, or them justify:
And some said, Let them live; some, Let them die;
Some said, John, print it; others said, Not so:
Some said, It might do good; others said, No.
  Now was I in a strait, and did not see
Which was the best thing to be done by me:
At last I thought, Since you are thus divided,
I print it will, and so the case decided.
  For, thought I, some I see would have it done,
Though others in that Channel do not run.
To prove then who advised for the best,
Thus I thought fit to put it to the test.
  I further thought, if now I did deny
Those that would have it thus, to gratify,
I did not know but hinder them I might
Of that which would to them be great delight.
  For those which were not for its coming forth,
I said to them, Offend you I am loth,
Yet since your Brethren pleased with it be,
Forbear to judge till you do further see.
  If that thou wilt not read, let it alone;
Some love the meat, some love to pick the bone:
Yea, that I might them better palliate,
I did too with them thus Expostulate:
  May I not write in such a style as this?

In such a method too, and yet not miss
Mine end, thy good? why may it not be done?
Dark Clouds bring Waters, when the bright bring none.
Yea, dark or bright, if they their Silver drops
Cause to descend, the Earth, by yielding Crops,
Gives praise to both, and carpeth not at either,
But treasures up the Fruit they yield together;
Yea, so commixes both, that in her Fruit
None can distinguish this from that: they suit
Her well, when hungry; but, if she be full,
She spues out both, and makes their blessings null.
  You see the ways the Fisher man doth take
To catch the Fish; what Engines doth he make?
Behold how he engageth all his Wits;
Also his Snares, Lines, Angles, Hooks, and Nets.
Yet Fish there be, that neither Hook, nor Line,
Nor Snare, nor Net, nor Engine can make thine;
They must be grop'd for, and be tickled too,
Or they will not be catch'd, whate'er you do.
  How doth the Fowler seek to catch his Game
By divers means, all which one cannot name?
His Gun, his Nets, his Lime-twigs, Light, and Bell;
He creeps, he goes, he stands; yea who can tell
Of all his postures? Yet there's none of these
Will make him master of what Fowls he please.
Yea, he must Pipe and Whistle to catch *this;*
Yet if he does so, *that* Bird he will miss.
  If that a Pearl may in a Toads-head dwell,[2]
And may be found too in an Oyster-shell;
If things that promise nothing do contain
What better is than Gold; who will disdain,
That have an inkling of it, there to look,
That they may find it? Now my little Book
(Though void of all those Paintings that may make
It with this or the other man to take)
Is not without those things that do excel
What do in brave but empty notions dwell.
  Well, yet I am not fully satisfied,
That this your Book will stand, when soundly try'd.
  Why, what's the matter? It is dark. What tho?
But it is feigned. What of that I tro?
Some men, by feigning words as dark as mine,

Make truth to spangle, and its rays to shine.
But they want solidness. Speak man thy mind.
They drowned the weak; Metaphors make us blind.
  Solidity indeed becomes the Pen
Of him that writeth things Divine to men;
But must I needs want solidness, because
By Metaphors I speak? Were not God's Laws,
His Gospel-Laws, in olden time held forth
By Types, Shadows, and Metaphors? Yet loth
Will any sober man be to find fault
With them, lest he be found for to assault
The highest Wisdom. No, he rather stoops,
And seeks to find out what by Pins and Loops,[3]
By Calves, and Sheep, by Heifers, and by Rams,[4]
By Birds, and Herbs, and by the blood of Lambs,[5]
God speaketh to him. And happy is he
That finds the light and grace that in them be.
  Be not too forward therefore to conclude
That I want solidness, that I am rude:
All things solid in shew not solid be;
All things in Parables despise not we;
Lest things most hurtful lightly we receive,
And things that good are, of our souls bereave.
  My dark and cloudy words they do but hold
The truth, as Cabinets inclose the Gold.
  The Prophets used much by Metaphors
To set forth Truth; yea, who so considers
Christ, his Apostles too, shall plainly see,
That Truths to this day in such Mantles be.
  Am I afraid to say that Holy Writ,
Which for its Style and Phrase puts down all Wit,
Is everywhere so full of all these things,
Dark Figures, Allegories?[6] Yet there springs
From that same Book that lustre, and those rays
Of light, that turns our darkest nights to days.
  Come, let my Carper to his Life now look,
And find there darker lines than in my Book
He findeth any, Yea, and let him know,
That in his best things there are worse lines too.
  May we but stand before impartial men,
To his poor One I dare adventure Ten,
That they will take my meaning in these lines

Far better than his lies in Silver Shrines.[7]
Come! Truth, although in Swaddling-clouts, I find,
Informs the Judgment, rectifies the Mind,
Pleases the Understanding, makes the Will
Submit; the Memory too it doth fill
With what doth our Imagination please;
Likewise it tends our troubles to appease.
  Sound words I know Timothy is to use,
And old Wives' Fables he is to refuse;
But yet grave Paul him nowhere doth forbid
The use of Parables; in which lay hid
That Gold, those Pearls, and precious stones that were
Worth digging for, and that with greatest care.
  Let me add one word more. O man of God,
Art thou offended? Dost thou wish I had
Put forth my matter in another dress,
Or that I had in things been more express?
Three things let me propound, then I submit
To those that are my betters, as is fit.
  1. I find not that I am denied the use
Of this my method, so I no abuse
Put on the Words, Things, Readers; or be rude
In handling Figure or Similitude,
In application; but, all that I may,
Seek the advance of Truth, this or that way.
Denied, did I say? Nay, I have leave,
(Example too, and that from them that have
God better pleased, by their words or ways,
Than any man that breatheth now-a-days)
Thus to express my mind, thus to declare
Things unto thee, that excellentest are.
  2. I find that men (as high as Trees) will write
Dialogue-wise;[8] yet no man doth them slight
For writing so: Indeed if they abuse
Truth, cursed be they, and the craft they use
To that intent; but yet let Truth be free
To make her sallies upon thee and me,
Which way it pleases God. For who knows how,
Better than he that taught us first to Plow,[9]
To guide our Mind and Pens for his Design?
And he makes base things usher in Divine.
  3. I find that Holy Writ in many places

Hath semblance with this method, where the cases
Do call for one thing, to set forth another;
Use it I may then, and yet nothing smother
Truth's golden Beams: nay, by this method may
Make it cast forth its rays as light as day.
  And now, before I do put up my Pen,
I'll shew the profit of my Book, and then
Commit both thee and it unto that hand
That pulls the strong down, and makes weak ones stand.
  This Book it chalketh out before thine eyes
The man that seeks the everlasting Prize;
It shews you whence he comes, whither he goes,
What he leaves undone, also what he does;
It also shews you how he runs and runs,
Till he unto the Gate of Glory comes.
  It shews too, who set out for life amain,
As if the lasting Crown they would obtain,
Here also you may see the reason why
They lose their labour and like Fools do die.
  This Book will make a Traveller of thee,
If by its Counsel thou wilt ruled be;
It will direct thee to the Holy Land,
If thou wilt its directions understand:
Yea, it will make the slothful active be;
The blind also delightful things to see.
  Art thou for something rare and profitable?
Wouldest thou see a Truth within a Fable?
Art thou forgetful? Wouldest thou remember
From New-year's-day to the last of December?
Then read my Fancies, they will stick like Burrs,
And may be to the Helpless, Comforters.
  This Book is writ in such a Dialect
As may the minds of listless men affect:
It seems a novelty, and yet contains
Nothing but sound and honest Gospel strains.
  Would'st thou divert thyself from Melancholy?
Would'st thou be pleasant, yet be far from folly?
Would'st thou read Riddles, and their Explanation?
Or else be drowned in thy Contemplation?
Dost thou love picking meat? Or would'st thou see
A man i' th' Clouds, and hear him speak to thee?
Would'st thou be in a Dream, and yet not sleep?

Or would'st thou in a moment laugh and weep?
Wouldest thou lose thyself, and catch no harm,
And find thyself again without a charm?
Would'st read thyself, and read thou know'st not what,
And yet know whether thou art blest or not,
By reading the same lines? O then come hither,
And lay my Book, thy Head and Heart together.

JOHN BUNYAN

The Pilgrim's Progress

The Gaol.

As I walk'd through the wilderness of this world, I lighted on a certain place where was a Den, and I laid me down in that place to sleep; and as I slept I dreamed a Dream. I Dreamed, and behold I saw a man clothed with Rags, standing in a certain place, with his face from his own house, a Book in his hand, and a great Burden upon his back (Isa. 64:6; Luke 14:33; Ps. 38:4; Hab. 2:2; Acts 16:31). I looked, and saw him open the Book, and read therein; and as he read, he wept and trembled; and not being able longer to contain, he brake out with a lamentable cry, saying, What shall I do?

In this plight[10] therefore he went home, and refrained himself as long as he could, that his Wife and Children should not perceive his distress, but he could not be silent long, because that his trouble increased: wherefore at length he brake his mind to his Wife and Children; and thus he began to talk to them: O my dear Wife, said he, and you the Children of my bowels, I your dear friend am in myself undone by reason of a Burden that lieth hard upon me;

moreover, I am for certain informed that this our City will be burned with fire from Heaven; in which fearful overthrow, both myself, with thee my Wife, and you my sweet babes, shall miserably come to ruin, except (the which yet I see not) some way of escape can be found, whereby we may be delivered. At this his Relations[11] were sore amazed; not for that they believed that what he said to them was true, but because they thought that some frenzy distemper had got into his head; therefore, it drawing towards night, and they hoping that sleep might settle his brains, with all haste they got him to bed: But the night was as troublesome to him as the day; wherefore, instead of sleeping, he spent it in sighs and tears. So, when the morning was come, they would know how he did; and he told them, Worse and worse: he also set to talking to them again, but they began to be hardened: they also thought to drive away his distemper by harsh and surly carriages to him; sometimes they would deride, sometimes they would chide, and sometimes they would quite neglect him: wherefore he began to retire himself to his chamber, to pray for and pity them, and also to condole his own misery; he would also walk solitarily in the fields, sometimes reading, and sometimes praying: and thus for some days he spent his time.

Now, I saw upon a time, when he was walking in the fields, that he was, as he was wont, reading in his Book, and greatly distressed in his mind; and as he read, he burst out, as he had done before, crying, What shall I do to be saved?

I saw also that he looked this way and that way, as if he would run; yet he stood still, because, as I perceived, he could not tell which way to go. I looked then, and saw a Man named Evangelist, coming to him, and asked, Wherefore dost thou cry? He answered, Sir, I perceive by the Book in my hand, that I am condemned to die, and after that to come to Judgment; and I find that I am not willing to do the first, nor able to do the second. (Heb. 9:27; Job 16:21, 22; Ezek. 22:14.)

Then said Evangelist, Why not willing to die? since this life is attended with so many evils? The Man answered, Because I fear that this burden that is upon my back will sink me lower than the Grave, and I shall fall into Tophet[12] (Isa. 30:33). And, Sir, if I be not fit to go to Prison, I am not fit (I am sure)[13] to go to Judgment, and from thence to

Execution; and the thoughts of these things make me cry.

Then said Evangelist, If this be thy condition, why standest thou still? He answered, Because I know not whither to go. Then he gave him a Parchment-roll, and there was written within, Fly from the wrath to come (Matt. 3:7).

The Man therefore read it, and looking upon Evangelist very carefully, said, Whither must I fly? Then said Evangelist, pointing with his finger over a very wide Field, Do you see yonder Wicket-gate? (Matt. 7:13.) The Man said, No. Then said the other, Do you see yonder shining Light? (Ps. 119:105; II Pet. 1:19.) He said, I think I do. Then said Evangelist, Keep that Light in your eye, and go up directly thereto: so shalt thou see the Gate; at which when thou knockest, it shall be told thee what thou shalt do.

So I saw in my Dream that the Man began to run. Now he had not run far from his own door, but his Wife and Children, perceiving it, began to cry after him to return (Luke 14:26); but the Man put his fingers in his ears, and ran on, crying, Life! Life! Eternal Life! So he looked not behind him (Gen. 19:17), but fled towards the middle of the Plain.

The Neighbours also came out to see him run; and as he ran, some mocked, others threatened, and some cried after him to return: Now among those that did so, there were two that resolved to fetch him back by force (Jer. 20:10). The name of the one was Obstinate, and the name of the other Pliable. Now by this time the Man was got a good distance from them; but, however, they were resolved to pursue him, which they did, and in little time they overtook him. Then said the Man, Neighbours, wherefore are you come? They said, To persuade you to go back with us. But he said, That can by no means be; you dwell, said he, in the City of Destruction (the place also where I was born), I see it to be so; and dying there, sooner or later, you will sink lower than the Grave, into a place that burns with Fire and Brimstone: be content, good Neighbours, and go along with me.

OBSTINATE. What, said Obstinate, and leave our friends and our comforts behind us!

CHRISTIAN. Yes, said Christian (for that was his name), because that *all* which you shall forsake is not worthy to be compared with a *little* of that that I am seeking to enjoy (II Cor. 4:18); and if you will go along with me, and hold it, you shall fare as I myself; for there where I go is enough and to spare (Luke 15:17): Come away, and prove my words.

OBSTINATE. What are the things you seek, since you leave all the world to find them?

CHRISTIAN. I seek an Inheritance incorruptible, undefiled, and that fadeth not away, and it is laid up in Heaven (I Pet. 1:4; Heb. 11:16), and fast there, to be bestowed, at the time appointed, on them that diligently seek it. Read it so, if you will, in my Book.

OBSTINATE. Tush, said Obstinate, away with your Book; will you go back with us or no?

CHRISTIAN. No, not I, said the other, because I have laid my hand to the Plough (Luke 9:62).

OBSTINATE. Come then, Neighbour Pliable, let us turn again, and go home without him; there is a Company of these Craz'd-headed Coxcombs, that, when they take a fancy by the end,[14] are wiser in their own eyes than seven men that can render a reason.

PLIABLE. Then said Pliable, Don't revile; if what the good Christian says is true, the things he looks after are better than ours; my heart inclines to go with my Neighbour.

OBSTINATE. What! more fools still? Be ruled by me, and go back; who knows whither such a brain-sick fellow will lead you? Go back, go back, and be wise.

CHRISTIAN. Come with me, Neighbour Pliable; there are such things to be had which I spoke of, and many more Glories besides. If you believe not me, read here in this Book; and for the truth of what is exprest therein, behold, all is confirmed by the blood of Him that made it (Heb. 13:20, 21; 9:17-21).

PLIABLE. Well, Neighbour Obstinate, said Pliable, I begin to come to a point; I intend to go along with this good man, and to cast in my lot with him: but, my good Companion, do you know the way to this desired place?

CHRISTIAN. I am directed by a man, whose name is Evangelist, to speed me to a little Gate that is before us, where we shall receive instruction about the way.

PLIABLE. Come then, good Neighbour, let us be going.

Then they went both together.

OBSTINATE. And I will go back to my place, said Obstinate; I will be no companion of such misled, fantastical fellows.

Now I saw in my Dream, that when Obstinate was gone back, Christian and Pliable went talking over the Plain; and thus they began their discourse.

CHRISTIAN. Come, Neighbour Pliable, how do you do? I am glad you are persuaded to go along with me: Had even Obstinate himself but felt what I have felt of the Powers and Terrors of what is yet unseen, he would not thus lightly have given us the back.

PLIABLE. Come, Neighbour Christian, since there is none but us two here, tell me now further what the things are, and how to be enjoyed, whither we are going?

CHRISTIAN. I can better conceive of them with my Mind than speak of them with my Tongue: but yet, since you are desirous to know, I will read of them in my Book.

PLIABLE. And do you think that the words of your Book are certainly true?

CHRISTIAN. Yes, verily; for it was made by him that cannot lie (Titus 1:2).

PLIABLE. Well said; what things are they?

CHRISTIAN. There is an endless Kingdom to be inhabited, and everlasting Life to be given us, that we may inhabit that Kingdom for ever (Isa. 45:17; John 10:27-29).

PLIABLE. Well said; and what else?

CHRISTIAN. There are Crowns of Glory to be given us, and Garments that will make us shine like the Sun in the firmament of Heaven (II Tim. 4:8; Rev. 3:4; Matt. 13:43).

PLIABLE. This is excellent; and what else?

CHRISTIAN. There shall be no more crying, nor sorrow; for He that is owner of the place will wipe all tears from our eyes (Isa. 25:8; Rev. 7:16, 17; 21:4).

PLIABLE. And what company shall we have there?

CHRISTIAN. There we shall be with Seraphims and Cherubins, creatures that will dazzle your eyes to look on them (Isa. 6:2; I Thess. 4:16, 17; Rev. 7:17): There also you shall meet with thousands and ten thousands that have gone before us to that place; none of them are hurtful, but loving and holy; every one walking in the sight of God, and standing in his presence with acceptance for ever. In a word, there we shall see the Elders with their golden Crowns (Rev. 4:4; 14:2-4), there we shall see the Holy Virgins with their golden Harps, there we shall see men that by the World were cut in pieces, burnt in flames, eaten of beasts, drowned in the seas, for the love that they bare to the Lord of the place, all well, and clothed with Immortality as with a garment (John 12:25; II Cor. 5:2, 3, 5).

PLIABLE. The hearing of this is enough to ravish one's heart; but are these things to be enjoyed? How shall we get to be sharers hereof?

CHRISTIAN. The Lord, the Governor of that country, hath recorded *that* in this Book; the substance of which is, If we be truly willing to have it, he will bestow it upon us freely (Isa. 55:12; John 7:37; 6:37; Rev. 21:6; 22:17).

PLIABLE. Well, my good Companion, glad am I to hear of these things; come on, let us mend our pace.

CHRISTIAN. I cannot go so fast as I would, by reason of this Burden that is upon my back.

Now I saw in my Dream, that just as they had ended this talk, they drew near to a very miry Slough,[15] that was in the midst of the plain; and they being heedless did both fall suddenly into the bog. The name of the Slough was Despond.[16] Here therefore they wallowed for a time, being grievously bedaubed with dirt; and Christian, because of the Burden that was on his back, began to sink in the Mire.

PLIABLE. Then said Pliable, Ah, Neighbour Christian, where are you now?

CHRISTIAN. Truly, said Christian, I do not know.

PLIABLE. At that Pliable began to be offended, and angerly said to his Fellow, Is this the happiness you have told me all this while of? If we have such ill speed at our first setting out, what may we expect 'twixt this and our Journey's end? May I get out again with my life, you shall possess the brave Country alone for me. And with that he gave a desperate struggle or two, and got out of the Mire on that side of the Slough which was next to his own house: so away he went, and Christian saw him no more.

Wherefore Christian was left to tumble in the Slough of Despond alone: but still he endeavoured to struggle to that side of the Slough that was still further from his own house, and next to the Wicket-gate; the which he did, but could not get out, because of the Burden that was upon his back: But I beheld in my Dream, that a Man came to him, whose name was Help, and asked him, What he did there?

CHRISTIAN. Sir, said Christian, I was bid go this way by a Man called Evangelist; who directed me also to yonder Gate, that I might escape the wrath to come; and as I was going thither, I fell in here.

The Promises.

HELP. But why did you not look for the steps? [17]

CHRISTIAN. Fear followed me so hard, that I fled the next way, and fell in.

HELP. Then said he, Give me thy hand. So he gave him his hand, and he drew him out, and set him upon sound ground, and bid him go on his way (Ps. 40:2).

Then I stepped to him that plucked him out, and said, Sir, wherefore (since over this place is the way from the City of Destruction to yonder gate) is it that this Plat is not mended, that poor travellers might go thither with more security? And he said unto me, This miry Slough is such a place as cannot be mended; it is the descent whither the scum and filth that attends conviction for sin doth continually run, and therefore it is called the Slough of Despond; for still as the sinner is awakened about his lost condition, there ariseth in his soul many fears and doubts, and discouraging apprehensions, which all of them get together, and settle in this place: And this is the reason of the badness of this ground.

It is not the pleasure of the King that this place should remain so bad (Isa. 35:3, 4). His labourers also have, by the direction of His Majesty's Surveyors, been for above these sixteen hundred years[18] employed about this patch of ground, if perhaps it might have been mended: yea, and to my knowledge, said he, here hath been swallowed up at least twenty thousand cart-loads, yea, millions of wholesome Instructions, that have at all seasons been brought from all places of the King's Dominion (and they that can tell say they are the best materials to make good ground of the place); if so be it might have been mended, but it is the Slough of Despond still, and so will be when they have done what they can.

True, there are by the direction of the Lawgiver, certain good and substantial Steps, placed even through the very midst of this Slough; but at such time as this place doth much spue out its filth, as it doth against change of weather, these steps are hardly seen; or if they be, men through the dizziness of their heads, step besides; and then they are bemired to purpose, notwithstanding the steps be there; but the ground is good when they are once got in at the Gate (I Sam. 12:23).

Now I saw in my Dream, that by this time Pliable was got home to his House again. So his Neighbours came to visit him; and some of them called him wise Man for coming back, and some called him Fool for hazarding himself with Christian: others again did mock at his Cowardliness; saying, Surely since you began to venture, I would not have been so base to have given out for a few difficulties. So Pliable sat sneaking among them. But at last he got more confidence, and then they all turned their tales, and began to deride poor Christian behind his back. And thus much concerning Pliable.

Now as Christian was walking solitary by himself, he espied one afar off come crossing over the field to meet him; and their hap was to meet just as they were crossing the way of each other. The Gentleman's name that met him was Mr. Worldly Wiseman: [19] he dwelt in the Town of Carnal Policy, a very great Town, and also hard by from whence Christian came. This man then meeting with Christian, and having some inkling of him—for Christian's setting forth from the City of Destruction was much noised abroad, not only in the Town where he dwelt, but also it began to be the Town-talk in some other places—Master Worldly Wiseman therefore, having some guess of him, by beholding his laborious going, by observing his sighs and groans, and the like, began thus to enter into some talk with Christian.

WORLDLY WISEMAN. How now, good fellow, whither away after this burdened manner?

CHRISTIAN. A burdened manner indeed, as ever I think poor creature had. And whereas you ask me, Whither away? I tell you, Sir, I am going to yonder Wicket-gate before me; for there, as I am informed, I shall be put into a way to be rid of my heavy Burden.

WORLDLY WISEMAN. Hast thou a Wife and Children?

CHRISTIAN. Yes, but I am so laden with this Burden, that I cannot take that pleasure in them as formerly; methinks I am as if I had none (I Cor. 7:29).

WORLDLY WISEMAN. Wilt thou hearken to me if I give thee counsel?

CHRISTIAN. If it be good, I will; for I stand in need of good counsel.

WORLDLY WISEMAN. I would advise thee then, that thou with all speed get thyself rid of thy Burden; for thou wilt never be settled in thy mind till then; nor canst thou enjoy the benefits of the blessing which God hath bestowed upon thee till then.

CHRISTIAN. That is that which I seek for, even to be rid of this heavy burden; but get it off myself, I cannot; nor is there any man in our Country that can take it off my shoulders; therefore am I going this way, as I told you, that I may be rid of my burden.

WORLDLY WISEMAN. Who bid thee go this way to be rid of thy Burden?

CHRISTIAN. A man that appeared to me to be a very great and honourable person; his name as I remember is Evangelist.

WORLDLY WISEMAN. I beshrew him for his counsel; there is not a more dangerous and troublesome way in the world than is that unto which he hath directed thee; and that thou shalt find, if thou wilt be ruled by his counsel. Thou hast met with something (as I perceive) already; for I see the dirt of the Slough of Despond is upon thee; but that Slough is the beginning of the sorrows that do attend those that go on in that way: Hear me, I am older than thou; thou art like to meet with in the way which thou goest, Wearisomeness, Painfulness, Hunger, Perils, Nakedness, Sword, Lions, Dragons, Darkness, and in a word, Death, and what not! These things are certainly true, having been confirmed by many testimonies. And why should a man so carelessly cast away himself, by giving heed to a stranger?

CHRISTIAN. Why, Sir, this Burden upon my back is more terrible to me than are all these things which you have mentioned; nay, methinks I care not what I meet with in the way, so be I can also meet with deliverance from my Burden.

WORLDLY WISEMAN. How camest thou by thy Burden at first?

CHRISTIAN. By reading this Book in my hand.

WORLDLY WISEMAN. I thought so; and it is happened unto thee as to other weak men, who meddling with things too high for them, do suddenly fall into thy distractions; which distractions do not only unman men (as thine I perceive has done thee), but they run them upon desperate ventures, to obtain they know not what.

CHRISTIAN. I know what I would obtain; it is ease for my heavy burden.

WORLDLY WISEMAN. But why wilt thou seek for ease this way, seeing so many dangers attend it? Especially, since (hadst thou but patience to hear me) I could direct thee to the obtaining of what thou desirest, without the dangers that thou in this way wilt run thyself into; yea, and the remedy is at hand. Besides, I will add, that instead of those dangers, thou shalt meet with much safety, friendship, and content.

CHRISTIAN. Pray, Sir, open this secret to me.

WORLDLY WISEMAN. Why in yonder Village (the village is named Morality) there dwells a Gentleman whose name is Legality, a very judicious man, and a man of a very good name, that has skill to help men off with such burdens as thine are from their shoulders: yea, to my knowledge he hath done a great deal of good this way; ay, and besides, he hath skill to cure those that are somewhat crazed in their wits with their burdens. To him, as I said, thou mayest go, and be helped presently. His house is not quite a mile from this place, and if he should not be at home himself, he hath a pretty young man to his Son, whose name is Civility, that can do it (to speak on) as well as the old Gentleman himself; there, I say, thou mayest be eased of thy Burden; and if thou art not minded to go back to thy former habitation, as indeed I would not wish thee, thou mayest send for thy Wife and Children to thee to this village, where there are houses now stand empty, one of which thou mayest have at reasonable rates; Provision is there also cheap and good; and that which will make thy life the more happy is, to be sure, there thou shalt live by honest neighbours, in credit and good fashion.

Now was Christian somewhat at a stand, but presently he concluded, If this be true which this Gentleman hath said, my wisest course is to take his advice; and with that he thus farther spoke.

CHRISTIAN. Sir, which is my way to this honest man's house?

Mount Sinai.

WORLDLY WISEMAN. Do you see yonder high Hill?

CHRISTIAN. Yes, very well.

WORLDLY WISEMAN. By that Hill you must go, and the first house you come at is his.

So Christian turned out of his way to go to Mr. Legality's house for help; but behold, when he was got now hard by the Hill, it seemed so high, and also that side of it that was next the wayside, did hang so much over, that Christian was afraid to venture further, lest the Hill should fall on his head; wherefore there he stood still, and he wot not what to do. Also his Burden *now* seemed heavier to him than while he was in his way. There came also flashes of fire out of the Hill, that made Christian afraid that he should be burned (Ex. 19:16, 18; Heb. 12:21). Here therefore he sweat and did quake for fear. And now he began to be sorry that he had taken Mr. Worldly Wiseman's counsel. And with that he saw Evangelist coming to meet him; at the sight also of whom he began to blush for shame. So Evangelist drew nearer and nearer; and coming up to him, he looked upon him with a severe and dreadful countenance, and thus began to reason with Christian.

EVANGELIST. What doest thou here, Christian? said he: at which words Christian knew not what to answer; wherefore at present he stood speechless before him. Then said Evangelist further, Art not thou the man that I found crying without the walls of the City of Destruction?

CHRISTIAN. Yes, dear Sir, I am the man.

EVANGELIST. Did not I direct thee the way to the little Wicket-gate?

CHRISTIAN. Yes, dear Sir, said Christian.

EVANGELIST. How is it then that thou art so quickly turned aside? for thou art now out of the way.

CHRISTIAN. I met with a Gentleman so soon as I had got over the Slough of Despond, who persuaded me that I might, in the village before me, find a man that could take off my Burden.

EVANGELIST. What was he?

CHRISTIAN. He looked like a Gentleman, and talked much to me, and got me at last to yield; so I came hither: but when I beheld this Hill, and how it hangs over the way, I suddenly made a stand, lest it should fall on my head.

EVANGELIST. What said that Gentleman to you?

CHRISTIAN. Why, he asked whither I was going; and I told him.

EVANGELIST. And what said he then?

CHRISTIAN. He asked me if I had a family; and I told him. But, said I, I am so loaden with the Burden that is on my back, that I cannot take pleasure in them as formerly.

EVANGELIST. And what said he then?

CHRISTIAN. He bid me with speed get rid of my Burden; and I told him 'twas ease that I sought. And, said I, I am therefore going to yonder Gate, to receive further direction how I may get to the place of deliverance. So he said that he would shew me a better way, and short, not so attended with difficulties as the way, Sir, that you set me; which way, said he, will direct you to a Gentleman's house that hath skill to take off these Burdens: So I believed him, and turned out of that way into this, if haply I might be soon eased of my Burden. But when I came to this place, and beheld things as they are, I stopped for fear (as I said) of danger: but I now know not what to do.

EVANGELIST. Then, said Evangelist, stand still a little, that I may shew thee the words of God.

So he stood trembling.

Then said Evangelist, See that ye refuse not him that speaketh; for if they escaped not who refused him that spake on Earth, much more shall not we escape, if we turn away from him that speaketh from Heaven (Heb. 12:25). He said moreover, Now the just shall live by faith: but if any man draws back, my soul shall have no pleasure in him (Heb. 10:38). He also did thus apply them, Thou art the man that art running into this misery, thou hast begun to reject the counsel of the Most High, and to draw back thy foot from the way of peace, even almost to the hazarding of thy perdition.

Then Christian fell down at his foot as dead, crying, Woe is me, for I am undone: At the sight of which, Evangelist caught him by the right hand, saying, All manner of sin and blasphemies shall be forgiven unto men (Matt. 12:31; Mark 3:28); be not faithless, but believing. Then did Christian again a little revive, and stood up trembling, as at first before Evangelist.

Then Evangelist proceeded, saying, Give more earnest heed to the things that I shall tell thee of. I will now shew thee who it was that deluded thee, and who it was also to whom he sent thee. The man that met thee is one Worldly Wiseman, and rightly is he so called: partly because he savoureth only the doctrine of this world (I John 4:5), (therefore he always goes to the Town of Morality to church); and partly because he loveth that doctrine best, for it saveth him from the Cross (Gal. 6:12). And because he is of this carnal temper, therefore he seeketh to prevent my ways, though right. Now there are three things in this man's counsel that thou must utterly abhor.

1. His turning thee out of the way.

2. His labouring to render the Cross odious to thee.

3. And his setting thy feet in that way that leadeth unto the administration of Death.

First, Thou must abhor his turning thee out of the way; yea, and thine own consenting thereto: because this is to reject the counsel of God for the sake of the counsel of a Worldly Wiseman. The Lord says, Strive to enter in at the strait gate, the gate to which I sent thee; for strait is the gate that leadeth unto life, and few there be that find it (Luke 13:24; Matt. 7:13, 14). From this little Wicket-gate, and from the way thereto, hath this wicked man turned thee, to the bringing of thee almost to destruction; hate therefore his turning thee out of the way, and abhor thyself for hearkening to him.

Secondly, Thou must abhor his labouring to render the Cross odious unto thee; for thou art to prefer it before the treasures of Egypt (Heb. 11:25, 26). Besides, the King of glory hath told thee, that he that will save his life shall lose it: and He that comes after him, and hates not his father, and mother, and wife, and children, and brethren, and sisters, yea and his own life also, he cannot be my Disciple (Mark 8:35; John 12:25; Matt. 10:39; Luke 14:26). I say therefore, for a man to labour to persuade thee, that that shall be thy death, without which, the Truth hath said, thou canst not have eternal life; This doctrine thou must abhor.

Thirdly, Thou must hate his setting of thy feet in the way that leadeth to the ministration of death. And for this thou must consider to whom he sent thee, and also how unable that person was to deliver thee from thy Burden.

He to whom thou wast sent for ease, being by name Legality, is the Son of the Bond woman which now is, and is in bondage with her children[20] (Gal. 4:21-27); and is in a mystery this Mount Sinai, which thou hast feared will fall on thy head. Now if she with her children are in bondage, how canst thou expect by them to be made free? This Legality therefore is not able to set thee free from thy Burden. No man was as yet ever rid of his Burden by him; no, nor ever is like to be: ye cannot be justified by the Works of the Law; for by the deeds of the Law no man living can be rid of his Burden: therefore, Mr. Worldly Wiseman is an alien, and Mr. Legality a cheat; and for his son Civility, notwithstanding his simpering looks, he is but a hypocrite and cannot help thee. Believe me, there is nothing in all this noise, that thou hast heard of this sottish man, but a design to beguile thee of thy Salvation, by turning thee from the way in which I had set thee. After this Evangelist called aloud to the Heavens for confirmation of what he had said; and with that there came words and fire out of the Mountain under which poor Christian stood, that made the hair of his flesh stand. The words were thus pronounced, As many as are of the works of the Law are under the curse; for it is written, Cursed is every one that continueth not in all things which are written in the Book of the Law to do them (Gal. 3:10).

Now Christian looked for nothing but death, and began to cry out lamentably, even cursing the time in which he met with Mr. Worldly Wiseman, still calling himself a thousand fools for hearkening to his counsel: he also was greatly ashamed to think that this Gentleman's arguments, flowing only from the flesh, should have that prevalency with him as to cause him to forsake the right way. This done, he applied himself again to Evangelist in words and sense as follows.

CHRISTIAN. Sir, what think you! Is there hopes? May I now go back and go up to the Wicket-gate? Shall I not be abandoned for this, and sent back from thence ashamed? I am sorry I have hearkened to this man's counsel: But may my sin be forgiven?

EVANGELIST. Then said Evangelist to him, Thy sin is very great, for by it thou hast committed two evils: thou hast forsaken the way that is good, to tread in forbidden paths; yet will the man at the Gate receive thee, for he has good will for men; only, said he, take heed that thou turn not aside again, lest thou perish from the way, when his wrath is kindled but a little (Ps. 2:12). Then did Christian address himself to go back; and Evangelist, after he had kissed him, gave him one smile, and bid him God-speed. So he went on with haste, neither spake he to any man by the way; nor if any man asked him, would he vouchsafe them an answer. He went like one that was all the while treading on forbidden ground, and could by no means think himself safe, till again he was got into the way which he left to follow Mr. Worldly Wiseman's counsel. So in process of time Christian got up to the Gate. Now over the Gate there was written, Knock and it shall be opened unto you (Matt. 7:8). He knocked, therefore, more than once or twice, saying,

May I now enter here? Will he within
Open to sorry me, though I have been
An undeserving Rebel? Then shall I
Not fail to sing his lasting praise on high.

At last there came a grave person to the gate named Good-will, who asked Who was there? and whence he came? and what he would have?

CHRISTIAN. Here is a poor burdened sinner. I come from the City of Destruction, but am going to Mount Zion, that I may be delivered from the wrath to come. I would therefore, Sir, since I am informed that by this Gate is the way thither, know if you are willing to let me in.

GOOD-WILL. I am willing with all my heart, said he; and with that he opened the Gate.

So when Christian was stepping in, the other gave him a pull. Then said Christian, What means that? The other told him, A little distance from this Gate, there is erected a strong Castle, of which Beelzebub is the Captain; from thence both he and they that are with him shoot arrows at those that come up to this Gate, if haply they may die before they can enter in. Then said Christian, I rejoice and tremble. So when he was got in, the man of the Gate asked him who directed him thither?

CHRISTIAN. Evangelist bid me come hither and knock (as I did); and he said that you, Sir, would tell me what I must do.

GOOD-WILL. An open door is set before thee, and no man can shut it.

CHRISTIAN. Now I begin to reap the benefits of my hazards.

GOOD-WILL. But how is it that you came alone?

CHRISTIAN. Because none of my Neighbours saw their danger, as I saw mine.

GOOD-WILL. Did any of them know of your coming?

CHRISTIAN. Yes, my Wife and Children saw me at the first, and called after me to turn again; also some of my neighbours stood crying and calling after me to return; but I put my fingers in my ears, and so came on my way.

GOOD-WILL. But did none of them follow you, to persuade you to go back?

CHRISTIAN. Yes, both Obstinate and Pliable; but when they saw that they could not prevail, Obstinate went railing back, but Pliable came with me a little way.

GOOD-WILL. But why did he not come through?

A Man may have company when he sets out for Heaven, and yet go thither alone.

CHRISTIAN. We indeed came both together, until we came at the Slough of Despond, into the which we also suddenly fell. And then was my Neighbour Pliable discouraged, and would not adventure farther. Wherefore getting out again on that side next to his own house, he told me I should possess the brave country alone for him; so he went on his way, and I came mine: he after Obstinate, and I to this Gate.

GOOD-WILL. Then said Good-will, Alas, poor man, is the celestial glory of so small esteem with him, that he counteth it not worth running the hazards of a few difficulties to obtain it?

CHRISTIAN. Truly, said Christian,[21] I have said the truth of Pliable, and if I should also say all the truth of myself, it will appear there is no betterment 'twixt him and myself.[22] 'Tis true, he went back to his own house, but I also turned aside to go in the way of death, being persuaded thereto by the carnal arguments of one Mr. Worldly Wiseman.

GOOD-WILL. Oh, did he light upon you? What! he would have had you seek for ease at the hands of Mr. Legality. They are both of them a very cheat: But did you take his counsel?

CHRISTIAN. Yes, as far as I durst: I went to find out Mr. Legality, until I thought that the Mountain that stands by his house would have fallen upon my head; wherefore there I was forced to stop.

GOOD-WILL. That Mountain has been the death of many, and will be the death of many more; 'tis well you escaped being by it dashed in pieces.

CHRISTIAN. Why truly I do not know what had become of me there, had not Evangelist happily met me again, as I was musing in the midst of my dumps: [23] but 'twas God's mercy that he came to me again, for else I had never come hither. But now I am come, such a one as I am, more fit indeed for death by that Mountain than thus to stand talking with my Lord; but Oh, what a favour is this to me, that yet I am admitted entrance here.

GOOD-WILL. We make no objections against any; notwithstanding all that they have done before they come hither, they in no wise are cast out (John 6:37); and therefore, good Christian, come a little way with me, and I will teach thee about the way thou must go. Look before thee; dost thou see this narrow way? THAT is the way thou must go: it was cast up by the Patriarchs, Prophets, Christ, and his Apostles; and it is as straight as a rule can make it: This is the way thou must go.

CHRISTIAN. But said Christian, Are there no turnings nor windings, by which a Stranger may lose the way?

GOOD-WILL. Yes, there are many ways butt down upon this,[24] and they are crooked and wide: But thus thou mayest distinguish the right from the wrong, That only being straight and narrow (Matt. 7:14).

Then I saw in my Dream, that Christian asked him further if he could not help him off with his Burden that was upon his back; for as yet he had not got rid thereof, nor could he by any means get it off without help.

He told him, As to thy Burden, be content to bear it, until thou comest to the place of Deliverance; for there it will fall from thy back itself.

Then Christian began to gird up his loins, and to address himself to his Journey. So the other told him, That by that he was gone some distance from the Gate, he would come at the house of the Interpreter, at whose door he should knock; and he would shew him excellent[25] things. Then Christian took his leave of his Friend, and he again bid him God-speed.

Then he went on till he came at the house of the Interpreter, where he knocked over and over; at last one came to the door, and asked Who was there?

CHRISTIAN. Sir, here is a Traveller, who was bid by an acquaintance of the good-man of this house to call here for my profit; I would therefore speak with the Master of the house. So he called for the Master of the house, who after a little time came to Christian, and asked him what he would have?

CHRISTIAN. Sir, said Christian, I am a man that am come from the City of Destruction, and am going to the Mount Zion; and I was told by the Man that stands at the Gate, at the head of this way, that if I called here, you would shew me excellent things, such as would be a help to me in my Journey.

INTERPRETER. Then said the Interpreter, Come in. I will shew thee that which will be profitable to thee. So he commanded his man to light the Candle, and bid Christian follow him: so he had him into a private room, and bid his man open a door; the which when he had done, Christian saw a Picture of a very grave Person hang up against the wall; and this was the fashion of it. It had eyes lifted up to Heaven, the best of Books in his hand, the Law of Truth was written upon his lips, the World was behind his back. It stood as if it pleaded with men, and a Crown of Gold did hang over his head.

CHRISTIAN. Then said Christian, What means this?

INTERPRETER. The Man whose Picture this is, is one of a thousand;[26] he can beget children (I Cor. 4:15) travail in birth with children (Gal. 4:19), and nurse them himself when they are born (I Thess. 2:7). And whereas thou seest him with his eyes lift up to Heaven, the best of Books in his hand, and the Law of Truth writ on his lips, it is to shew thee that his work is to know and unfold dark things to sinners; even as also thou seest him stand as if he pleaded with men; and whereas thou seest the World as cast behind him, and that a Crown hangs over his head, that is to shew thee that slighting and despising things that are present, for the love that he hath to his Master's service, he is sure in the world that comes next to have Glory for his reward. Now, said the Interpreter, I have shewed thee this Picture first, because the Man whose Picture this is, is the only man whom the Lord of the place whither thou art going hath authorised to be thy guide in all difficult places thou mayest meet with in the way; wherefore take good heed to what I have shewed thee, and bear well in thy mind what thou hast seen, lest in thy Journey thou meet with some that pretend to lead thee right, but their way goes down to death.

Then he took him by the hand, and led him into a very large Parlour that was full of dust, because never swept; the which after he had reviewed a little while, the Interpreter called for a man to sweep. Now when he began to sweep, the dust began so abundantly to fly about, that Christian had almost therewith been choked. Then said the Interpreter to a Damsel that stood by, Bring hither the Water, and sprinkle the Room; the which when she had done, it was swept and cleansed with pleasure.

CHRISTIAN. Then said Christian, What means this?

INTERPRETER. The Interpreter answered, This parlour is the heart of a man[27] that was never sanctified by the sweet Grace of the Gospel: the dust is his Original Sin and inward Corruptions, that have defiled the whole man. He that began to sweep at first is the Law; but she that brought water, and did sprinkle it, is the Gospel. Now, whereas thou sawest that so soon as the first began to sweep, the dust did so fly about that the Room by him could not be cleansed, but that thou wast almost choked therewith; this is to shew thee, that the Law, instead of cleansing the heart (by its working) from sin, doth revive, put strength into, and increase it in the soul, even as it doth discover and forbid it, for it doth not give power to subdue (Rom. 5:20; 7:6; I Cor. 15:56).

Again, as thou sawest the Damsel sprinkle the room with water, upon which it was cleansed with pleasure; this is to shew thee, that when the Gospel comes in the sweet and precious influences thereof to the heart, then I say, even as thou sawest the Damsel lay the dust by sprinkling the floor with Water, so is sin vanquished and subdued, and the soul made clean, through the faith of it, and consequently fit for the King of Glory to inhabit (John 15:3, 13; Eph. 5:26; Acts 15:9; Rom. 16:25, 26).

I saw moreover in my Dream, that the Interpreter took him by the hand, and had him into a little room, where sat two little Children, each one in his chair. The name of the eldest was Passion, and the name of the other Patience. Passion seemed to be much discontent; but Patience was very quiet. The Christian asked, What is the reason of the discontent of Passion? The Interpreter answered, The Governor of them[28] would have him stay for his best things till the beginning of the next year; but he will have all now; but Patience is willing to wait.

Then I saw that one came to Passion,[29] and brought him a bag of Treasure, and poured it down at his feet, the which he took up and rejoiced therein; and withal, laughed Patience to scorn. But I beheld but a while, and he had lavished all away, and had nothing left him but Rags.

CHRISTIAN. Then said Christian to the Interpreter, Expound this matter more fully to me.

INTERPRETER. So he said, These two Lads are figures: Passion, of the men of this world; and Patience, of the men of that which is to come; for as here thou seest, Passion will have all now this year, that is to say, in this world; so are the men of this world: they must have all their good things now, they cannot stay till next year, that is, until the next world, for their portion of good. That proverb, A Bird in the Hand is worth two in the Bush, is of more authority with them than are all the Divine testimonies of the good of the world to come. But as thou sawest that he had quickly lavished all away, and had presently left him nothing but Rags; so will it be with all such men at the end of this world.

CHRISTIAN. Then said Christian, Now I see that Patience has the best wisdom, and that upon many accounts. 1. Because he stays for the best things. 2. And also because he will have the Glory of his, when the other has nothing but Rags.

INTERPRETER. Nay, you may add another; to wit, The glory of the next world will never wear out; but these are suddenly gone. Therefore Passion had not so much reason to laugh at Patience, because he had his good things first, as Patience will have to laugh at Passion, because he had his best things last; for first must give place to last, because last must have his time to come: but last gives place to nothing; for there is not another to succeed. He, therefore, that hath his portion first must needs have a time to spend it; but he that hath his portion last must have it lastingly. Therefore it is said of Dives, In thy lifetime thou receivedst thy good things, and likewise Lazarus evil things; but now he is comforted, and thou art tormented (Luke 16).

CHRISTIAN. Then I perceive 'tis not best to covet things that are now, but to wait for things to come.

INTERPRETER. You say the truth: For the things that are seen are Temporal; but the things that are not seen are Eternal (II Cor. 4:18). But though this be so, yet since things present and our fleshly appetite are such near neighbours one to another; and, again, because things to come and carnal sense are such strangers one to another: therefore it is, that the first of these so suddenly fall into amity, and that distance is so continued between the second.

Then I saw in my Dream that the Interpreter took Christian by the hand, and led him into a place where was a Fire burning against a wall,[30] and one standing by it always casting much Water upon it to quench it; yet did the Fire burn higher and hotter.

Then said Christian, What means this?

The Interpreter answered, This Fire is the work of Grace that is wrought in the heart; he that casts Water upon it, to extinguish and put it out, is the Devil; but in that thou seest the Fire notwithstanding burn higher and hotter, thou shalt also see the reason of that. So he had him about to the backside of the wall, where he saw a man with a Vessel of Oil in his hand, of the which he did also continually cast (but secretly) into the Fire.

Then said Christian, What means this?

The Interpreter answered, This is Christ, who continually, with the Oil of his Grace, maintains the work already begun in the heart: by the means of which, notwithstanding what the Devil can do, the souls of his people prove gracious still (II Cor. 12:9). And in that thou sawest that the man stood behind the wall to maintain the Fire, that is to teach thee that it is hard for the tempted to see how this work of Grace is maintained in the soul.

I saw also that the Interpreter took him again by the hand, and led him into a pleasant place, where was builded a stately Palace, beautiful to behold; at the sight of which Christian was greatly delighted: He saw also upon the top thereof, certain persons walking, who were clothed all in gold.

Then said Christian, May we go in thither?

Then the Interpreter took him, and led him up toward the door of the Palace; and behold, at the door stood a great company of men, as desirous to go in, but durst not. There also sat a man at a little distance from the door, at a table-side, with a Book and his Inkhorn before him, to take the name of him that should enter therein: He saw also, that in the doorway stood many men in armour to keep it, being resolved to do the Man that would enter what hurt and mischief they could. Now was Christian somewhat in a muse.[31] At last, when every man started back for fear of the armed men, Christian saw a man of a very stout countenance come up to the man that sat there to write, saying, Set down my name, Sir: the which when he had done, he saw the man draw his Sword, and put an Helmet upon his head, and rush toward the door upon the armed men, who laid upon him with deadly force; but the man, not at all discouraged, fell to cutting and hacking most fiercely. So, after he had received and given many wounds to those that attempted to keep him out (Acts 14:22), he cut his way through them all, and pressed forward into the Palace; at which there was a pleasant voice heard from those that were within, even of the Three[32] that walked upon the top of the Palace.

Come in, Come in;
Eternal Glory thou shalt win.

So he went in, and was clothed with such garments as they. Then Christian smiled, and said, I think verily I know the meaning of this.

Now, said Christian, let me go hence. Nay stay, said the Interpreter, till I have shewed thee a little more, and after that thou shalt go on thy way. So he took him by the hand again, and led him into a very dark room, where there sat a Man in an Iron Cage.[33]

Now the Man, to look on, seemed very sad; he sat with his eyes looking down to the ground, his hands folded together; and he sighed as if he would break his heart. Then said Christian, What means this? At which the Interpreter bid him talk with the Man.

Then said Christian to the Man, What art thou? The Man answered, I am what I was not once.

CHRISTIAN. What wast thou once?

MAN. The man said, I was once a fair and flourishing Professor,[34] both in mine own eyes, and also in the eyes of others; I once was, as I thought, fair for the Celestial City (Luke 8:13), and had then even joy at the thoughts that I should get thither.

CHRISTIAN. Well, but what art thou now?

MAN. I am now a man of Despair, and am shut up in it, as in this Iron Cage. I cannot get out; Oh now I cannot.

CHRISTIAN. But how camest thou in this condition?

MAN. I left off to watch and be sober; I laid the reins upon the neck of my lusts; I sinned against the light of the Word and the goodness of God; I have grieved the Spirit, and he is gone; I tempted the Devil, and he is come to me; I have provoked God to anger, and he has left me; I have so hardened my heart, that I cannot repent.

Then said Christian to the Interpreter, But are there no hopes for such a man as this? Ask him, said the Interpreter.

CHRISTIAN. Nay, said Christian, pray Sir, do you.

INTERPRETER. Then said the Interpreter, Is there no hope, but you must be kept in the Iron Cage of Despair?

MAN. No, none at all.

INTERPRETER. Why? the Son of the Blessed is very pitiful.

MAN. I have crucified him to myself afresh (Heb. 6:6), I have despised his Person (Luke 19:14), I have despised his Righteousness, I have counted his Blood an unholy thing, I have done despite to the Spirit of Grace (Heb. 10:28, 29): Therefore I have shut myself out of all the Promises, and there now remains to me nothing but threatenings, dreadful threatenings, fearful threatenings of certain Judgment, which shall devour me as an Adversary.

INTERPRETER. For what did you bring yourself into this condition?

MAN. For the Lusts, Pleasures, and Profits of this World; in the enjoyment of which I did then promise myself much delight; but now even every one of those things also bite me, and gnaw me like a burning worm.

INTERPRETER. But canst thou not now repent and turn?

MAN. God hath denied me repentance: his Word gives me no encouragement to believe; yea, himself hath shut me up in this Iron Cage; nor can all the men in the world let me out. O Eternity! Eternity! how shall I grapple with the misery that I must meet with in Eternity!

INTERPRETER. Then said the Interpreter to Christian, Let this man's misery be remembered by thee, and be an everlasting caution to thee.

CHRISTIAN. Well, said Christian, this is fearful; God help me to watch and be sober, and to pray that I may shun the causes of this man's misery. Sir, is it not time for me to go on my way now?

INTERPRETER. Tarry till I shall shew thee one thing more, and then thou shalt go on thy way.

So he took Christian by the hand again, and led him into a Chamber, where there was one rising out of bed; and as he put on his raiment, he shook and trembled. Then said Christian, Why doth this man thus tremble? The Interpreter then bid him tell to Christian the reason of his so doing. So he began and said: This night, as I was in my sleep, I dreamed, and behold the Heavens grew exceeding black; also it thundered and lightened in most fearful wise, that it put me into an agony. So I looked up in my Dream, and saw the Clouds rack at an unusual rate,[35] upon which I heard a great sound of a Trumpet (I Cor. 15:52; I Thess. 4:16), and saw also a Man sit upon a Cloud, attended with the thousands of Heaven (Jude 15); they were all in flaming fire (II Thess. 1:8), also the Heavens were in a burning flame. I heard then a Voice saying, Arise ye Dead, and come to Judgment; and with that the Rocks rent, the Graves opened, and the Dead that were therein came forth (John 5:28; Rev. 20:11-14). Some of them were exceeding glad, and looked upward; and some sought to hide themselves under the Mountains (Isa. 26:21; Mic. 7:16, 17; Ps. 50:1-3). Then I saw the Man that sat upon the Cloud open the Book (Dan. 7:10), and bid the World draw near. Yet there was, by reason of a fiery flame that issued out and came from before him, a convenient distance betwixt him and them, as betwixt the Judge and the Prisoners at the bar (Mal. 3:2, 3; Dan. 7:9, 10). I heard it also proclaimed to them that attended on the Man that sat on the Cloud, Gather together the Tares, the Chaff, and Stubble, and cast them into the burning Lake. And with that, the bottomless pit opened, just whereabout I stood; out of the mouth of which there came in an abundant manner smoke and coals of fire, with hideous noises. It was also said to the same persons, Gather my Wheat into my Garner (Matt. 3:12; 13:30; Mal. 4:1; Luke 3:17). And with that I saw many catch'd up and carried away into the Clouds (I Thess. 4:16, 17), but I was left behind. I also sought to hide myself, but I could not, for the Man that sat upon the Cloud still kept his eye upon me: my sins also came into mind, and my Conscience did accuse me on every side (Rom. 2:14, 15). Upon this I awaked from my sleep.

CHRISTIAN. But what was it that made you so afraid of this sight?

MAN. Why, I thought that the day of Judgment was come, and that I was not ready for it: but this frighted me most, that the Angels gathered up several, and left me behind; also the pit of Hell opened her mouth just where I stood: my Conscience too within afflicted me; and as I thought, the Judge had always his eye upon me, shewing indignation in his countenance.

Then said the Interpreter to Christian, Hast thou considered all these things?

CHRISTIAN. Yes, and they put me in hope and fear.

INTERPRETER. Well, keep all things so in thy mind that they may be as a Goad in thy sides, to prick thee forward in the way thou must go. Then Christian began to gird up his loins, and to address himself to his Journey. Then said the Interpreter, The Comforter be always with thee, good Christian, to guide thee in the way that leads to the City.

Now I saw in my Dream that the highway up which Christian was to go was fenced on either side with a Wall, and that Wall is called Salvation (Isa. 26:1). Up this way therefore did burdened Christian run, but not without great difficulty, because of the load on his back.

He ran thus till he came at a place somewhat ascending, and upon that place stood a Cross, and a little below in the bottom, a Sepulchre. So I saw in my Dream, that just as Christian came up with the Cross, his Burden loosed from off his shoulders,[36] and fell from off his back, and began to tumble, and so continued to do, till it came to the mouth of the Sepulchre, where it fell in, and I saw it no more.

Who's this? the Pilgrim. How! 'tis very true,
Old things are past away, all's become new.
Strange! he's another man, upon my word,
They be fine Feathers that make a fine Bird.

Then was Christian glad and lightsome, and said with a merry heart, He hath given me rest by his sorrow, and life by his death. Then he stood still awhile to look and wonder; for it was very surprising to him, that the sight of the Cross should thus ease him of his Burden. He looked therefore, and looked again, even till the springs that were in his head sent the waters down his cheeks (Zech. 12:10). Now as he stood looking and weeping, behold three Shining Ones came to him and saluted him with Peace be to thee; so the first said to him, Thy sins be forgiven (Mark 2:5): the second stript him of his Rags, and clothed him with Change of Raiment; the third also set a mark in his forehead, and gave him a Roll with a Seal upon it (Zech 3:4; Eph. 1:13), which he bid him look on as he ran, and that he should give it in at the Celestial Gate. So they went their way. Then Christian gave three leaps for joy, and went out singing,

Thus far did I come laden with my sin;
Nor could aught ease the grief that I was in
Till I came hither: What a place is this!
Must here be the beginning of my bliss?
Must here the Burden fall from off my back?
Must here the strings that bound it to me crack?

Blest Cross! blest Sepulchre! blest rather be
The Man that there was put to shame for me.

I saw then in my Dream that he went on thus, even until he came at a bottom, where he saw, a little out of the way, three men fast asleep, with fetters upon their heels. The name of the one was Simple, another Sloth, and the third Presumption.

Christian then seeing them lie in this case, went to them, if peradventure he might awake them, and cried, You are like them that sleep on the top of a mast (Prov. 23:34), for the Dead Sea is under you, a gulf that hath no bottom. Awake therefore and come away; be willing also, and I will help you off with your Irons. He also told them, If he that goeth about like a roaring lion comes by, you will certainly become a prey to his teeth (I Pet. 5:8). With that they looked upon him, and began to reply in this sort: Simple said, I see no danger; Sloth said, Yet a little more sleep; and Presumption said, Every Fatt must stand upon his own bottom.[37] And so they lay down to sleep again, and Christian went on his way.

Yet was he troubled to think that men in that danger should so little esteem the kindness of him that so freely offered to help them, both by awakening of them, counselling of them, and proffering to help them off with their Irons. And as he was troubled thereabout, he espied two men come tumbling over the Wall, on the left hand of the narrow way; and they made up a pace to him. The name of the one was Formalist, and the name of the other Hypocrisy. So, as I said, they drew up unto him, who thus entered with them into discourse.

CHRISTIAN. Gentlemen, Whence came you, and whither do you go?

FORMALIST and HYPOCRISY. We were born in the land of Vain-glory, and are going for praise to Mount Zion.

CHRISTIAN. Why came you not in at the Gate which standeth at the beginning of the way? Know you not that it is written, That he that cometh not in by the Door, but climbeth up some other way, the same is a Thief and a Robber? (John 10:1.)

FORMALIST and HYPOCRISY. They said, That to go to the Gate for entrance was by all their countrymen counted too far about; and that therefore their usual way was to make a short cut of it, and to climb over, as they had done.

CHRISTIAN. But will it not be counted a Trespass against the Lord of the City whither we are bound, thus to violate his revealed will?

FORMALIST and HYPOCRISY. They told him, That as for that, he needed not to trouble his head thereabout; for what they did they had custom for; and could produce, if need were, Testimony that would witness it for more than a thousand years.

CHRISTIAN. But, said Christian, will your practice stand a Trial at Law?

FORMALIST and HYPOCRISY. They told him, That custom, it being of so long a standing as above a thousand years, would doubtless now be admitted as a thing legal by any impartial Judge; and besides, said they, so be we get into the way, what's matter which way we get in? if we are in, we are in; thou art but in the way, who, as we perceive, came in at the Gate; and we are also in the way, that came tumbling over the wall: wherein now is thy condition better than ours?

CHRISTIAN. I walk by the Rule of my Master, you walk by the rude working of your fancies. You are counted thieves already by the Lord of the way; therefore I doubt you will not be found true men at the end of the way. You come in by yourselves without his direction, and shall go out by yourselves without his mercy.

To this they made him but little answer; only they bid him look to himself. Then I saw that they went on every man in his way, without much conference one with another; save that these two men told Christian, that as to Laws and Ordinances,[38] they doubted not but they should as conscientiously do them as he. Therefore, said they, we see not wherein thou differest from us, but by the Coat that is on thy back, which was, as we tro, given thee by some of thy Neighbours, to hide the shame of thy nakedness.

CHRISTIAN. By Laws and Ordinances you will not be saved (Gal. 2:16), since you came not in by the door. And as for this Coat[39] that is on my back, it was given me by the Lord of the place whither I go; and that, as you say, to cover my nakedness with. And I take it as a token of his kindness to me, for I had nothing but rags before. And, besides, thus I comfort myself as I go: Surely, think I, when I come to the gate of the City, the Lord thereof will know me for good, since I have his Coat on my back; a Coat that he gave me freely in the day that he stript me of my rags. I have moreover a Mark in my forehead, of which perhaps you have taken no notice, which one of my Lord's most intimate associates fixed there in the day that my Burden fell off my shoulders. I will tell you, moreover, that I had then given me a Roll sealed, to comfort me by reading as I go in the way; I was also bid to give it in at the Celestial Gate, in token of my certain going in after it; all which things I doubt you want, and want them because you came not in at the Gate.

To these things they gave him no answer; only they looked upon each other and laughed. Then I saw that they went on all, save that Christian kept before, who had no more talk but with himself, and that sometimes sighingly, and sometimes comfortably; also he would be often reading in the Roll that one of the Shining Ones gave him, by which he was refreshed.

I beheld, then, that they all went on till they came to the foot of an Hill, at the bottom of which was a Spring. There was also in the same place two other ways besides that which came straight from the Gate; one turned to the left hand, and the other to the right, at the bottom of the Hill; but the narrow way lay right up the Hill, and the name of the going up the side of the Hill is called Difficulty. Christian now went to the Spring, and drank thereof to refresh himself (Isa. 49:10), and then began to go up the Hill, saying,

This Hill, though high, I covet to ascend;
The difficulty will not me offend;
For I perceive the way to life lies here:
Come, pluck up, Heart, let's neither faint nor fear:
Better, though difficult, the right way to go,
Than wrong, though easy, where the end is woe.

The other two also came to the foot of the Hill; but when they saw that the Hill was steep and high, and that there were two other ways to go; and supposing also that these two ways might meet again with that up which Christian went, on the other side of the Hill; therefore they were resolved to go in those ways. Now the name of one of those ways was Danger, and the name of the other Destruction. So the one took the way which is called Danger, which led him into a great Wood; and the other took directly up the way to Destruction, which led him into a wide field, full of dark Mountains[40] where he stumbled and fell, and rose no more.

I looked then after Christian to see him go up the Hill, where I perceived he fell from running to going, and from going to clambering upon his hands and his knees, because of the steepness of the place. Now about the mid-way to the top of the Hill was a pleasant Arbour, made by the Lord of the Hill for the refreshment of weary travellers; thither therefore Christian got, where also he sat down to rest him. Then he pulled his Roll out of his bosom, and read therein to his comfort; he also now began afresh to take a review of the Coat, or Garment, that was given him as he stood by the Cross. Thus pleasing himself awhile he at last fell into a slumber, and thence into a fast sleep, which detained him in that place until it was almost night; and in his sleep his Roll fell out of his hand. Now as he was sleeping, there came one to him and awaked him, saying, Go to the Ant, thou sluggard, consider her ways and be wise (Prov. 6:6). And with that Christian suddenly started up, and sped him on his way, and went apace till he came to the top of the Hill.

Now when he was got up to the top of the Hill, there came two men running against him amain; the name of the one was Timorous, and the name of the other Mistrust. To whom Christian said, Sirs, what's the matter you run the wrong way? [41] Timorous answered, that they were going to the City of Zion, and had got up that difficult place; but, said he, the further we go, the more danger we meet with; wherefore we turned, and are going back again.

Yes, said Mistrust, for just before us lie a couple of Lions[42] in the way, whether sleeping or waking we know not, and we could not think, if we came within reach, but they would presently pull us in pieces.

CHRISTIAN. Then said Christian, You make me afraid, but whither shall I fly to be safe? If I go back to mine own country, that is prepared for Fire and Brimstone; and I shall certainly perish there. If I can get to the Celestial City, I am sure to be in safety there. I must venture: To go back is nothing but death; to go forward is fear of death, and life everlasting beyond it. I will yet go forward. So Mistrust and Timorous ran down the Hill, and Christian went on his way. But thinking again of what he heard from the men, he felt in his bosom for his Roll, that he might read therein and be comforted; but he felt, and found it not. Then was Christian in great distress, and knew not what to do, for he wanted that which used to relieve him, and that which should have been his pass into the Celestial City. Here therefore he began to be much perplexed, and knew not what to do. At last he bethought himself that he had slept in the Arbour that is on the side of the Hill; and falling down upon his knees, he asked God's forgiveness for that his foolish fact,[43] and then went back to look for his Roll. But all the way he went back, who can sufficiently set forth the sorrow of Christian's heart? Sometimes he sighed, sometimes he wept, and oftentimes he chid himself, for being so foolish to fall asleep in that place, which was erected only for a little refreshment from his weariness. Thus therefore he went back, carefully looking on this side and on that, all the way as he went, if happily he might find[44] his Roll, that had been his comfort so many times in his Journey. He went thus till he came again within sight of the Arbour where he sat and slept; but that sight renewed his sorrow the more, by bringing again, even afresh, his evil of sleeping into his mind. Thus therefore he now went on bewailing his sinful sleep, saying, O wretched man that I am, that I should sleep in the daytime! (Rev. 2:5; I Thess. 5:7, 8) that I should sleep in the midst of difficulty! that I should so indulge the flesh, as to use that rest for ease to my flesh, which the Lord of the Hill had erected only for the relief of the spirits of Pilgrims! How many steps have I took in vain! (thus it happened to Israel for their sin [Num. 15:25], they were sent back again by the way of the Red Sea) and I am made to tread those steps with sorrow, which I might have trod with delight, had it not been for this sinful sleep. How far might I have been on my way by this time! I am made to tread those steps thrice over, which I needed not to have trod but once; yea, now also I am like to be benighted, for the day is almost spent. Oh that I had not slept!

Now by this time he was come to the Arbour again, where for a while he sat down and wept; but at last, as Christian would have it, looking sorrowfully down under the settle, there he espied his Roll; the which he with trembling and haste catched up, and put it into his bosom. But who can tell how joyful this man was when he had gotten his Roll again! for this Roll was the assurance of his life and acceptance at the desired Haven. Therefore he laid it up in his bosom, gave thanks to God for directing his eye to the place where it lay, and with joy and tears betook himself again to his Journey.

But Oh how nimbly now did he go up the rest of the Hill! Yet before he got up, the Sun went down upon Christian; and this made him again recall the vanity of his sleeping to his remembrance; and thus he again began to condole with himself: Ah! thou sinful sleep: how for thy sake am I like to be benighted in my Journey! I must walk without the Sun, darkness must cover the path of my feet, and I must hear the noise of doleful creatures,[45] because of my sinful sleep. Now also he remembered the story that Mistrust and Timorous told him of, how they were frighted with the sight of the Lions. Then said Christian to himself again, These beasts range in the night for their prey; and if they should meet with me in the dark, how should I shift them?[46] How should I escape being by them torn in pieces? Thus he went on his way. But while he was thus bewailing his unhappy miscarriage, he lift up his eyes, and behold there was a very stately Palace before him, the name whereof was Beautiful;[47] and it stood just by the High-way side.

So I saw in my Dream that he made haste and went forward, that if possible he might get Lodging there. Now before he had gone far, he entered into a very narrow passage, which was about a furlong off of the Porter's lodge; and looking very narrowly before him as he went, he espied two Lions in the way. Now, thought he, I see the dangers that Mistrust and Timorous were driven back by. (The Lions were chained, but he saw not the chains.) Then he was afraid, and thought also himself to go back after them, for he thought nothing but death was before him: But the Porter at the lodge, whose name is Watchful (Mark 13:34), perceiving that Christian made a halt as if he would go back, cried unto him, saying, Is thy strength so small? Fear not the Lions, for they are chained,[48] and are placed there for trial of faith where it is, and for discovery of those that have none. Keep in the midst of the Path, and no hurt shall come unto thee.

Then I saw that he went on, trembling for fear of the Lions, but taking good heed to the directions of the Porter; he heard them roar, but they did him no harm. Then he clapped his hands, and went on, till he came and stood before the Gate where the Porter was. Then said Christian to the Porter, Sir, what house is this? and may I lodge here to-night? The Porter answered, This house was built by the Lord of the Hill, and he built it for the relief and security of Pilgrims.

The Porter also asked whence he was, and whither he was going?

CHRISTIAN. I am come from the City of Destruction, and am going to Mount Zion; but because the Sun is now set, I desire, if I may, to lodge here to-night.

PORTER. What is your name?

CHRISTIAN. My name is now Christian, but my name at the first was Graceless; I came of the race of Japheth, whom God will persuade to dwell in the Tents of Shem (Gen. 9:27).

PORTER. But how doth it happen that you come so late? The Sun is set.

CHRISTIAN. I had been here sooner, but that, wretched man that I am! I slept in the Arbour that stands on the Hill-side; nay, I had, notwithstanding that, been here much sooner, but that in my sleep I lost my evidence,[49] and came without it to the brow of the Hill; and then feeling for it, and finding it not, I was forced with sorrow of heart to go back to the place where I slept my sleep, where I found it, and now I am come.

PORTER. Well, I will call out one of the Virgins of this place, who will, if she likes your talk, bring you in to the rest of the Family, according to the rules of the house. So Watchful the Porter, rang a bell, at the sound of which came out at the door of the house a grave and beautiful Damsel named Discretion, and asked why she was called.

The Porter answered, This man is in a Journey from the City of Destruction to Mount Zion, but being weary and benighted, he asked me if he might lodge here to-night; so I told him I would call for thee, who, after discourse had with him, mayest do as seemeth thee good, even according to the Law of the house.

Then she asked him whence he was, and whither he was going; and he told her. She asked him also, how he got into the way; and he told her. Then she asked him, what he had seen and met with in the way; and he told her. And last she asked his name; so he said, It is Christian, and I have so much the more a desire to lodge here to-night, because, by what I perceive, this place was built by the Lord of the Hill, for the relief and security of Pilgrims. So she smiled, but the water stood in her eyes; and after a little pause she said, I will call forth two or three more of the Family. So she ran to the door, and called out Prudence, Piety, and Charity,[50] who, after a little more discourse with him, had him in to the Family; and many of them, meeting him at the threshold of the house, said, Come in thou blessed of the Lord; this house was built by the Lord of the Hill on purpose to entertain such Pilgrims in. Then he bowed his head, and followed them into the house. So when he was come in and set down, they gave him something to drink, and consented together, that until supper was ready, some of them should have some particular discourse with Christian, for the best improvement of time; and they appointed Piety, and Prudence, and Charity to discourse with him; and thus they began.

PIETY. Come, good Christian, since we have been so loving to you, to receive you into our house this night, let us, if perhaps we may better ourselves thereby, talk with you of all things that have happened to you in your Pilgrimage.

CHRISTIAN. With a very good will, and I am glad that you are so well disposed.

PIETY. What moved you at first to betake you to a Pilgrim's life?

CHRISTIAN. I was driven out of my Native Country by a dreadful sound that was in mine ears: to wit, that unavoidable destruction did attend me if I abode in that place where I was.

PIETY. But how did it happen that you came out of your Country this way?

CHRISTIAN. It was as God would have it; for when I was under the fears of destruction, I did not know whither to go; but by chance there came a Man, even to me, as I was trembling and weeping, whose name is Evangelist, and he directed me to the Wicket-gate, which else I should never have found; and so set me into the way that hath led me directly to this House.

PIETY. But did you not come by the house of the Interpreter?

CHRISTIAN. Yes, and did see such things there, the remembrance of which will stick by me as long as I live; especially three things: to wit, How Christ, in despite of Satan, maintains his work of Grace in the heart; how the man had sinned himself quite out of hopes of God's mercy; and also the Dream of him that thought in his sleep the day of Judgment was come.

PIETY. Why, did you hear him tell his dream?

CHRISTIAN. Yes, and a dreadful one it was. I thought it made my heart ache as he was telling of it; but yet I am glad I heard it.

PIETY. Was that all that you saw at the House of the Interpreter?

CHRISTIAN. No: he took me and had me where he shewed me a stately Palace, and how the people were clad in Gold that were in it; and how there came a venturous Man and cut his way through the armed men that stood in the door to keep him out, and how he was bid to come in and win eternal Glory. Methought those things did ravish my heart; I could have stayed at that good Man's house a twelvemonth, but that I knew I had farther to go.

PIETY. And what saw you else in the way?

CHRISTIAN. Saw! Why, I went but a little farther, and I saw one, as I thought in my mind, hang bleeding upon the Tree; and the very sight of him made my burden fall off my back (for I groaned under a weary burden), but then it fell down from off me. 'Twas a strange thing to me, for I never saw such a thing before; yea, and while I stood looking up (for then I could not forbear looking) three Shining Ones came to me. One of them testified that my sins were forgiven me; another stript me of my Rags, and gave me this broidered Coat which you see; and the third set the Mark which you see in my forehead, and gave me this sealed Roll (and with that he plucked it out of his bosom).

PIETY. But you saw more than this, did you not?

CHRISTIAN. The things that I have told you were the best; yet some other small matters I saw, as namely I saw three Men, Simple, Sloth, and Presumption, lie asleep a little out of the way as I came, with Irons upon their heels; but do you think I could awake them? I also saw Formalist and Hypocrisy come tumbling over the wall, to go, as they pretended, to Zion; but they were quickly lost, even as I myself did tell them, but they would not believe. But, above all, I found it hard work to get up this Hill, and as hard to come by the Lions' mouths; and truly if it had not been for the good Man, the Porter that stands at the Gate, I do not know but that after all I might have gone back again; but now I thank God I am here, and I thank you for receiving of me.

Then Prudence thought good to ask him a few questions, and desired his answer to them.

PRUDENCE. Do you not think sometimes of the Country from whence you came?

CHRISTIAN. Yes, but with much shame and detestation: truly, if I had been mindful of that Country from whence I came out, I might have had opportunity to have returned; but now I desire a better Country, that is, an Heavenly (Heb. 11:15, 16).

PRUDENCE. Do you not yet bear away with you some of the things that then you were conversant withal?

CHRISTIAN. Yes, but greatly against my will; especially my inward and carnal cogitations; with which all my countrymen, as well as myself, were delighted; but now all those things are my grief; and might I but choose mine own things, I would choose never to think of those things more; but when I would be doing of that which is best, that which is worst is with me (Rom. 7).

PRUDENCE. Do you not find sometimes, as if those things were vanquished, which at other times are your perplexity?

CHRISTIAN. Yes, but that is but seldom; but they are to me golden hours in which such things happen to me.

PRUDENCE. Can you remember by what means you find your annoyances at times, as if they were vanquished?

CHRISTIAN. Yes, when I think what I saw at the Cross, that will do it; and when I look upon my broidered Coat, that will do it; also when I look into the Roll that I carry in my bosom, that will do it; and when my thoughts wax warm about whither I am going, that will do it.

PRUDENCE. And what is it that makes you so desirous to go to Mount Zion?

CHRISTIAN. Why, there I hope to see him alive that did hang dead on the Cross; and there I hope to be rid of all those things that to this day are in me an annoyance to me; there, they say, there is no death (Isa. 25:8; Rev. 21:4); and there I shall dwell with such Company as I like best. For to tell you truth, I love him, because I was by him eased of my Burden, and I am weary of my inward sickness; I would fain be where I shall die no more, and with the Company that shall continually cry, Holy, Holy, Holy.

Then said Charity to Christian, Have you a family? Are you a married man?

CHRISTIAN. I have a Wife and four small Children.

CHARITY. And why did you not bring them along with you?

CHRISTIAN. Then Christian wept, and said, Oh how willingly would I have done it, but they were all of them utterly averse to my going on Pilgrimage.

CHARITY. But you should have talked to them, and have endeavoured to have shewn them the danger of being behind.

CHRISTIAN. So I did and told them also what God had shewed to me of the destruction of our City; but I seemed to them as one that mocked, and they believed me not (Gen. 19:14).

CHARITY. And did you pray to God that he would bless your counsel to them?

CHRISTIAN. Yes, and that with much affection; for you must think that my Wife and poor Children were very dear unto me.

CHARITY. But did you tell them of your own sorrow, and fear of destruction? for I suppose that destruction was visible enough to you.

CHRISTIAN. Yes, over, and over, and over. They might also see my fears in my countenance, in my tears, and also in my trembling under the apprehension of the Judgment that did hang over our heads; but all was not sufficient to prevail with them to come with me.

CHARITY. But what could they say for themselves, why they came not?

CHARITY. Why, my Wife was afraid of losing this World, and my children were given to the foolish Delights of youth: so what by one thing, and what by another, they left me to wander in this manner alone.

CHARITY. But did you not with your vain life, damp all that you by words used by way of persuasion to bring them away with you?

CHRISTIAN. Indeed I cannot commend my life; for I am conscious to myself of many failings therein: I know also that a man by his conversation may soon overthrow what by argument or persuasion he doth labour to fasten upon others for their good. Yet this I can say, I was very wary of giving them occasion, by any unseemly action, to make them averse to going on Pilgrimage. Yea, for this very thing they would tell me I was too precise, and that I denied myself of things (for their sakes) in which they saw no evil. Nay, I think I may say, that if what they saw in me did hinder them, it was my great tenderness in sinning against God, or of doing any wrong to my Neighbour.

CHARITY. Indeed Cain hated his Brother, because his own works were evil, and his Brother's righteous (I John 3:12); and if thy Wife and Children have been offended with thee for this, they thereby shew themselves to be implacable to good, and thou hast delivered thy soul from their blood (Ezek. 3:19).

Now I saw in my Dream that thus they sat talking together until supper was ready. So when they had made ready, they sat down to meat. Now the Table was furnished with fat things, and with Wine that was well refined: and all their talk at the Table was about the LORD of the Hill; as namely, about what HE had done, and wherefore HE did what He did, and why HE had builded that House: and by what they said, I perceived that he had been a great Warrior and had fought with and slain him that had the power of Death (Heb. 2:14, 15), but not without great danger to himself, which made me love him the more.

For, as they said, and as I believe (said Christian) he did it with the loss of much blood; but that which put Glory of Grace into all he did was, that he did it out of pure love to his Country. And, besides, there were some of them of the household that said they had seen and spoke with him since he did die on the Cross; and they have attested that they had it from his own lips, that he is such a lover of poor Pilgrims that the like is not to be found from the East to the West.

They moreover gave an instance of what they affirmed, and that was, He had stript himself of his glory,[51] that he might do this for the Poor; and that they heard him say and affirm, That he would not dwell in the Mountain of Zion alone. They said, moreover, that he had made many Pilgrims Princes, though by nature they were Beggars born, and their original had been the dunghill (I Sam. 2:8; Ps. 113:7).

Thus they discoursed together till late at night; and after they had committed themselves to their Lord for protection, they betook themselves to rest. The Pilgrim they laid in a large upper chamber, whose window opened towards the Sun rising: the name of the chamber was Peace, where he slept till break of day, and then he awoke and sang,

Where am I now? Is this the love and care
Of Jesus, for the men that Pilgrims are
Thus to provide! That I should be forgiven!
And dwell already the next door to Heaven!

So in the morning they all got up, and after some more discourse, they told him that he should not depart till they had shewed him the Rarities of that place. And first they had him into the Study, where they shewed him Records of the greatest antiquity; in which, as I remember in my Dream, they shewed him first the Pedigree of the Lord of the Hill, that he was the Son of the Ancient of Days, and came by an Eternal Generation. Here also was more fully recorded the Acts that he had done, and the names of many hundreds that he had taken into his service; and how he had placed them in such Habitations that could neither by length of Days, nor decays of Nature, be dissolved.

Then they read to him some of the worthy Acts that some of his servants had done: as, how they had subdued Kingdoms, wrought Righteousness, obtained Promises, stopped the mouths of Lions, quenched the violence of Fire, escaped the edge of the Sword; out of weakness were made strong, waxed valiant in fight, and turned to flight the Armies of the Aliens (Heb. 11:33, 34).

Then they read again in another part of the Records of the house, where it was shewed how willing their Lord was to receive into his favour any, even any, though they in time past had offered great affronts to his Person and proceedings. Here also were several other Histories of many other famous things, of all which Christian had a view; as of things both Ancient and Modern: together with Prophecies and Predictions of things that have their certain accomplishment, both to the dread and amazement of Enemies, and the comfort and solace of Pilgrims.

The next day they took him and had him into the Armoury, where they shewed him all manner of Furniture, which their Lord had provided for Pilgrims, as Sword, Shield, Helmet, Breastplate,[52] All-prayer, and Shoes that would not wear out. And there was here enough of this to harness out as many men for the service of their Lord as there be Stars in the Heaven for multitude.

They also shewed him some of the Engines with which some of his Servants had done wonderful things. They shewed him

Moses' Rod;[53] the Hammer and Nail with which Jael[54] slew Sisera; the Pitchers, Trumpets, and Lamps, too, with which Gideon[55] put to flight the Armies of Midian: then they shewed him the Ox's goad wherewith Shamgar[56] slew six hundred men: they shewed him also the Jaw-bone with which Samson did such mighty feats: they shewed him moreover the Sling and Stone with which David[57] slew Goliath of Gath; and the Sword also with which their Lord will kill the Man of Sin[58] in the day that he shall rise up to the prey. They shewed him besides many excellent things, with which Christian was much delighted. This done, they went to their rest again.

Then I saw in my Dream, that on the morrow he got up to go forwards, but they desired him to stay till the next day also; and then, said they, we will (if the day be clear) shew you the Delectable Mountains;[59] which, they said, would yet further add to his comfort, because they were nearer the desired Haven than the place where at present he was. So he consented and stayed. When the morning was up, they had him to the top of the House, and bid him look South; so he did: and behold at a great distance (Isa. 33:16, 17) he saw a most pleasant Mountainous Country, beautified with Woods, Vineyards, Fruits of all sorts, Flowers also, with Springs and Fountains, very delectable to behold. Then he asked the name of the Country: they said it was Immanuel's Land; and it is as common, said they, as this Hill is, to and for all the Pilgrims. And when thou comest there, from thence, said they, thou mayest see to the gate of the Celestial City, as the Shepherds that live there will make appear.

Now he bethought himself of setting forward, and they were willing he should: but first, said they, let us go again into the Armoury: so they did; and when they came there, they harnessed him from head to foot with what was of proof, lest perhaps he should meet with assaults in the way.

He being therefore thus accoutred, walketh out with his friends to the Gate, and there he asked the Porter if he saw any Pilgrims pass by. Then the Porter answered, Yes.

CHRISTIAN. Pray, did you know him?

PORTER. I asked his name, and he told me it was Faithful.

CHRISTIAN. Oh, said Christian, I know him; he is my Townsman, my near Neighbour, he comes from the place where I was born: How far do you think he may be before?

PORTER. He is got by this time below the Hill.

CHRISTIAN. Well, said Christian, good Porter, the Lord be with thee, and add to all thy blessings much increase, for the kindness that thou hast shewed to me.

Then he began to go forward; but Discretion, Piety, Charity, and Prudence, would accompany him down to the foot of the Hill. So they went on together, reiterating their former discourses, till they came to go down the Hill. Then said Christian, As it was difficult coming up, so (so far as I can see) it is dangerous going down. Yes, said Prudence, so it is; for it is a hard matter for a man to go down into the Valley of Humiliation, as thou art now, and to catch no slip by the way; therefore, said they, are we come out to accompany thee down the Hill. So he began to go down, but very warily; yet he caught a slip or two.

Then I saw in my Dream that these good Companions, when Christian was gone down to the bottom of the Hill, gave him a loaf of Bread, a bottle of Wine, and a cluster of Raisins;[60] and then he went on his way.

But now, in this Valley of Humiliation, poor Christian was hard put to it; for he had gone but a little way before he espied a foul Fiend coming over the field to meet him; his name is Apollyon.[61] Then did Christian begin to be afraid, and to cast in his mind whether to go back or to stand his ground: but he considered again that he had no Armour for his back, and therefore thought that to turn the back to him might give him the greater advantage with ease to pierce him with his Darts. Therefore he resolved to venture and stand his ground. For, thought he, had I no more in mine eye than the saving of my life, 'twould be the best way to stand.

So he went on, and Apollyon met him. Now the Monster was hideous to behold; he was clothed with scales like a Fish (and they are his pride); he had wings like a Dragon, feet like a Bear, and out of his belly came Fire and Smoke; and his mouth was as the mouth of a Lion. When he was come up to Christian, he beheld him with a disdainful countenance, and thus began to question with him.

APOLLYON. Whence come you? and whither are you bound?

CHRISTIAN. I am come from the City of Destruction, which is the place of all evil, and am going to the City of Zion.

APOLLYON. By this I perceive thou art one of my Subjects, for all that Country is mine, and I am the Prince and God of it. How is it then that thou hast run away from thy King? Were it not that I hope thou mayest do me more service, I would strike thee now at one blow to the ground.

CHRISTIAN. I was born indeed in your dominions, but your service was hard, and your wages such as a man could not live on, for the wages of sin is death (Rom. 6:23); therefore when I was come to years, I did as other considerate persons do, look out, if perhaps I might mend myself.

APOLLYON. There is no Prince that will thus lightly lose his subjects, neither will I as yet lose thee: but since thou complainest of thy service and wages, be content to go back; what our Country will afford, I do here promise to give thee.

CHRISTIAN. But I have let myself[62] to another, even to the King of Princes, and how can I with fairness go back with thee?

APOLLYON. Thou hast done in this, according to the Proverb, changed a bad for a worse; but it is ordinary for those that have professed themselves his Servants, after a while to give him the slip, and return again to me: Do thou so too, and all shall be well.

CHRISTIAN. I have given him my faith, and sworn my allegiance to him; how then can I go back from this, and not be hanged as a Traitor?

APOLLYON. Thou didst the same to me, and yet I am willing to pass by all, if now thou wilt yet turn again and go back.

CHRISTIAN. What I promised thee was in my nonage; and besides I count that the Prince under whose Banner now I stand is able to absolve me; yea, and to pardon also what I did as to my compliance with thee; and besides, O thou destroying Apollyon, to speak truth, I like his Service, his Wages, his Servants, his Government, his Company, and Country, better than thine; and therefore leave off to persuade me further; I am his Servant, and I will follow him.

APOLLYON. Consider again when thou art in cool blood, what thou art like to meet with in the way that thou goest. Thou knowest that for the most part his Servants come to an ill end, because they are transgressors against me and my ways: How many of them have been put to shameful deaths! and besides, thou countest his service better than mine, whereas he never came yet from the place where he is, to deliver any that served him out of our hands; but as for me, how many times, as all the World very well knows, have I delivered, either by power or fraud, those that have faithfully served me, from him and his, though taken by them; and so I will deliver thee.

CHRISTIAN. His forbearing at present to deliver them is on purpose to try their love, whether they will cleave to him to the end; and as for the ill end thou sayest they come to, that is most glorious in their account; for, for present deliverance, they do not much expect it; for they stay for their Glory, and then they shall have it, when their Prince comes in his and the Glory of the Angels.

APOLLYON. Thou hast already been unfaithful in thy service to him, and how dost thou think to receive wages of him?

CHRISTIAN. Wherein, O Apollyon, have I been unfaithful to him?

APOLLYON. Thou didst faint at first setting out, when thou wast almost choked in the Gulf of Despond; thou didst attempt wrong ways to be rid of thy Burden, whereas thou shouldest have stayed till thy Prince had taken it off; thou didst sinfully sleep and lose thy choice thing; thou wast almost persuaded to go back, at the sight of the Lions; and when thou talkest of thy Journey, and of what thou hast heard and seen, thou art inwardly desirous of vain-glory in all that thou sayest or doest.

CHRISTIAN. All this is true, and much more which thou hast left out; but the Prince whom I serve and honour is merciful, and ready to forgive; but, besides, these infirmities possessed me in thy Country, for there I sucked them in, and I have groaned under them, been sorry for them, and have obtained Pardon of my Prince.

APOLLYON. Then Apollyon broke out into a grievous rage, saying, I am an enemy to this Prince; I hate his Person, his Laws, and People; I am come out on purpose to withstand thee.

CHRISTIAN. Apollyon, beware what you do, for I am in the King's Highway,[63] the way of Holiness, therefore take heed to yourself.

APOLLYON. Then Apollyon strodled[64] quite over the whole breadth of the way, and said, I am void of fear in this matter, prepare thyself to die; for I swear by my infernal Den, that thou shalt go no farther; here will I spill thy soul.

And with that he threw a flaming Dart at his breast, but Christian had a Shield in his hand, with which he caught it, and so prevented the danger of that.

Then did Christian draw, for he saw 'twas time to bestir him: and Apollyon as fast made at him, throwing Darts as thick as Hail; by the which, notwithstanding all that Christian could do to avoid it, Apollyon wounded him in his head, his hand, and foot: This made Christian give a little back; Apollyon therefore followed his work amain, and Christian again took courage and resisted as manfully as he could. This sore Combat lasted for above half a day, even till Christian was almost quite spent; for you must know that Christian, by reason of his wounds, must needs grow weaker and weaker.

Then Apollyon espying his opportunity, began to gather up close to Christian, and wrestling with him, gave him a dreadful fall; and with that Christian's Sword flew out of his hand. Then said Apollyon, I am sure of thee now: and with that he had almost pressed him to death, so that Christian began to despair of life. But as God would have it, while Apollyon was fetching of his last blow, thereby to make a full end of this good man, Christian nimbly reached out his hand for his Sword, and caught it, saying, Rejoice not against me, O mine Enemy! when I fall I shall arise (Mic. 7:8); and with that gave him a deadly thrust, which made him give back, as one that had received his mortal wound: Christian perceiving that, made at him again, saying, Nay, in all these things we are more than conquerors through him that loved us (Rom. 8:37; James 4:7). And with that Apollyon spread forth his Dragon's wings, and sped him away, that Christian for a season saw him no more.[65]

In this Combat no man can imagine, unless he had seen and heard as I did, what yelling and hideous roaring Apollyon made all the time of the fight, he spake like a Dragon; and on the other side, what sighs and groans brast[66] from Christian's heart. I never saw him all the while give so much as one pleasant look, till he perceived he had wounded Apollyon with his two-edged Sword; then indeed he did smile, and look upward; but 'twas the dreadfullest sight that ever I saw.

So when the Battle was over, Christian said, I will here give thanks to him that hath delivered me out of the mouth of the Lion, to him that did help me against Apollyon. And so he did, saying,

Great Beelzebub, the Captain of this Fiend,
Design'd my ruin; therefore to this end
He sent him harness'd out: and he with rage
That hellish was, did fiercely me engage:
But blessed Michael helped me, and I
By dint of Sword did quickly make him fly.
Therefore to him let me give lasting praise,
And thank and bless his holy name always.

Then there came to him a hand, with some of the leaves of the Tree of Life,[67] the which Christian took, and applied to the wounds that he had received in the Battle, and was healed immediately. He also sat down in that place to eat Bread, and to drink of the Bottle that was given him a little before; so being refreshed, he addressed himself to his Journey, with his Sword drawn in his hand; for he said, I know not but some other Enemy may be at hand. But he met with no other affront from Apollyon[68] quite through this Valley.

Now at the end of this Valley was another, called the Valley of the Shadow of Death, and Christian must needs go through it, because the way to the Celestial City lay through the midst of it. Now, this Valley is a very solitary place. The Prophet Jeremiah thus describes it: A wilderness, a land of deserts and of pits, a land of drought, and of the shadow of death, a land that no man (but a Christian) passeth through, and where no man dwelt (Jer. 2:6).

Now here Christian was worse put to it than in his fight with Apollyon, as by the sequel you shall see.

I saw then in my Dream, that when Christian was got to the borders of the Shadow of Death, there met him two men, Children of them that brought up an evil report[69] of the good land (Num. 13:32), making haste to go back; to whom Christian spake as follows—

CHRISTIAN. Whither are you going?

MEN. They said, Back, back; and we would have you to do so too, if either life or peace is prized by you.

CHRISTIAN. Why, what's the matter? said Christian.

MEN. Matter! said they; we were going that way as you are going, and went as far as we durst; and indeed we were almost past coming back; for had we gone a little farther, we had not been here to bring the news to thee.

CHRISTIAN. But what have you met with? said Christian.

MEN. Why we were almost in the Valley of the Shadow of

Death (Ps. 44:19; 107:10); but that by good hap we looked before us, and saw the danger before we came to it.

CHRISTIAN. But what have you seen? said Christian.

MEN. Seen! Why, the Valley itself, which is as dark as pitch; we also saw there the Hobgoblins, Satyrs,[70] and Dragons of the Pit; we heard also in that Valley a continual howling and yelling, as of a people under unutterable misery, who there sat bound in affliction and irons; and over that Valley hangs the discouraging clouds of Confusion; Death also doth always spread his wings over it (Job 3:5; 10:22). In a word it is every whit dreadful, being utterly without Order.

CHRISTIAN. Then said Christian, I perceive not yet, by what you have said, but that this is my way to the desired Haven (Jer. 2:6).

MEN. Be it thy way; we will not choose it for ours. So they parted, and Christian went on his way, but still with his Sword drawn in his hand, for fear lest he should be assaulted.

I saw then in my Dream, so far as this Valley reached, there was on the right hand a very deep Ditch; that Ditch is it unto which the blind have led the blind in all ages, and have both there miserably perished. Again, behold on the left hand, there was a very dangerous Quag, into which, if even a good man falls, he can find no bottom for his foot to stand on. Into that Quag King David once did fall, and had no doubt therein been smothered, had not he that is able plucked him out (Ps. 69:14).

The pathway was here also exceeding narrow, and therefore good Christian was the more put to it; for when he sought in the dark to shun the Ditch on the one hand, he was ready to tip over into the mire on the other; also when he sought to escape the mire, without great carefulness he would be ready to fall into the Ditch. Thus he went on, and I heard him here sigh bitterly; for, besides the dangers mentioned above, the pathway was here so dark, that oft-times, when he lift up his foot to set forward, he knew not where, or upon what he should set it next.

About the midst of this valley, I perceived the mouth of Hell to be, and it stood also hard by the wayside. Now, thought Christian, what shall I do? And ever and anon the flame and smoke would come out in such abundance, with sparks and hideous noises (things that cared not for Christian's Sword, as did Apollyon before) that he was forced to put up his Sword, and betake himself to another weapon, called All-prayer (Eph. 6:18). So he cried in my hearing, O Lord I beseech thee deliver my Soul (Ps. 116:4). Thus he went on a great while, yet still the flames would be reaching towards him: also he heard doleful voices, and rushings to and fro, so that sometimes he thought he should be torn in pieces, or trodden down like mire in the Streets. This frightful sight was seen, and these dreadful noises were heard by him for several miles together; and coming to a place where he thought he heard a company of Fiends coming forward to meet him, he stopped, and began to muse what he had best to do. Sometimes he had half a thought to go back; then again he thought he might be half way through the Valley; he remembered also how he had already vanquished many a danger, and that the danger of going back might be much more than for to go forward; so he resolved to go on. Yet the Fiends seemed to come nearer and nearer; but when they were come even almost at him, he cried out with a most vehement voice, I will walk in the strength of the Lord God; so they gave back, and came no farther.

One thing I would not let slip; I took notice that now poor Christian was so confounded that he did not know his own voice; and thus I perceived it: just when he was come over against the mouth of the burning Pit, one of the wicked ones got behind him, and stepped up softly to him, and whisperingly suggested many grievous blasphemies[71] to him, which he verily thought had proceeded from his own mind. This put Christian more to it than anything that he met with before, even to think that he should now blaspheme him that he loved so much before; yet, if he could have helped it, he would not have done it; but he had not the discretion neither to stop his ears, nor to know from whence those blasphemies came.

When Christian had travelled in this disconsolate condition some considerable time, he thought he heard the voice of a man, as going before him, saying, Though I walk through the Valley of the Shadow of Death, I will fear none ill,[72] for thou art with me (Ps. 23:4).

Then was he glad, and that for these reasons:

First, Because he gathered from thence, that some who feared God were in this Valley as well as himself.

Secondly, For that he perceived God was with them, though

in that dark and dismal State; and why not, thought he, with me? though by reason of the impediment that attends this place, I cannot perceive it (Job 9:10).

Thirdly, For that he hoped, could he overtake them, to have company by and by. So he went on, and called to him that was before; but he knew not what to answer, for that he also thought himself to be alone. And by and by the day broke; then said Christian, He hath turned the Shadow of Death into the morning (Amos 5:8).

Now morning being come, he looked back, not out of desire to return, but to see, by the light of the day, what hazards he had gone through in the dark. So he saw more perfectly the Ditch that was on the one hand and the Quag that was on the other; also how narrow the way was which lay betwixt them both; also now he saw the Hobgoblins, and Satyrs, and Dragons of the Pit, but all afar off; for after break of day they came not nigh; yet they were discovered to him, according to that which is written, He discovereth deep things out of darkness, and bringeth out to light the Shadow of Death (Job 12:22).

Now was Christian much affected with his deliverance from all the dangers of his solitary way; which dangers, though he feared them more before, yet he saw them more clearly now, because the light of the day made them conspicuous to him. And about this time the Sun was rising, and this was another mercy to Christian; for you must note, that though the first part of the Valley of the Shadow of Death was dangerous, yet this second part which he was yet to go, was, if possible, far more dangerous: for from the place where he now stood, even to the end of the Valley, the way was all along set so full of Snares, Traps, Gins, and Nets here, and so full of Pits, Pitfalls, deep Holes, and Shelvings down there, that had it now been dark as it was when he came the first part of the way, had he had a thousand souls, they had in reason been cast away; but as I said, just now the Sun was rising. Then said he, His candle shineth on my head, and by his light I go through darkness (Job 29:3).

In this light therefore he came to the end of the Valley. Now I saw in my Dream, that at the end of this Valley lay blood, bones, ashes, and mangled bodies of men, even of Pilgrims that had gone this way formerly; and while I was musing what should be the reason, I espied a little before me a Cave, where two Giants, Pope and Pagan, dwelt in old time; by whose power and tyranny the men whose bones, blood, ashes, etc., lay there, were cruelly put to death. But by this place Christian went without much danger, whereat I somewhat wondered; but I have learned since that Pagan has been dead many a day; and as for the other, though he be yet alive, he is by reason of age, and also of the many shrewd brushes that he met with in his younger days, grown so crazy, and stiff in his joints, that he can now do little more than sit in his Cave's mouth, grinning at Pilgrims as they go by, and biting his nails, because he cannot come at them.[73]

So I saw that Christian went on his way; yet at the sight of the Old Man that sat in the mouth of the Cave, he could not tell what to think, specially because he spake to him, though he could not go after him, saying, You will never mend till more of you be burned: but he held his peace, and set a good face on't, and so went by and catched no hurt.

Now as Christian went on his way, he came to a little ascent, which was cast up on purpose that Pilgrims might see before them. Up there therefore Christian went, and looking forward he saw Faithful before him upon his Journey. Then said Christian aloud, Ho, ho, So-ho; stay, and I will be your Companion. At that Faithful looked behind him; to whom Christian cried again, Stay, stay, till I come up to you: But Faithful answered, No, I am upon my life, and the Avenger of Blood [74] is behind me.

At this Christian was somewhat moved, and putting to all his strength, he quickly got up with Faithful, and did also overrun[75] him, so the last was first. Then did Christian vain-gloriously smile, because he had gotten the start of his Brother; but not taking good heed to his feet, he suddenly stumbled and fell, and could not rise again, until Faithful came up to help him.

Then I saw in my Dream they went very lovingly on together, and had sweet discourse of all things that had happened to them in their Pilgrimage; and thus Christian began:

CHRISTIAN. My honoured and well-beloved Brother Faithful, I am glad that I have overtaken you; and that God has so tempered our spirits, that we can walk as Companions in this so pleasant a path.

FAITHFUL. I had thought, dear Friend, to have had your company quite from our Town; but you did get the start of me, wherefore I was forced to come thus much of the way alone.

CHRISTIAN. How long did you stay in the City of Destruction, before you set out after me on your Pilgrimage?

FAITHFUL. Till I could stay no longer; for there was great talk presently after you was gone out, that our City would in short time with Fire from Heaven be burned down to the ground.

CHRISTIAN. What, did your Neighbours talk so?

FAITHFUL. Yes, 'twas for a while in everybody's mouth.

CHRISTIAN. What, and did no more of them but you come out to escape the danger?

FAITHFUL. Though there was, as I said, a great talk thereabout, yet I do not think they did firmly believe it. For in the heat of the discourse, I heard some of them deridingly speak of you and of your desperate Journey (for so they called this your Pilgrimage), but I did believe, and do still, that the end of our City will be with Fire and Brimstone from above; and therefore I have made mine escape.

CHRISTIAN. Did you hear no talk of Neighbour Pliable?

FAITHFUL. Yes, Christian, I heard that he followed you till he came at the Slough of Despond, where, as some said, he fell in; but he would not be known to have so done; but I am sure he was soundly bedabbled with that kind of dirt.

CHRISTIAN. And what said the Neighbours to him?

FAITHFUL. He hath since his going back been had greatly in derision, and that among all sorts of people; some do mock and despise him; and scarce will any set him on work. He is now seven times worse than if he had never gone out of the City.

CHRISTIAN. But why should they be so set against him, since they also despise the way that he forsook?

FAITHFUL. Oh, they say, Hang him, he is a Turncoat, he was not true to his profession: I think God has stirred up even his Enemies to hiss at him, and make him a Proverb, because he hath forsaken the way (Jer. 29:18, 19).

CHRISTIAN. Had you no talk with him before you came out?

FAITHFUL. I met him once in the Streets, but he leered away[76] on the other side, as one ashamed of what he had done; so I spake not to him.

CHRISTIAN. Well, at my first setting out, I had hopes of that man; but now I fear he will perish in the overthrow of the City, for it is happened to him according to the true Proverb, The Dog is turned to his Vomit again, and the Sow that was washed to her wallowing in the Mire (II Pet. 2:22).

FAITHFUL. They are my fears of him too; but who can hinder that which will be?

CHRISTIAN. Well, Neighbour Faithful, said Christian, let us leave him, and talk of things that more immediately concern ourselves. Tell me now, what you have met with in the way as you came; for I know you have met with some things, or else it may be writ for a wonder.

FAITHFUL. I escaped the Slough that I perceive you fell into, and got up to the Gate without that danger; only I met with one whose name was Wanton, that had like to have done me a mischief.

CHRISTIAN. 'Twas well you escaped her Net; Joseph was hard put to it by her, and he escaped her as you did; but it had like to have cost him his life (Gen. 39:11-13). But what did she do to you?

FAITHFUL. You cannot think (but that you know something) what a flattering tongue she had; she lay at me hard to turn aside with her, promising me all manner of content.

CHRISTIAN. Nay, she did not promise you the content of a good conscience.

FAITHFUL. You know what I mean, all carnal and fleshly content.

CHRISTIAN. Thank God you have escaped her: The abhorred of the Lord shall fall into her Ditch (Prov. 22:14).

FAITHFUL. Nay, I know not whether I did wholly escape her or no.

CHRISTIAN. Why, I trow you did not consent to her desires?

FAITHFUL. No, not to defile myself; for I remembered an old writing that I had seen, which saith, Her steps take hold of Hell (Prov. 5:5). So I shut mine eyes, because I would not be bewitched with her looks (Job 31:1): then she railed on me, and I went my way.

CHRISTIAN. Did you meet with no other assault as you came?

FAITHFUL. When I came to the foot of the Hill called Difficulty, I met with a very aged Man, who asked me, What I was, and whither bound? I told him, That I was a Pilgrim, going to the Celestial City. Then said the old man, Thou lookest like an honest fellow; wilt thou be content to dwell with me for the wages that I shall give thee? Then I asked him his name, and where he dwelt? He said his name was Adam the First, and he dwelt in the town of Deceit (Eph. 4:22). I asked him then, What was his work? and what the wages that he would give? He told me, That his work was many delights; and his wages, that I should be his Heir at last. I further asked him, What House he kept, and what other Servants he had? So he told me, That his House was maintained with all the dainties in the world; and that his Servants were those of his own begetting. Then I asked how many Children he had? He said that he had but three Daughters: The Lust of the Flesh, The Lust of the Eyes, and The Pride of Life (I John 2:16), and that I should marry them all if I would. Then I asked how long time he would have me live with him? And he told me, As long as he lived himself.

CHRISTIAN. Well, and what conclusion came the old man and you to at last?

FAITHFUL. Why, at first, I felt myself somewhat inclinable to go with the man, for I thought he spake very fair; but looking in his forehead, as I talked with him, I saw there written, Put off the old man with his deeds.

CHRISTIAN. And how then?

FAITHFUL. Then it came burning hot into my mind, whatever he said, and however he flattered, when he got me home to his House, he would sell me for a slave.[77] So I bid him forbear to talk, for I would not come near the door of his House. Then he reviled me, and told me that he would send such a one after me, that should make my way bitter to my Soul. So I turned to go away from him; but just as I turned myself to go thence, I felt him take hold of my flesh, and give me such a deadly twitch back,[78] that I thought he had pulled part of me after himself. This made me cry, O wretched Man! (Rom. 7:24.) So I went on my way up the Hill.

Now when I had got about halfway up, I looked behind me, and saw one coming after me, swift as the wind; so he overtook me just about the place where the Settle stands.

CHRISTIAN. Just there, said Christian, did I sit down to rest me; but being overcome with sleep, I there lost this Roll out of my bosom.

FAITHFUL. But, good Brother, hear me out. So soon as the man overtook me, he was but a word and a blow, for down he knocked me, and laid me for dead. But when I was a little come to myself again, I asked him wherefore he served me so? He said, Because of my secret inclining to Adam the First: and with that he struck me another deadly blow on the breast, and beat me down backward, so I lay at his foot as dead as before. So when I came to myself again I cried him mercy; but he said, I know not how to shew mercy, and with that knocked me down again. He had doubtless made an end of me, but that one came by, and bid him forbear.

CHRISTIAN. Who was that that bid him forbear?

FAITHFUL. I did not know him at first, but as he went by I perceived the holes in his hands and in his side; then I concluded that he was our Lord. So I went up the Hill.

CHRISTIAN. That man that overtook you was Moses:[79] He spareth none, neither knoweth he how to shew mercy to those that transgress his Law.

FAITHFUL. I know it very well; it was not the first time that he has met with me. 'Twas he that came to me when I dwelt securely at home, and that told me, He would burn my house over my head if I stayed there.

CHRISTIAN. But did you not see the house that stood there on the top of that Hill, on the side of which Moses met you?

FAITHFUL. Yes, and the Lions too, before I came at it: but for the Lions, I think they were asleep,[80] for it was about Noon; and because I had so much of the day before me, I passed by the Porter, and came down the Hill.

CHRISTIAN. He told me, indeed, that he saw you go by, but I wish you had called at the house, for they would have shewed you so many Rarities, that you would scarce have forgot them to the day of your death. But pray tell me, Did you meet nobody in the Valley of Humility?

FAITHFUL. Yes, I met with one Discontent, who would willingly have persuaded me to go back again with him; his reason was, for that the Valley was altogether without honour. He told me, moreover, that there to go was the way to disobey all my friends, as Pride, Arrogancy, Self-conceit, Worldly-glory, with others, who he knew, as he said, would be very much offended if I made such a Fool of myself as to wade through this Valley.

CHRISTIAN. Well, and how did you answer him?

FAITHFUL. I told him, That although all these that he named might claim kindred of me, and that rightly (for indeed they were my Relations according to the flesh), yet since I became a Pilgrim, they have disowned me, as I also have rejected them; and therefore they were to me now no more than if they had never been of my lineage. I told him, moreover, that as to this Valley, he had quite misrepresented the thing; for before Honour is Humility, and a haughty spirit before a fall (Prov. 15:33; 16:18). Therefore, said I, I had rather go through this Valley to the honour that was so accounted by the wisest, than choose that which he esteemed most worthy our affections.

CHRISTIAN. Met you with nothing else in that Valley?

FAITHFUL. Yes, I met with Shame; but of all the men that I met with in my Pilgrimage, he, I think, bears the wrong name. The other would be said nay, after a little argumentation (and somewhat else), but this boldfaced Shame would never have done.

CHRISTIAN. Why, what did he say to you?

FAITHFUL. What! why he objected against Religion itself; he said it was a pitiful low sneaking business for a man to mind Religion; he said that a tender conscience was an unmanly thing; and that for a man to watch over his words and ways, so as to tie up himself from that hectoring liberty that the brave spirits of the times accustom themselves unto, would make him the ridicule of the times. He objected also, that but few of the Mighty, Rich, or Wise, were ever of my opinion; nor any of them neither, before they were persuaded to be Fools, and to be of a voluntary fondness to venture the loss of all, for nobody else knows what. (I Cor. 1:26; 3:18; Phil. 3:7, 8; John 7:48.) He, moreover, objected the base and low estate and condition of those that were chiefly the Pilgrims; also their ignorance of the times in which they lived, and want of understanding in all Natural Science. Yea, he did hold me to it at that rate also, about a great many more things than here I relate; as, that it was a shame to sit whining and mourning under a Sermon, and a shame to come sighing and groaning home; that it was a shame to ask my Neighbour forgiveness for petty faults, or to make restitution where I had taken from any. He said also that Religion made a man grow strange to the great, because of a few vices (which he called by finer names), and made him own and respect the base because of the same Religious Fraternity. And is not this, said he, a shame?

CHRISTIAN. And what did you say to him?

FAITHFUL. Say! I could not tell what to say at first. Yea, he put me so to it, that my blood came up in my face; even this Shame fetched it up, and had almost beat me quite off. But at last I began to consider, That that which is highly esteemed among Men is had in abomination with God (Luke 16:15). And I thought again, this Shame tells me what men are; but it tells me nothing what God or the Word of God is. And I thought, moreover, that at the day of doom, we shall not be doomed to death or life according to the hectoring spirits of the world, but according to the Wisdom and Law of the Highest. Therefore, thought I, what God says is best, is best, though all the men in the world are against it. Seeing then that God prefers his Religion, seeing God prefers a tender Conscience, seeing they that make themselves Fools for the Kingdom of Heaven are wisest; and that the poor man that loveth Christ is richer than the greatest man in the world that hates him: Shame depart, thou art an Enemy to my Salvation; shall I entertain thee against my Sovereign Lord? How then shall I look him in the face at his coming? Should I now be ashamed of his ways and Servants, how can I expect the blessing? (Mark 8:38.) But indeed this Shame was a bold Villain; I could scarce shake him out of my company; yea, he would be haunting of me, and continually whispering me in the ear, with some one or other of the infirmities that attend Religion; but at last I told him, 'Twas but in vain to attempt further in this business; for those things that he disdained, in those did I see most glory; and so at last I got past this importunate one.

CHRISTIAN. I am glad, my Brother, that thou didst withstand this Villain so bravely; for of all, as thou sayest, I think he has the wrong name; for he is so bold as to follow us in the Streets, and to attempt to put us to shame before all men; that is, to make us ashamed of that which is good: but if he was not himself audacious, he would never attempt to do as he does; but let us still resist him; for notwithstanding all his bravadoes, he promoteth the Fool and none else. The Wise shall inherit glory, said Solomon, but shame shall be the promotion of Fools (Prov. 3:35).

FAITHFUL. I think we must cry to Him for help against Shame, that would have us to be valiant for the Truth upon the Earth.

CHRISTIAN. You say true; but did you meet nobody else in that Valley?

FAITHFUL. No, not I; for I had Sun-shine all the rest of the way through that, and also through the Valley of the Shadow of Death.

CHRISTIAN. 'Twas well for you; I am sure it fared far otherwise with me; I had for a long season, as soon almost as I entered into that Valley, a dreadful Combat with that foul Fiend Apollyon; yea, I thought verily he would have killed me, especially when he got me down and crushed me under him, as if he would have crushed me to pieces; for as he threw me, my Sword flew out of my hand; nay, he told me, He was sure of me: but I cried to God, and he heard me, and delivered me out of all my troubles. Then I entered into the Valley of the Shadow of Death, and had no light for almost half the way through it. I thought I should have been killed there, over and over; but at last day brake, and the Sun rose, and I went through that which was behind with far more ease and quiet.

Moreover, I saw in my Dream, that as they went on, Faithful, as he chanced to look on one side, saw a man whose name is Talkative, walking at a distance besides them (for in this place there was room enough for them all to walk). He was a tall man, and something more comely at a distance than at hand. To this man Faithful addressed himself in this manner.

FAITHFUL. Friend, whither away? Are you going to the Heavenly Country?

TALKATIVE. I am going to that same place.

FAITHFUL. That is well; then I hope we may have your good company.

TALKATIVE. With a very good will will I be your Companion.

FAITHFUL. Come on then, and let us go together, and let us spend our time in discoursing of things that are profitable.

TALKATIVE. To talk of things that are good, to me is very acceptable, with you or with any other; and I am glad that I have met with those that incline to so good a work; for to speak the truth, there are but few that care thus to spend their time (as they are in their travels), but choose much rather to be speaking of things to no profit; and this hath been a trouble to me.

FAITHFUL. That is indeed a thing to be lamented; for what things so worthy of the use of the tongue and mouth of men on Earth as are the things of the God of Heaven?

TALKATIVE. I like you wonderful well, for your saying is full of conviction; and I will add, What thing so pleasant, and what so profitable, as to talk of the things of God? What things so pleasant? (that is, if a man hath any delight in things that are wonderful), for instance, if a man doth delight to talk of the History or the Mystery of things; or if a man doth love to talk of Miracles, Wonders, or Signs, where shall he find things recorded so delightful, and so sweetly penned, as in the Holy Scripture?

FAITHFUL. That's true; but to be profited by such things in our talk should be that which we design.

TALKATIVE. That's it that I said; for to talk of such things is most profitable; for by so doing, a man may get knowledge of many things; as of the vanity of earthly things, and the benefit of things above (thus in general): but more particularly, by this a man may learn the necessity of the New-birth, the insufficiency of our works, the need of Christ's righteousness, etc. Besides, by this a man may learn by talk, what it is to repent, to believe, to pray, to suffer, or the like; by this also a man may learn what are the great promises and consolations of the Gospel, to his own comfort. Further, by this a man may learn to refute false opinions, to vindicate the truth, and also to instruct the ignorant.

FAITHFUL. All this is true, and glad am I to hear these things from you.

TALKATIVE. Alas! the want of this is the cause that so few understand the need of faith, and the necessity of a work of Grace in their Soul, in order to eternal life; but ignorantly live in the works of the Law, by which a man can by no means obtain the Kingdom of Heaven.

FAITHFUL. But by your leave, Heavenly knowledge of these is the gift of God; no man attaineth to them by human industry, or only by the talk of them.

TALKATIVE. All this I know very well; for a man can receive nothing, except it be given him from Heaven; all is of Grace, not of Works: I could give you an hundred Scriptures for the confirmation of this.

O brave Talkative!

FAITHFUL. Well then, said Faithful, what is that one thing that we shall at this time found our discourse upon?

TALKATIVE. What you will: I will talk of things Heavenly,

or things Earthly; things Moral, or things Evangelical; things Sacred, or things Profane; things past, or things to come; things foreign, or things at home; things more Essential, or things Circumstantial; provided that all be done to our profit.

Now did Faithful begin to wonder; and stepping to Christian (for he walked all this while by himself), he said to him (but softly), What a brave Companion have we got! Surely this man will make a very excellent Pilgrim.

At this Christian modestly smiled, and said, This man with whom you are so taken will beguile with this tongue of his twenty of them that know him not.

FAITHFUL. Do you know him then?

CHRISTIAN. Know him? Yes, better than he knows himself.

FAITHFUL. Pray what is he?

CHRISTIAN. His name is Talkative; he dwelleth in our Town: I wonder that you should be a stranger to him, only I consider that our Town is large.

FAITHFUL. Whose son is he? And whereabout doth he dwell?

CHRISTIAN. He is the son of one Say-well; he dwelt in Prating Row; and is known of all that are acquainted with him by the name of Talkative in Prating Row; and notwithstanding his fine tongue, he is but a sorry fellow.

FAITHFUL. Well, he seems to be a very pretty[81] man.

CHRISTIAN. That is, to them that have not thorough acquaintance with him, for he is best abroad, near home he is ugly enough: your saying that he is a pretty man, brings to my mind what I have observed in the work of the Painter, whose Pictures shew best at a distance, but very near more unpleasing.

FAITHFUL. But I am ready to think you do but jest, because you smiled.

CHRISTIAN. God forbid that I should jest (though I smiled) in this matter, or that I should accuse any falsely; I will give you a further discovery of him: This man is for any company, and for any talk; as he talketh now with you, so will he talk when he is on the Ale-bench; and the more drink he hath in his crown, the more of these things he hath in his mouth; Religion hath no place in his heart, or house, or conversation; all he hath lieth in his tongue, and his Religion is to make a noise therewith.

FAITHFUL. Say you so! Then am I in this man greatly deceived.

CHRISTIAN. Deceived! you may be sure of it. Remember the Proverb, They say and do not: but the Kingdom of God is not in word, but in power (Matt. 23:3; I Cor. 4:20). He talketh of Prayer, of Repentance, of Faith, and of the New-birth; but he knows but only to talk of them. I have been in his Family, and have observed him both at home and abroad; and I know what I say of him is the truth. His house is as empty of Religion as the white of an Egg is of savour. There is there neither Prayer, nor sign of Repentance for sin; yea, the brute in his kind serves God far better than he. He is the very stain, reproach, and shame of Religion to all that know him (Rom. 2:24, 25); it can hardly have a good word in all that end of the Town where he dwells, through him. Thus say the common people that know him, A saint abroad, and a Devil at home. His poor Family finds it so; he is such a churl, such a railer at, and so unreasonable with his Servants,[82] that they neither know how to do for, or speak to him. Men that have any dealings with him say 'tis better to deal with a Turk than with him; for fairer dealing they shall have at their hands. This Talkative (if it be possible) will go beyond them, defraud, beguile, and over-reach them. Besides, he brings up his Sons to follow his steps; and if he findeth in any of them a foolish timorousness (for so he calls the first appearance of a tender conscience), he calls them fools and blockheads, and by no means will employ them in much, or speak to their commendations before others. For my part I am of opinion, that he has by his wicked life caused many to stumble and fall; and will be, if God prevent not, the ruin of many more.

FAITHFUL. Well, my Brother, I am bound to believe you; not only because you say you know him, but also because like a Christian you make your reports of men. For I cannot think that you speak these things of ill-will, but because it is even so as you say.

CHRISTIAN. Had I known him no more than you, I might perhaps have thought of him as at the first you did; yea, had he received this report at their hands only that are enemies to Religion, I should have thought it had been a slander (a lot that often falls from bad men's mouths upon good men's names and professions); but all these things, yea and a great many more as bad, of my own knowledge, I can prove him guilty of. Besides, good men are ashamed of him; they can neither call him Brother, nor Friend; the very naming of him among them makes them blush, if they know him.

FAITHFUL. Well, I see that saying and doing are two things, and hereafter I shall better observe this distinction.

CHRISTIAN. They are two things indeed, and are as diverse as are the Soul and the Body; for as the Body without the Soul is but a dead Carcass, so Saying, if it be alone, is but a dead Carcass also. The Soul of Religion is the practick part: Pure Religion and undefiled, before God and the Father, is this, To visit the fatherless and widows in their affliction, and to keep himself unspotted from the world (James 1:27; see ver. 22-26). This Talkative is not aware of; he thinks that hearing and saying will make a good Christian, and thus he deceiveth his own soul. Hearing is but as the sowing of the Seed; talking is not sufficient to prove that fruit is indeed in the heart and life; and let us assure ourselves, that at the day of Doom men shall be judged according to their fruits (Matt. 13:18-23; 25:14-46). It will not be said then, Did you believe? but, Were you Doers, or Talkers only? and accordingly shall they be judged. The end of the world is compared to our Harvest, and you know men at Harvest regard nothing but fruit. Not that anything can be accepted that is not of Faith; but I speak this to shew you how insignificant the profession of Talkative will be at that day.

FAITHFUL. This brings to my mind that of Moses, by which he describeth the beast that is clean (Lev. 11:3, 6; Deut. 14:7). He is such an one that parteth the Hoof and cheweth the Cud; not that parteth the Hoof only, or that cheweth the Cud only. The Hare cheweth the Cud, but yet is unclean, because he parteth not the Hoof. And this truly resembleth Talkative; he cheweth the Cud, he seeketh knowledge, he cheweth upon the Word; but he divideth not the Hoof, he parteth not with the way of sinners; but as the Hare, he retaineth the foot of a Dog, or Bear, and therefore is unclean.[83]

CHRISTIAN. You have spoken, for aught I know, the true Gospel sense of those Texts: And I will add another thing. Paul calleth some men, yea and those great Talkers, too, sounding Brass and tinkling Cymbals; that is, as he expounds them in another place, Things without life, giving sound (I Cor. 13:1-3; 14:7). Things without life, that is, without the true Faith and Grace of the Gospel; and consequently things that shall never be placed in the Kingdom of Heaven among those that are the Children of life; though their sound, by their talk, be as if it were the tongue or voice of an Angel.

FAITHFUL. Well, I was not so fond of his company at first, but I am as sick of it now. What shall we do to be rid of him?

CHRISTIAN. Take my advice, and do as I bid you, and you shall find that he will soon be sick of your company too, except God shall touch his heart and turn it.

FAITHFUL. What would you have me to do?

CHRISTIAN. Why, go to him, and enter into some serious discourse about the power of Religion; and ask him plainly (when he has approved of it, for that he will) whether this thing be set up in his Heart, House, or Conversation.

FAITHFUL. Then Faithful stepped forward again, and said to Talkative, Come, what cheer? How is it now?

TALKATIVE. Thank you, well. I thought we should have had a great deal of talk by this time.

FAITHFUL. Well, if you will, we will fall to it now; and since you left it with me to state the question, let is be this: How doth the saving Grace of God discover itself, when it is in the heart of man?

TALKATIVE. I perceive then that our talk must be about the power of things: Well, 'tis a very good question, and I shall be willing to answer you. And take my answer in brief thus: First, Where the Grace of God is in the heart, it causeth there a great outcry against sin. Secondly—

FAITHFUL. Nay hold, let us consider of one at once: I think you should rather say, It shews itself by inclining the soul to abhor its sin.

TALKATIVE. Why, what difference is there between crying out against, and abhorring of sin?

FAITHFUL. Oh! a great deal; A man may cry out against sin, of policy; but he cannot abhor it, but by virtue of a godly antipathy against it: I have heard many cry out against sin in the Pulpit, who yet can abide it well enough in the heart, house, and conversation. Joseph's Mistress cried out with a loud voice, as if she had been very holy; but she would willingly, notwithstanding that, have committed uncleanness with him (Gen. 39:15). Some cry out against sin, even as the Mother cries out against her Child in her lap, when she calleth it slut and naughty girl, and then falls to hugging and kissing it.

TALKATIVE. You lie at the catch,[84] I perceive.

FAITHFUL. No, not I; I am only for setting things right. But what is the second thing whereby you would prove a discovery of a work of Grace in the heart?

TALKATIVE. Great knowledge of Gospel Mysteries.

FAITHFUL. This sign should have been first; but first or last, it is also false; for knowledge, great knowledge may be obtained in the mysteries of the Gospel, and yet no work of Grace in the Soul (I Cor. 13:2). Yea, if a man have all knowledge, he may yet be nothing, and so consequently be no child of God. When Christ said, Do you know all these things? and the disciples had answered, Yes; he addeth, Blessed are ye if ye do them. He doth not lay the blessing in the knowing of them, but in the doing of them. For there is a knowledge that is not attended with doing; he that knoweth his Master's will, and doeth it not. A man may know like an angel, and yet be no Christian; therefore your sign of it is not true. Indeed to know is a thing that pleaseth Talkers and Boasters; but to do is that which pleaseth God. Not that the heart can be good without knowledge, for without that the heart is naught. There is therefore knowledge and knowledge. Knowledge that resteth in the bare speculation of things, and knowledge that is accompanied with the Grace of faith and love, which puts a man upon doing even the will of God from the heart: the first of these will serve the Talker; but without the other the true Christian is not content. Give me understanding and I shall keep thy Law; yea I shall observe it with my whole heart.

TALKATIVE. You lie at the catch again, this is not for edification.

FAITHFUL. Well, if you please, propound another sign how this work of Grace discovereth itself where it is.

TALKATIVE. Not I, for I see we shall not agree.

FAITHFUL. Well, if you will not, will you give me leave to do it?

TALKATIVE. You may use your liberty.

FAITHFUL. A work of Grace in the soul discovereth itself, either to him that hath it, or to standers-by.

To him that hath it, thus: It gives him conviction of sin, especially of the defilement of his nature and the sin of unbelief (for the sake of which he is sure to be damned, if he findeth not mercy at God's hand by faith in Jesus Christ). (John 16:8, 9; Rom. 7:24; Mark 16:16.) This sight and sense of things[85] worketh in him sorrow and shame for sin; he findeth moreover revealed in him the Saviour of the world, and the absolute necessity of closing with him for life, at the which he findeth hungerings and thirstings after him, to which hungerings, etc., the promise is made (Ps. 38:18; Jer. 31:19; Gal. 2:16; Acts 4:12; Matt. 5:6; Rev. 21:6). Now according to the strength or weakness of his Faith in his Saviour, so is his joy and peace, so is his love to holiness, so are his desires to know him more, and also to serve him in this World. But though I say it discovereth itself thus unto him, yet it is but seldom that he is able to conclude that this is a work of Grace; because his corruptions now, and his abused reason, make his mind to misjudge in this matter; therefore in him that hath this work, there is required a very sound Judgment before he can with steadiness conclude that this is a work of Grace.

To others it is thus discovered:

1. By an experimental confession of his Faith in Christ.

2. By a life answerable to that confession, to wit, a life of holiness; heart-holiness, family-holiness (if he hath a Family), and by conversation-holiness in the World: which in the general teacheth him inwardly to abhor his sin and himself for that in secret, to suppress it in his Family, and to promote holiness in the World; not by talk only, as an Hypocrite or Talkative person may do, but by a practical subjection, in Faith and Love, to the power of the Word (Rom. 10:10; Phil. 1:27; Matt. 5:9; John 24:15; Ps. 50:20; Job 42:5,6; Ezek 29:43): And now, Sir, as to this brief description of the work of Grace, and also the discovery of it, if you have aught to object, object; if not, then give me leave to propound to you a second question.

TALKATIVE. Nay, my part is not now to object, but to hear, let me therefore have your second question.

FAITHFUL. It is this. Do you experience the first part of this description of it? and doth your life and conversation testify the same? or standeth your religion in Word or in Tongue, and not in Deed and Truth? Pray, if you incline to answer me in this, say no more than you know the God above will say Amen to; and also nothing but what your conscience can justify you in; for, not he that commendeth himself is approved, but whom the Lord commendeth (II Cor. 10:18). Besides, to say I am thus and thus, when my Conversation and all my Neighbours tell me I lie, is great wickedness.

TIVE. Then Talkative at first began to blush, but recovering himself, thus he replied, You come now to Experience, to Conscience, and God; and to appeals to him for justification of what is spoken: This kind of discourse I did not expect, nor am I disposed to give an answer to such questions, because I count not myself bound thereto, unless you take upon you to be a Catechiser; and, though you should do so, yet I may refuse to make you my Judge. But I pray will you tell me why you ask me such questions?

FAITHFUL. Because I saw you forward to talk, and because I knew not that you had aught else but notion. Besides, to tell you all the truth, I have heard of you that you are a man whose Religion lies in talk, and that your conversation gives this your Mouth-profession the lie. They say you are a spot among Christians, and that religion fareth the worse for your ungodly Conversation, that some have already stumbled at your wicked ways, and that more are in danger of being destroyed thereby; your Religion, and an Ale-house, and Covetousness, and Uncleanness, and Swearing and Lying, and vain Company-keeping, etc., will stand together. The Proverb is true of you which is said of a Whore, to wit, That she is a shame to all Women; so you are a shame to all Professors.

TALKATIVE. Since you are ready to take up reports, and to judge so rashly as you do, I cannot but conclude you are some peevish[86] or melancholy man, not fit to be discoursed with; and so adieu.

CHRISTIAN. Then came up Christian, and said to his Brother, I told you how it would happen; your words and his lusts could not agree; he had rather leave your company than reform his life. But he is gone, as I said; let him go, the loss is no man's but his own, he has saved us the trouble of going from him; for he continuing (as I suppose he will do) as he is, he would have been but a blot in our company: besides, the Apostle says, From such withdraw thyself.

A good riddance.

FAITHFUL. But I am glad we had this little discourse with him, it may happen that he will think of it again; however, I have dealt plainly with him, and so am clear of his blood, if he perisheth.

CHRISTIAN. You did well to talk so plainly to him as you did. There is but little of this faithful dealing with men now-a-days, and that makes Religion so stink in the nostrils of many, as it doth; for they are these Talkative Fools whose Religion is only in word, and are debauched and vain in their Conversation, that (being so much admitted into the fellowship of the godly) do stumble the World,[87] blemish Christianity, and grieve the sincere. I wish that all men would deal with such as you have done: then should they either be made more conformable to Religion, or the company of Saints would be too hot for them.

How Talkative at first lifts up his Plumes!
How bravely doth he speak! How he presumes
To drive down all before him! But so soon
As Faithful talks of Heart-work, like the Moon
That's past the full, into the wane he goes.
And so will all but he that Heart-work knows.

Thus they went on talking of what they had seen by the way, and so made that way easy, which would otherwise, no doubt, have been tedious to them; for now they went through a Wilderness.

Now when they were got almost quite out of this Wilderness, Faithful chanced to cast his eye back, and espied one coming after them, and he knew him. Oh! said Faithful to his Brother, Who comes yonder? Then Christian looked, and said, It is my good friend Evangelist. Ay, and my good friend too, said Faithful, for 'twas he that set me in the way to the Gate. Now was Evangelist come up unto them, and thus saluted them:

EVANGELIST. Peace be with you, dearly beloved, and peace be to your helpers.[88]

CHRISTIAN. Welcome, welcome, my good Evangelist, the sight of thy countenance brings to my remembrance thy ancient kindness and unwearied labouring for my eternal good.

FAITHFUL. And a thousand times welcome, said good Faithful: thy company, O sweet Evangelist, how desirable is it to us poor Pilgrims!

EVANGELIST. Then said Evangelist, How hath it fared with you, my friends, since the time of our last parting? What have you met with, and how have you behaved yourselves?

Then Christian and Faithful told him of all things that had happened to them in the way; and how, and with what difficulty, they had arrived to that place.

IST. Right glad am I, said Evangelist, not that you have met with trials, but that you have been victors; and for that you have (notwithstanding many weaknesses) continued in the way to this very day.

I say, right glad am I of this thing, and that for mine own sake and yours: I have sowed and you have reaped; and the day is coming when both he that sowed and they that reaped shall rejoice together; that is, if you hold out: for in due time ye shall reap, if you faint not (John 4:36; Gal. 6:9). The Crown is before you, and it is an incorruptible one; so run that you may obtain it.[89] (I Cor. 9:24-27.) Some there be that set out for this Crown, and after they have gone far for it, another comes in, and takes it from them; hold fast therefore that you have, let no man take your Crown (Rev. 3:11). You are not yet out of the gunshot of the Devil; you have not resisted unto blood, striving against sin; let the Kingdom be always before you, and believe steadfastly concerning things that are invisible. Let nothing that is on this side the other world get within you; and above all, look well to your own hearts, and to the lusts thereof, for they are deceitful above all things, and desperately wicked; set your faces like a flint;[90] you have all power in Heaven and Earth on your side.

CHRISTIAN. Then Christian thanked him for his exhortation, but told him withal, that they would have him speak further to them for their help the rest of the way, and the rather, for that they well knew that he was a Prophet, and could tell them of things that might happen unto them, and also how they might resist and overcome them.

To which request Faithful also consented. So Evangelist began as followeth:

EVANGELIST. My Sons, you have heard, in the words of the truth of the Gospel, that you must through many tribulations enter into the Kingdom of Heaven. And again, that in every City bonds and afflictions abide you; and therefore you cannot expect that you should go long on your Pilgrimage without them, in some sort or other. You have found something of the truth of these testimonies upon you already, and more will immediately follow; for now, as you see you are almost out of this Wilderness, and therefore you will soon come into a Town that you will by and by see before you; and in that Town you will be hardly beset with enemies, who will strain hard but they will kill you;[91] and be ye sure that one or both of you must seal the testimony which you hold with blood; but be you faithful unto death, and the King will give you a Crown of life. He that shall die there, although his death will be unnatural, and his pain perhaps great, he will yet have the better of his fellow; not only because he will be arrived at the Celestial City soonest, but because he will escape many miseries that the other will meet with in the rest of his Journey. But when you are come to the Town, and shall find fulfilled what I have here related, then remember your friend, and quit yourselves like men, and commit the keeping of your souls to your God in well-doing, as unto a faithful Creator.

Then I saw in my Dream, that when they were got out of the Wilderness, they presently saw a Town before them, and the name of that town is Vanity; and at the Town there is a Fair kept, called Vanity Fair:[92] it is kept all the year long; it beareth the name of Vanity Fair, because the Town where 'tis kept is lighter than Vanity; and also because all that is there sold, or that cometh thither, is Vanity. As is the saying of the wise, All that cometh is Vanity (Isa. 40:17; Eccles. 1:2, 14; 2:11, 17).

This Fair is no new erected business, but a thing of ancient standing; I will shew you the original of it.

Almost five thousand years agone, there were Pilgrims walking to the Celestial City, as these two honest persons are; and Beelzebub, Apollyon, and Legion,[93] with their Companions, perceiving by the path that the Pilgrims made, that their way to the City lay through this Town of Vanity, they contrived here to set up a Fair; a Fair wherein should be sold all sorts of Vanity, and that it should last all the year long: therefore at this Fair are all such Merchandise sold as Houses, Lands, Trades, Places, Honours, Preferments, Titles, Countries, Kingdoms, Lusts, Pleasures, and Delights of all sorts, as Whores, Bawds, Wives, Husbands, Children, Masters, Servants, Lives, Blood, Bodies, Souls, Silver, Gold, Pearls, Precious Stones, and what not.

And moreover, at this Fair there is at all times to be seen Jugglings, Cheats, Games, Plays, Fools, Apes, Knaves, and Rogues, and that of all sorts.

Here are to be seen, too, and that for nothing, Thefts, Murders, Adulteries, False-swearers, and that of a blood-red colour.

in other Fairs of less moment, there are the several Rows of Streets under their proper names, where such and such Wares are vended; so here likewise you have the proper Places, Rows, Streets (*viz.* Countries and Kingdoms) where the Wares of this Fair are soonest to be found: Here is the Britain Row, the French Row, the Italian Row, the Spanish Row, the German Row, where several sorts of Vanities are to be sold. But as in other Fairs, some one commodity is as the chief of all the Fair, so the ware of Rome and her Merchandise is greatly promoted in this Fair; only our English Nation, with some others, have taken a dislike thereat.

Now, as I said, the way to the Celestial City lies just through this Town where this lusty Fair is kept; and he that will go to the City, and yet not go through this Town, must needs go out of the World (I Cor. 5:10). The Prince of Princes himself, when here, went through this Town to his own Country, and that upon a Fair-day too; yea, and as I think, it was Beelzebub, the chief Lord of this Fair, that invited him to buy of his Vanities (Matt. 4:8, 9; Luke 4:5-7): yea, would have made him Lord of the Fair, would he but have done him reverence as he went through the Town. Yea, because he was such a person of honour, Beelzebub had him from Street to Street, and shewed him all the Kingdoms of the World in a little time, that he might (if possible) allure that Blessed One to cheapen and buy some of his Vanities. But he had no mind to the Merchandise, and therefore left the Town, without laying out so much as one Farthing upon these Vanities. This Fair, therefore, is an ancient thing, of long standing, and a very great Fair.

Now these Pilgrims, as I said, must needs go through this Fair. Well, so they did: but behold, even as they entered into the Fair, all the people in the Fair were moved, and the Town itself as it were in a hubbub about them; and that for several reasons: for

First, The Pilgrims were clothed with such kind of Raiment as was diverse from the Raiment of any that traded in that Fair. The people therefore of the Fair made a great gazing upon them: some said they were Fools, some they were Bedlams,[94] and some they are Outlandish-men.[95]

Secondly, And as they wondered at their Apparel, so they did likewise at their Speech; for few could understand what they said: they naturally spoke the language of Canaan,[96] but they that kept the Fair were the men of this World; so that, from one end of the Fair to the other, they seemed Barbarians[97] each to the other (I Cor. 2:7, 8).

Thirdly, But that which did not a little amuse the Merchandisers was, that these Pilgrims set very light by all their Wares, they cared not so much as to look upon them; and if they called upon them to buy, they would put their fingers in their ears, and cry, Turn away mine eyes from beholding Vanity (Ps. 119:37), and look upwards, signifying that their trade and traffic was in Heaven (Phil. 3:19, 20).

One chanced mockingly, beholding the carriages of the men,[98] to say unto them, What will ye buy? But they, looking gravely upon him, answered, We buy the Truth (Prov. 23:23). At that there was an occasion taken to despise the men the more; some mocking, some taunting, some speaking reproachfully, and some calling upon others to smite them. At last things came to an hubbub and great stir in the Fair, insomuch that all order was confounded. Now was word presently brought to the Great One of the Fair, who quickly came down and deputed some of his most trusty friends to take these men into examination, about whom the Fair was almost overturned. So the men were brought to examination; and they that sat upon them asked them whence they came, whither they went, and what they did there in such an unusual Garb? The men told them that they were Pilgrims and Strangers in the World, and that they were going to their own Country, which was the Heavenly Jerusalem (Heb. 11:13-16); and that they had given none occasion to the men of the Town, nor yet to the Merchandisers, thus to abuse them, and to let them in their Journey,[99] except it was for that, when one asked them what they would buy, they said they would buy the Truth. But they that were appointed to examine them did not believe them to be any other than Bedlams and Mad, or else such as came to put all things into a confusion in the Fair. Therefore they took them and beat them, and besmeared them with dirt, and then put them into the Cage, that they might be made a spectacle to all the men of the Fair. There, therefore, they lay for some time, and were made the objects of any man's sport, or malice, or revenge, the Great One of the Fair laughing still at all that befell them. But the men being patient, and not rendering railing for railing, but contrariwise blessing, and giving good bad, and kindness for injuries done, some men in hat were more observing, and less prejudiced than the rest, began to check and blame the baser sort for their continual abuses done by them to the men; they, therefore, in angry manner let fly at them[100] again, counting them as bad as the men in the Cage, and telling them that they seemed confederates, and should be made partakers of their misfortunes. The other replied, that for ought they could see, the men were quiet, and sober, and intended nobody any harm; and that there were many that traded in their Fair that were more worthy to be put into the Cage, yea, and Pillory too, than were the men that they had abused. Thus, after divers words had passed on both sides (the men behaving themselves all the while very wisely and soberly before them), they fell to some blows among themselves, and did harm one to another. Then were these two poor men brought before their examiner again, and there charged as being guilty of the late hubbub that had been in the Fair. So they beat them pitifully and hanged irons upon them, and led them in chains up and down the Fair, for an example and a terror to others, lest any should further speak in their behalf, or join themselves unto them. But Christian and Faithful behaved themselves yet more wisely, and received the ignominy and shame that was cast upon them with so much meekness and patience that it won to their side (though but few in comparison of the rest) several of the men in the Fair. This put the other party yet into a greater rage, insomuch that they concluded the death of these two men. Wherefore they threatened, that the Cage nor irons should serve their turn, but that they should die, for the abuse they had done, and for d[illegible]ling the men of the Fair.

Then were they remanded to the Cage again, until further order should be taken with them. So they put them in, and made their feet fast in the Stocks.

Here also they called again to mind what they had heard from their faithful friend Evangelist, and were the more confirmed in their way and sufferings, by what he told them would happen to them. They also now comforted each other, that whose lot it was to suffer, even he should have the best on't;[101] therefore each man secretly wished that he might have that preferment: but committing themselves to the Allwise disposal of Him that ruleth all things, with much content they abode in the condition in which they were, until they should be otherwise disposed of.

Then a convenient time being appointed, they brought them forth to their Trial, in order to their condemnation. When the time was come, they were brought before their enemies, and arraigned. The Judge's name was Lord Hate-good. Their Indictment was one and the same in substance, though somewhat varying in form, the contents whereof was this:

That they were enemies to and disturbers of their Trade; that they had made Commotions and Divisions in the Town, and had won a party to their own most dangerous Opinions in contempt of the Law of their Prince.

Now, Faithful, play the Man, speak for thy God;
Fear not the wicked's malice, nor their rod:
Speak boldly, man, the Truth is on thy side;
Die for it, and to Life in triumph ride.

Then Faithful began to answer, that he had only set himself against that which had set itself against Him that is higher than the highest. And said he, as for Disturbance, I make none, being myself a man of Peace; the Party that were won to us, were won by beholding our Truth and Innocence, and they are only turned from the worse to the better. And as to the King you talk of, since he is Beelzebub, the enemy of our Lord, I defy him and all his Angels.

Then Proclamation was made, that they that had aught to say for their Lord the King against the Prisoner at the Bar, should forthwith appear and give in their evidence. So there came in three witnesses, to wit, Envy, Superstition, and Pickthank. They were then asked if they knew the Prisoner at the Bar; and what they had to say for their Lord the King against him.

Then stood forth Envy, and said to this effect: My Lord, I have known this man a long time, and will attest upon my Oath before this honourable Bench, that he is—

JUDGE. Hold! Give him his Oath.

So they sware him.

Then he said, My Lord, this man, notwithstanding his plausible name, is one of the vilest men in our Country. He neither regardeth Prince nor People, Law nor Custom; but doth all that he can to possess all men with certain of his disloyal notions, which he in the general calls Principles of

Faith and Holiness. And in particular, I heard him once myself affirm, That Christianity and the Customs of our Town of Vanity were diametrically opposite, and could not be reconciled. By which saying, my Lord, he doth at once not only condemn all our laudable doings, but us in the doing of them.

JUDGE. Then did the Judge say to him, Hast thou any more to say?

ENVY. My Lord, I could say much more, only I would not be tedious to the Court. Yet if need be, when the other Gentlemen have given in their Evidence, rather than anything shall be wanting that will despatch him, I will enlarge my Testimony against him.

So he was bid stand by. Then they called Superstition, and bid him look upon the Prisoner. They also asked, what he could say for their Lord the King against him. Then they sware him; so he began:

SUPERSTITION. My Lord, I have no great acquaintance with this man, nor do I desire to have further knowledge of him; however, this I know, that he is a very pestilent fellow, from some discourse that the other day I had with him in this Town; for then talking with him, I heard him say that our Religion was naught, and such by which a man could by no means please God. Which sayings of his, my Lord, your Lordship very well knows, what necessarily thence will follow, to wit, That we still do worship in vain, are yet in our sins, and finally shall be damned; and this is that which I have to say.

Then was Pickthank[102] sworn, and bid say what he knew in behalf of their Lord the King, against the Prisoner at the Bar.

PICKTHANK. My Lord, and you, Gentlemen all, This fellow I have known of a long time, and have heard him speak things that ought not to be spoke; for he hath railed on our noble Prince Beelzebub, and hath spoken contemptibly of his honourable Friends, whose names are the Lord Old Man, the Lord Carnal Delight, the Lord Luxurious, the Lord Desire of Vain-Glory, my old Lord Lechery, Sir Having Greedy, with all the rest of our Nobility; and he hath said, moreover, that if all men were of his mind, if possible, there is not one of these Noblemen should have any longer a being in this Town; besides, he hath not been afraid to rail on you, my Lord, who are now appointed to be his Judge, calling you an ungodly villain, with many other suchlike vilifying terms, with which he hath bespattered most of the Gentry of our Town.

Sins are all Lords and great ones.[103]

When this Pickthank had told his tale, the Judge directed his speech to the Prisoner at the Bar, saying, Thou Runagate, Heretic, and Traitor, hast thou heard what these honest Gentlemen have witnessed against thee?

FAITHFUL. May I speak a few words in my own defence?

JUDGE. Sirrah, sirrah, thou deservest to live no longer, but to be slain immediately upon the place; yet that all men may see our gentleness towards thee, let us see what thou hast to say.

FAITHFUL. 1. I say then, in answer to what Mr. Envy hath spoken, I never said aught but this, That what Rule or Laws or Custom or People, were flat against the Word of God, are diametrically opposite to Christianity. If I have said amiss in this, convince me of my error, and I am ready here before you to make my recantation.

2. As to the second, to wit, Mr. Superstition, and his charge against me, I said only this, That in the worship of God there is required a Divine Faith; but there can be no Divine Faith without a Divine Revelation of the will of God: therefore whatever is thrust into the Worship of God that is not agreeable to a Divine Revelation, cannot be done but by a human faith, which faith will not profit to Eternal Life.

3. As to what Mr. Pickthank hath said, I say (avoiding terms, as that I am said to rail, and the like) that the Prince of this Town, with all the rabblement his attendants, by this Gentlemen named, are more fit for a being in Hell, than in this Town and Country: and so, the Lord have mercy upon me.

Then the Judge called to the Jury (who all this while stood by, to hear and observe), Gentlemen of the Jury, you see this man about whom so great an uproar hath been made in this Town: you have also heard what these worthy Gentlemen have witnessed against him; also you have heard his reply and confession: It lieth now in your breasts to hang him or save his life; but yet I think meet to instruct you into our Law.

There was an Act made in the days of Pharaoh the Great, the Servant to our Prince, that lest those of a contrary

Religion should multiply and grow too strong for him, their Males should be thrown into the river (Ex. 1). There was also an Act made in the days of Nebuchadnezzar the Great, another of his servants, that whoever would not fall down and worship his Golden Image should be thrown into a Fiery Furnace (Dan. 3:4-6). There was also an Act made in the days of Darius, that whoso, for some time, called upon any God but him should be cast into the Lions' Den (Dan. 6:7-9). Now the substance of these Laws this Rebel has broken, not only in thought (which is not to be borne) but also in word and deed; which must therefore needs be intolerable.

For that of Pharaoh, his Law was made upon a supposition to prevent mischief, no Crime being yet apparent; but here is a Crime apparent. For the second and third, you see he disputeth against our Religion; and for the Treason he hath confessed, he deserveth to die the death.

Then went the Jury out, whose names were, Mr. Blind-man, Mr. No-good, Mr. Malice, Mr. Love-lust, Mr. Live-loose, Mr. Heady, Mr. High-mind, Mr. Enmity, Mr. Lyar, Mr. Cruelty, Mr. Hate-light, and Mr. Implacable; who every one gave in his private Verdict against him among themselves, and afterwards unanimously concluded to bring him in guilty before the Judge. And first among themselves, Mr. Blind-man, the Foreman, said, I see clearly that this man is an Heretic. Then said Mr. No-good, Away with such a fellow from the earth. Ay, said Mr. Malice, for I hate the very looks of him. Then said Mr. Love-lust, I could never endure him. Nor I, said Mr. Live-loose, for he would always be condemning my way. Hang him, hang him, said Mr. Heady. A sorry Scrub,[104] said Mr. High-mind. My heart riseth against him, said Mr. Enmity. He is a rogue, said Mr. Lyar. Hanging is too good for him, said Mr. Cruelty. Let us despatch him out of the way, said Mr. Hate-light. Then said Mr. Implacable, Might I have all the world given me, I could not be reconciled to him; therefore let us forthwith bring him in guilty of death. And so they did; therefore he was presently condemned to be had from the place where he was, to the place from whence he came, and there to be put to the most cruel death that could be invented.

They therefore brought him out, to do with him according to their Law; and first they Scourged him, then they Buffeted him, then they Lanced his flesh with Knives; after that they

Stoned him with stones, then pricked him with their Swords; and last of all they burned him to ashes at the Stake. Thus came Faithful to his end.

Now I saw that there stood behind the multitude a Chariot and a couple of Horses,[105] waiting for Faithful, who (so soon as his adversaries had despatched him) was taken up into it, and straightway was carried up through the Clouds, with sound of Trumpet, the nearest way to the Celestial Gate. But as for Christian, he had some respite, and was remanded back to prison; so he there remained for a space: But he that over-rules all things, having the power of their rage in his own hand, so wrought it about, that Christian for that time escaped them, and went his way. And as he went he sang, saying,

Well, Faithful, thou hast faithfully profest
Unto thy Lord; with him thou shalt be blest,
When faithless ones, with all their vain delights,
Are crying out under their hellish plights:
Sing, Faithful, sing, and let thy name survive;
For though they kill'd thee, thou art yet alive.

Now I saw in my Dream, that Christian went not forth alone, for there was one whose name was Hopeful (being made so by the beholding of Christian and Faithful in their words and behaviour, in their sufferings at the Fair) who joined himself unto him, and entering into a brotherly covenant, told him that he would be his Companion. Thus one died to make Testimony to the Truth, and another rises out of his ashes to be a Companion with Christian in his Pilgrimage. This Hopeful also told Christian, that there were many more of the men in the Fair that would take their time and follow after.

So I saw that quickly after they were got out of the Fair, they overtook one that was going before them, whose name was By-ends:[106] so they said to him, What Countryman, Sir? and how far go you this way? He told them that he came from the Town of Fair-speech, and he was going to the Celestial City (but told them not his name).

From Fair-speech, said Christian. Is there any good that lives there? (Prov. 26:25.)

BY-ENDS. Yes, said By-ends, I hope.

CHRISTIAN. Pray, Sir, what may I call you?

BY-ENDS. I am a Stranger to you, and you to me: if you be going this way, I shall be glad of your company; if not, I must be content.

CHRISTIAN. This Town of Fair-speech, said Christian, I have heard of it, and, as I remember, they say it's a wealthy place.

BY-ENDS. Yes, I will assure you that it is; and I have very many rich Kindred there.

CHRISTIAN. Pray, who are your Kindred there? if a man may be so bold.

BY-ENDS. Almost the whole Town; and in particular, my Lord Turn-about, my Lord Time-server, my Lord Fair-speech (from whose ancestors that Town first took its name), also Mr. Smooth-man, Mr. Facing-both-ways, Mr. Anything; and the Parson of our Parish, Mr. Two-tongues, was my Mother's own Brother by Father's side; and to tell you the truth, I am a Gentleman of good Quality, yet my Great Grandfather was but a Waterman, looking one way and rowing another; and I got most of my estate by the same occupation.

CHRISTIAN. Are you a married man?

BY-ENDS. Yes, and my Wife is a very virtuous woman, the Daughter of a virtuous woman; she was my Lady Feigning's Daughter, therefore she came of a very honourable Family, and is arrived to such a pitch of breeding that she knows how to carry it to all,[107] even to Prince and Peasant. 'Tis true we somewhat differ in Religion from those of the stricter sort, yet but in two small points: First, we never strive against Wind and Tide: Secondly, we are always most zealous when Religion goes in his Silver Slippers; we love much to walk with him in the Street, if the Sun shines, and the People applaud him.

Then Christian stepped a little aside to his fellow Hopeful, saying, It runs in my mind that this is one By-ends of Fair-speech, and if it be he, we have as very a Knave in our company as dwelleth in all these parts. Then said Hopeful, Ask him; methinks he should not be ashamed of his name. So Christian came up with him again, and said, Sir, you talk as if you knew something more than all the world doth; and if I take not my mark amiss, I deem I have half a guess of you: Is not your name Mr. By-ends of Fair-speech?

BY-ENDS. This is not my name, but indeed it is a nickname that is given me by some that cannot abide me; and I must be content to bear it as a reproach, as other good men have borne theirs before me.

CHRISTIAN. But did you never give an occasion to men to call you by this name?

BY-ENDS. Never, never! The worst that ever I did to give them an occasion to give me this name was, that I had always the luck to jump in my Judgment[108] with the present way of the times whatever it was, and my chance was to get thereby; but if things are thus cast upon me, let me count them a blessing, but let not the malicious load me therefore with reproach.

CHRISTIAN. I thought indeed that you were the man that I heard of, and to tell you what I think, I fear this name belongs to you more properly than you are willing we should think it doth.

BY-ENDS. Well, if you will thus imagine, I cannot help it; you shall find me a fair company-keeper, if you will still admit me your associate.

CHRISTIAN. If you will go with us, you must go against Wind and Tide, the which, I perceive, is against your opinion; you must also own Religion in his Rags, as well as when in his Silver Slippers, and stand by him, too, when bound in Irons, as well as when he walketh the Streets with applause.

BY-ENDS. You must not impose, nor lord it over my Faith; leave me to my liberty, and let me go with you.

CHRISTIAN. Not a step farther, unless you will do in what I propound as we.

Then said By-ends, I shall never desert my old Principles, since they are harmless and profitable. If I may not go with you, I must do as I did before you overtook me, even go by myself, until some overtake me that will be glad of my company.

Now I saw in my Dream that Christian and Hopeful forsook him, and kept their distance before him; but one of them looking back, saw three men following Mr. By-ends, and behold, as they came up with him, he made them a very low congee, and they also gave him a compliment. The men's names were Mr. Hold-the-World, Mr. Money-love, and Mr. Save-all; men that Mr. By-ends had formerly been acquainted with; for in their minority they were School-fellows, and were taught by one Mr. Gripe-man, a School-master in Love-gain, which is a Market-town in the County of Coveting, in the North. This School-master taught them the Art of Getting either by violence, cozenage, flattery, lying, or by putting on a guise of Religion; and these four Gentlemen had attained much of the Art of their Master, so that they could each of them have kept such a School themselves.

Well when they had, as I said, thus saluted each other, Mr. Money-love said to Mr. By-ends, Who are they upon the Road before us? For Christian and Hopeful were yet within view.

BY-ENDS. They are a couple of far countrymen, that after their mode are going on Pilgrimage.

MONEY-LOVE. Alas! Why did they not stay, that we might have had their good company? for they, and we, and you, Sir, I hope, are all going on Pilgrimage.

BY-ENDS. We are so indeed; but the men before us are so rigid, and love so much their own notions, and do also so lightly esteem the opinions of others, that let a man be never so godly, yet if he jumps not with them in all things, they thrust him quite out of their company.

SAVE-ALL. That's bad; but we read of some that are righteous overmuch; and such men's rigidness prevails with them to judge and condemn all but themselves. But I pray what, and how many, were the things wherein you differed?

BY-ENDS. Why, they after their head-strong manner conclude that it is duty to rush on their Journey all weathers, and I am for waiting for Wind and Tide. They are for hazarding all for God at a clap,[109] and I am for taking all advantages to secure my Life and Estate. They are for holding their notions, though all other men are against them; but I am for Religion in what, and so far as, the times and my safety will bear it. They are for Religion when in Rags and Contempt; but I am for him when he walks in his Golden Slippers in the Sunshine, and with applause

HOLD-THE-WORLD. Ay, and hold you there still, good Mr. By-ends; for, for my part, I can count him but a Fool, that having the liberty to keep what he has, shall be so unwise as to lose it. Let us be wise as Serpents; 'tis best to make hay when the Sun shines; you see how the Bee lieth still all winter, and bestirs her only when she can have Profit and Pleasure. God sends sometimes Rain and sometimes Sunshine; if they be such fools to go through the first, yet let us be content to take fair weather along with us. For my part I like that Religion best that will stand with the security of God's good blessings unto us; for who can imagine that is ruled by his Reason, since God has bestowed upon us the good things of this Life, but that he would have us keep them for his sake? Abraham and Solomon grew rich in Religion. And Job says, that a good man shall lay up gold as Dust. But he must not be such as the men before us, if they be as you have described them.

SAVE-ALL. I think that we are all agreed in this matter, and therefore there needs no more words about it.

MONEY-LOVE. No, there needs no more words about this matter indeed; for he that believes neither Scripture nor Reason (and you see we have both on our side) neither knows his own liberty, nor seeks his own safety.

BY-ENDS. My brethren, we are, as you see, going all on Pilgrimage; and for our better diversion from things that are bad, give me leave to propound unto you this question:

Suppose a man, a Minister, or a Tradesman,[110] etc., should have an advantage lie before him to get the good blessings of this life, yet so as that he can by no means come by them, except, in appearance at least, he becomes extraordinary zealous in some points of Religion that he meddled not with before; may he not use this means to attain his end, and yet be a right honest man?

MONEY-LOVE. I see the bottom of your question, and, with these Gentlemen's good leave, I will endeavour to shape you an answer. And first, to speak to your question as it concerns a Minister himself: Suppose a Minister, a worthy man, possess'd but of a very small benefice, and has in his eye a greater, more fat and plump by far; he has also now an opportunity of getting of it, yet so as by being more studious, by preaching more frequently and zealously, and because the temper of the people requires it, by altering of some of his Principles; for my part I see no reason but a man may do this (provided he has a Call), ay, and more a great deal besides, and yet be an honest man. For why?

1. His desire of a greater benefice is lawful (this cannot be contradicted), since 'tis set before him by Providence; so then he may get it if he can, making no question for Conscience' sake.

2. Besides, his desire after that benefice makes him more studious, a more zealous Preacher, etc., and so makes him a

better man; yea makes him better improve his parts, which is according to the Mind of God.

3. Now as for his complying with the temper of his people, by disserting,[111] to serve them, some of his Principles, this argueth, 1. That he is of a self-denying temper; 2. Of a sweet and winning deportment; 3. And so more fit for the Ministerial function.

4. I conclude then, that a Minister that changes a small for a great, should not for so doing be judged as covetous; but rather, since he has improved in his parts and industry thereby, be counted as one that pursues his Call, and the opportunity put into his hand to do Good.

And now to the second part of the question, which concerns the Tradesman you mentioned. Suppose such an one to have but a poor employ in the world, but, by becoming Religious, he may mend his Market, perhaps get a rich Wife, or more and far better Customers to his Shop; for my part I see no reason but this may be lawfully done. For why?

1. To become Religious is a Virtue, by what means soever a man becomes so.

2. Nor is it unlawful to get a rich Wife, or more custom to my Shop.

3. Besides, the man that gets these by becoming religious, gets that which is good, of them that are good, by becoming good himself; so then here is a good Wife, and good Customers, and good Gain, and all these by becoming religious, which is good: therefore, to become religious to get all these is a good and profitable design.

This answer thus made by this Mr. Money-love to Mr. By-ends' question was highly applauded by them all; wherefore they concluded upon the whole that it was most wholesome and advantageous. And because, as they thought, no man was able to contradict it, and because Christian and Hopeful were yet within call, they jointly agreed to assault them with the question as soon as they overtook them, and the rather because they had opposed Mr. By-ends before. So they called after them, and they stopped, and stood still till they came up to them; but they concluded as they went that not Mr. By-ends, but old Mr. Hold-the-World, should propound the question to them, because, as they supposed, their answer to him would be without the remainder of that heat that was kindled betwixt Mr. By-ends and them at their parting a little before.

So they came up to each other, and after a short salutation, Mr. Hold-the-World propounded the question to Christian and his fellow, and bid them to answer it if they could.

CHRISTIAN. Then said Christian, Even a babe in Religion may answer ten thousand such questions. For if it be unlawful to follow Christ for loaves, as it is (John 6), how much more abominable is it to make of him and Religion a Stalking-horse to get and enjoy the world. Nor do we find any other than Heathens, Hypocrites, Devils, and Witches,[112] that are of this opinion.

1. Heathens; for when Hamor and Shechem[113] had a mind to the Daughter and Cattle of Jacob, and saw that there was no way for them to come at them but by becoming circumcised, they said to their companions, If every male of us be circum-sized, as they are circumcised, shall not their Cattle, and their substance, and every beast of theirs, be ours? Their Daughter and their Cattle were that which they sought to obtain, and their Religion the Stalking-horse they made use of to come at them. Read the whole story, Gen. 34:20-23.

2. The Hypocritical Pharisees were also of this Religion; Long Prayers were their Pretence, but to get widows' houses was their Intent; and greater damnation was from God their Judgment, Luke 20:46, 47.

3. Judas the Devil[114] was also of this Religion; he was religious for the Bag, that he might be possessed of what was therein; but he was lost, cast away, and the very Son of Perdition.

4. Simon the Witch was of this Religion too; for he would have had the Holy Ghost, that he might have got Money therewith, and his sentence from Peter's mouth was according, Acts 8:19-22.

5. Neither will it out of my mind, but that that man that takes up Religion for the World will throw away Religion for the World; for so surely as Judas designed the World in becoming religious, so surely did he also sell Religion and his Master for the same. To answer the question therefore affirmatively, as I perceive you have done, and to accept of as authentic such answer, is both Heathenish, Hypocritical, and Devilish, and your Reward will be according to your

Works. Then they stood staring one upon another, but had not wherewith to answer Christian. Hopeful also approved of the soundness of Christian's answer; so there was a great Silence among them. Mr. By-ends and his company also staggered and kept behind, that Christian and Hopeful might outgo them. Then said Christian to his fellow, If these men cannot stand before the sentence of men, what will they do with the sentence of God? And if they are mute when dealt with by vessels of Clay, what will they do when they shall be rebuked by the flames of a devouring Fire?

Then Christian and Hopeful out-went them, and went till they came at a delicate Plain called Ease,[115] where they went with much content; but that Plain was but narrow, so they were quickly got over it. Now at the farther side of that Plain was a little Hill called Lucre, and in that Hill a Silver-Mine, which some of them that had formerly gone that way, because of the rarity of it, had turned aside to see; but going too near the brink of the pit, the ground being deceitful under them broke, and they were slain; some also had been maimed there, and could not to their dying day be their own men again.

Then I saw in my Dream, that a little off the road, over against the Silver-Mine, stood Demas (gentleman-like) to call to Passengers to come and see; who said to Christian and his fellow, Ho, turn aside hither, and I will shew you a thing.[116]

CHRISTIAN. What thing so deserving as to turn us out of the way?

DEMAS. Here is a Silver-Mine, and some digging in it for Treasure. If you will come, with a little pains you may richly provide for yourselves.

HOPEFUL. Then said Hopeful, Let us go see.

CHRISTIAN. Not I, said Christian; I have heard of this place before now, and how many have there been slain; and besides, that Treasure is a snare to those that seek it, for it hindereth them in their Pilgrimage. Then Christian called to Demas, saying, Is not the place dangerous? Hath it not hindered many in their pilgrimage? (Hos. 4:18.)

DEMAS. Not very dangerous, except to those that are careless: but withal he blushed as he spake.

CHRISTIAN. Then said Christian to Hopeful, Let us not stir a step, but still keep on our way.

HOPEFUL. I will warrant you when By-ends comes up, if he hath the same invitation as we, he will turn in thither to see.

CHRISTIAN. No doubt thereof, for his Principles lead him that way, and a hundred to one but he dies there.

DEMAS. Then Demas called again, saying, But will you not come over and see?

CHRISTIAN. Then Christian roundly answered, saying, Demas, thou art an Enemy to the right ways of the Lord of this way, and hast been already condemned for thine own turning aside, by one of his Majesty's Judges[117] (II Tim. 4:10); and why seekest thou to bring us into the like condemnation? Besides, if we at all turn aside, our Lord the King will certainly hear thereof, and will there put us to shame, where we would stand with boldness before him.

Demas cried again, that he also was one of their fraternity; and that, if they would tarry a little, he also himself would walk with them.

CHRISTIAN. Then said Christian, What is thy name? Is it not it by the which I have called thee?

DEMAS. Yes, my name is Demas, I am the son of Abraham.

CHRISTIAN. I know you, Gehazi was your Great Grandfather, and Judas your Father, and you have trod in their steps. It is but a devilish prank that thou usest; thy Father was hanged for a Traitor, and thou deservest no better reward (II Kings 5:20; Matt. 26:14, 15; 27:1-6). Assure thyself, that when we come to the King we will do him word of this thy behaviour. Thus they went their way.

By this time By-ends and his Companions were come again within sight, and they at the first beck went over to Demas. Now whether they fell into the Pit by looking over the brink thereof, or whether they went down to dig, or whether they were smothered in the bottom by the damps that commonly arise, of these things I am not certain; but this I observed, that they never were seen again in the way. Then sang Christian,

By-ends and Silver Demas both agree;
One calls, the other runs, that he may be
A sharer in his Lucre; so these two
Take up in this World, and no farther go.

Now I saw that, just on the other side of this Plain, the Pilgrims came to a place where stood an old Monument, hard by the Highway side, at the sight of which they were both concerned, because of the strangeness of the form thereof; for it seemed to them as if it had been a Woman transformed into the shape of a Pillar;[118] here therefore they stood looking upon it, but could not for a time tell what they should make thereof. At last Hopeful espied written above upon the head thereof, a writing in an unusual hand; but he being no Scholar, called to Christian (for he was learned) to see if he could pick out the meaning; so he came, and after a little laying of letters together, he found the same to be this, Remember Lot's Wife. So he read it to his fellow; after which they both concluded that that was the Pillar of Salt into which Lot's Wife was turned, for her looking back with a covetous heart, when she was going from Sodom for safety (Gen. 19:26). Which sudden and amazing sight gave them occasion of this discourse.

CHRISTIAN. Ah, my Brother, this is a seasonable sight; it came opportunely to us after the invitation which Demas gave us to come over to view the Hill Lucre; and had we gone over as he desired us, and as thou wast inclining to do, my Brother, we had, for aught I know, been made ourselves like this woman, a spectacle for those that shall come after to behold.

HOPEFUL. I am sorry that I was so foolish, and am made to wonder that I am not now as Lot's Wife; for wherein was the difference 'twixt her sin and mine? she only looked back, and I had a desire to go see. Let Grace be adored, and let me be ashamed that ever such a thing should be in mine heart.

CHRISTIAN. Let us take notice of what we see here, for our help for time to come: This woman escaped one Judgment, for she fell not by the destruction of Sodom; yet she was destroyed by another, as we see she is turned into a Pillar of Salt.

HOPEFUL. True, and she may be to us both Caution and Example; Caution that we should shun her sin, or a sign of what Judgment will overtake such as shall not be prevented by this caution. So Korah, Dathan, and Abiram, with the two hundred and fifty men that perished in their sin, did also become a sign or example to others to beware (Num. 26:9, 10). But above all, I muse at one thing, to wit, how Demas and his fellows can stand so confidently yonder to look for that treasure, which this Woman, but for looking behind her after (for we read not that she stepped one foot out of the way), was turned into a pillar of salt; especially since the Judgment which overtook her did make her an example within sight of where they are; for they cannot choose but see her, did they but lift up their eyes.

CHRISTIAN. It is a thing to be wondered at, and it argueth that their hearts are grown desperate in the case; and I cannot tell who to compare them to so fitly, as to them that pick pockets in the presence of the Judge, or that will cut purses under the Gallows. It is said of the men of Sodom that they were sinners exceedingly, because they were sinners before the Lord (Gen. 13:13); that is, in his eyesight, and notwithstanding the kindnesses that he had shewed them; for the land of Sodom was now like the Garden of Eden heretofore (Gen. 13:10). This therefore provoked him the more to jealousy, and made their plague as hot as the fire of the Lord out of Heaven could make it. And it is most rationally to be concluded that such, even such as these are, that shall sin in the sight, yea, and that too in despite of such examples that are set continually before them to caution them to the contrary, must be partakers of severest Judgments.

HOPEFUL. Doubtless thou hast said the truth; but what a mercy is it, that neither thou, but especially I, am not made myself this example: this ministereth occasion to us to thank God, to fear before him, and always to remember Lot's Wife.

I saw then that they went on their way to a pleasant River, which David the King called the River of God, but John the River of the Water of Life (Ps. 65:9; Rev. 22:1-3; Ezek. 47). Now their way lay just upon the bank of the River; here therefore Christian and his Companion walked with great delight; they drank also of the water of the River, which was pleasant and enlivening to their weary spirits: besides, on the banks of this River, on either side, were green Trees that bore all manner of Fruit; and the Leaves of the Trees were good for Medicine; with the Fruit of these Trees they were also much delighted; and the Leaves they ate to prevent Surfeits and other Diseases that are incident to those that heat their blood by Travels. On either side of the River was also a Meadow, curiously beautified with Lilies; and it was green all the year long. In this Meadow they lay down and slept, for here they might lie down safely (Ps. 23:2; Isa. 14:30). When they awoke, they gathered again of the Fruit of the Trees, and drank again of the water of the River; and then lay down again to sleep. Thus they did several days and nights. Then they sang,

Behold ye how these Crystal streams do glide
(To comfort Pilgrims) by the Highway side;
The Meadows green, beside their fragrant smell,
Yield dainties for them: And he that can tell
What pleasant Fruit, yea Leaves, these Trees do yield,
Will soon sell all,[119] that he may buy this Field.

So when they were disposed to go on (for they were not as yet at their Journey's end) they ate and drank, and departed.

Now I beheld in my dream, that they had not journeyed far, but the River and the way for a time parted; at which they were not a little sorry, yet they durst not go out of the way. Now the way from the River was rough, and their feet tender by reason of their Travels; so the soul of the Pilgrims was much discouraged because of the way (Num. 21:4). Wherefore, still as they went on, they wished for better way. Now a little before them, there was on the left hand of the road a Meadow, and a Stile to go over into it, and that Meadow is called By-path Meadow.[120] Then said Christian to his fellow, If this Meadow lieth along by our wayside, let's go over into it. Then he went to the Stile to see, and behold a Path lay along by the way on the other side of the fence. 'Tis according to my wish, said Christian, here is the easiest going; come, good Hopeful, and let us go over.

HOPEFUL. But how if this Path should lead us out of the way?

CHRISTIAN. That's not like, said the other; look, doth it not go along by the wayside? So Hopeful, being persuaded by his fellow, went after him over the Stile. When they were gone over, and were got into the Path, they found it very easy for their feet: and withal, they looking before them espied a man walking as they did (and his name was Vain-confidence), so they called after him, and asked him whither that way led? He said, To the Celestial Gate. Look, said Christian, did I not tell you so? by this you may see we are right. So they followed, and he went before them. But behold the night came on, and it grew very dark, so that they that were behind lost the sight of him that went before.

He, therefore, that went before (Vain-confidence by name),

not seeing the way before him, fell into a deep Pit (Isa. 9:16), which was on purpose there made by the Prince of those grounds to catch vain-glorious fools withal, and was dashed in pieces with his fall.

Now Christian and his fellow heard him fall. So they called to know the matter, but there was none to answer, only they heard a groaning. Then said Hopeful, Where are we now? Then was his fellow silent, as mistrusting that he had led him out of the way; and now it began to rain, and thunder, and lighten in a very dreadful manner, and the water rose amain.

Then Hopeful groaned in himself, saying, Oh that I had kept on my way!

CHRISTIAN. Who could have thought that this Path should have led us out of the way?

HOPEFUL. I was afraid on't at the very first, and therefore gave you that gentle caution. I would have spoke plainer, but that you are older than I.

CHRISTIAN. Good Brother, be not offended; I am sorry I have brought thee out of the way, and that I have put thee into such eminent[121] danger; pray, my Brother, forgive me, I did not do it of an evil intent.

HOPEFUL. Be comforted, my Brother, for I forgive thee; and believe too that this shall be for our good.

CHRISTIAN. I am glad I have with me a merciful Brother; but we must not stand thus, let's try to go back again.

HOPEFUL. But, good Brother, let me go before.

CHRISTIAN. No, if you please, let me go first, that if there be any danger, I may be first therein, because by my means we are both gone out of the way.

HOPEFUL. No, said Hopeful, you shall not go first, for your mind being troubled may lead you out of the way again. Then for their encouragement, they heard the voice of one saying, Let thine heart be towards the Highway, even the way that thou wentest, turn again (Jer. 31:21). But by this time the waters were greatly risen, by reason of which the way of going back was very dangerous. (Then I thought that it is easier going out of the way when we are in, than going in when we are out.) Yet they adventured to go back; but it was so dark, and the flood was so high, that in their going back they had like to have been drowned nine or ten times.

Neither could they, with all the skill they had, get again to the Stile that night. Wherefore at last, lighting under a little shelter, they sat down there till the day brake; but being weary they fell asleep. Now there was not far from the place where they lay, a Castle called Doubting Castle,[122] the owner whereof was Giant Despair, and it was in his grounds they now were sleeping: wherefore he, getting up in the morning early, and walking up and down in his fields, caught Christian and Hopeful asleep in his grounds. Then with a grim and surly voice he bid them awake, and asked them whence they were? and what they did in his grounds? They told him they were Pilgrims, and that they had lost their way. Then said the Giant, You have this night trespassed on me, by trampling in and lying on my grounds, and therefore you must go along with me. So they were forced to go, because he was stronger than they. They also had but little to say, for they knew themselves in a fault. The Giant therefore drove them before him, and put them into his Castle into a very dark Dungeon, nasty and stinking to the spirits of these two men. Here then they lay from Wednesday morning till Saturday night, without one bit of bread, or drop of drink, or light, or any to ask how they did; they were therefore here in evil case, and were far from friends and acquaintance (Ps. 88:18). Now in this place Christian had double sorrow, because 'twas through his unadvised haste that they were brought into this distress.

Now Giant Despair had a Wife, and her name was Diffidence. So when he was gone to bed, he told his Wife what he had done, to wit, that he had taken a couple of Prisoners and cast them into his Dungeon for trespassing on his grounds. Then he asked her also what he had best do further to them. So she asked him what they were, whence they came, and whither they were bound; and he told her. Then she counselled him that when he arose in the morning he should beat them without any mercy. So when he arose, he getteth him a grievous Crab-tree Cudgel, and goes down into the Dungeon to them, and there first falls to rating of them as if they were dogs, although they gave him never a word of distaste. Then he falls upon them, and beats them fearfully, in such sort that they were not able to help themselves, or to turn them upon the floor. This done, he withdraws and leaves them there to condole their misery, and to mourn under their distress: so all that day they spent the time in nothing but sighs and bitter lamentations. The next night she talking with her Husband about them further, and understanding that they were yet alive, did advise him to counsel them to make away themselves. So when morning was come, he goes to them in a surly manner as before, and perceiving them to be very sore with the stripes that he had given them the day before, he told them that, since they were never like to come out of that place, their only way would be forthwith to make an end of themselves, either with Knife, Halter, or Poison. For why, said he, should you choose life, seeing it is attended with so much bitterness? But they desired him to let them go. With that he looked ugly upon them, and rushing to them had doubtless made an end of them himself, but that he fell into one of his Fits[123] (for he sometimes in Sun-shine[124] weather fell into Fits) and lost for a time the use of his hand; wherefore he withdrew, and left them as before, to consider what to do. Then did the Prisoners consult between themselves, whether 'twas best to take his counsel or no; and thus they began to discourse:

CHRISTIAN. Brother, said Christian, what shall we do? The life that we now live is miserable: for my part I know not whether it is best to live thus, or to die out of hand. My soul chooseth strangling rather than life (Job 7:15), and the Grave is more easy for me than this Dungeon. Shall we be ruled by the Giant?

HOPEFUL. Indeed our present condition is dreadful, and death would be far more welcome to me than thus for ever to abide; but yet let us consider, the Lord of the Country to which we are going hath said, Thou shalt do no murder, no not to another man's person; much more then are we forbidden to take his counsel to kill ourselves. Besides, he that kills another can but commit murder upon his body; but for one to kill himself is to kill body and soul at once.[125] And, moreover, my Brother, thou talkest of ease in the Grave; but hast thou forgotten the Hell whither for certain the murderers go? For no murderer hath eternal life, etc. And let us consider again, that all the Law is not in the hand of Giant Despair. Others, so far as I can understand, have been taken by him as well as we, and yet have escaped out of his hand. Who knows but that God that made the world may cause that Giant Despair may die? or that at some time or other he may forget to lock us in? or but he may in short time have another of his Fits before us, and may lose the use of his limbs? and if ever that should come to pass again, for my part I am resolved to pluck up the heart of a man, and to try my utmost to get from under his hand. I was a fool that I did not try to do it before; but, however, my Brother, let's be patient, and endure a while; the time may come that may give us a happy release; but let us not be our own murderers. With these words Hopeful at present did moderate the mind of his Brother; so they continued together (in the dark) that day, in their sad and doleful condition.

Well, towards evening the Giant goes down into the Dungeon again, to see if his Prisoners had taken his counsel; but when he came there he found them alive, and truly, alive was all; for now, what for want of Bread and Water, and by reason of the Wounds they received when he beat them, they could do little but breathe: but, I say, he found them alive; at which he fell into a grievous rage, and told them that seeing they had disobeyed his counsel, it should be worse with them than if they had never been born.

At this they trembled greatly, and I think that Christian fell into a Swound;[126] but coming a little to himself again, they renewed their discourse about the Giant's counsel, and whether yet they had best to take it or no. Now Christian again seemed to be for doing it, but Hopeful made his second reply as followeth:

HOPEFUL. My Brother, said he, rememberest thou not how valiant thou hast been heretofore? Apollyon could not crush thee, nor could all that thou didst hear, or see, or feel in the Valley of the Shadow of Death. What hardship, terror, and amazement hast thou already gone through, and art thou now nothing but fear? Thou seest that I am in the Dungeon with thee, a far weaker man by nature than thou art; also this Giant has wounded me as well as thee, and hath also cut off the Bread and Water from my mouth; and with thee I mourn without the light. But let's exercise a little more patience; remember how thou playedst the man at Vanity Fair, and wast neither afraid of the Chain, nor Cage, nor yet of bloody Death: wherefore let us (at least to avoid the same that becomes not a Christian to be found in) bear up with patience as well as we can.

Now night being come again, and the Giant and his Wife being in bed, she asked him concerning the Prisoners, and if they had taken his counsel: To which he replied, They are sturdy Rogues, they choose rather to bear all hardship than to make away themselves. Then said she, Take them into the Castle-yard to-morrow, and shew them the Bones and Skulls of those that thou hast already despatch'd, and make them believe, ere a week comes to an end, thou also wilt tear them in pieces, as thou hast done their fellows before them.

So when the morning was come, the Giant goes to them again, and takes them into the Castle-yard and shews them as his Wife had bidden him. These, said he, were Pilgrims as you are, once, and they trespassed in my grounds, as you have done; and when I thought fit, I tore them in pieces, and so within ten days I will do you. Go get you down to your Den[127] again; and with that he beat them all the way thither. They lay therefore all day on Saturday in a lamentable case, as before. Now when night was come, and when Mrs. Diffidence and her Husband the Giant were got to bed they began to renew their discourse of their Prisoners; and withal the old Giant wondered that he could neither by his blows nor counsel bring them to an end. And with that his Wife replied, I fear, said she, that they live in hope that some will come to relieve them, or that they have pick-locks about them, by the means of which they hope to escape. And sayest thou so, my dear? said the Giant. I will therefore search them in the morning.

Well on Saturday about midnight they began to pray, and continued in Prayer till almost break of day.

Now a little before it was day, good Christian, as one half amazed, brake out in this passionate speech: What a fool, quoth he, am I, thus to lie in a stinking Dungeon, when I may as well walk at liberty. I have a Key[128] in my bosom called Promise, that will, I am persuaded, open any Lock in Doubting Castle. Then said Hopeful, That's good news; good Brother, pluck it out of thy bosom and try.

Then Christian pulled it out of his bosom, and began to try at the Dungeon door, whose bolt (as he turned the Key) gave back, and the door flew open with ease, and Christian and Hopeful both came out. Then he went to the outward door that leads into the Castle-yard, and with his Key opened that door also. After he went to the iron Gate, for that must be opened too, but that Lock went damnable hard, yet the Key did open it. Then they thrust open the Gate to make their escape with speed, but that Gate as it opened made such a creaking that it waked Giant Despair, who hastily rising to pursue his Prisoners, felt his limbs to fail, for his Fits took him again, so that he could by no means go after them. Then they went on, and came to the King's Highway again, and so were safe, because they were out of his Jurisdiction.

Now when they were gone over the Stile, they began to contrive with themselves what they should do at that Stile to prevent those that should come after from falling into the hands of Giant Despair. So they consented to erect[129] there a Pillar, and to engrave upon the side thereof this sentence, Over this Stile is the way to Doubting Castle, which is kept by Giant Despair, who despiseth the King of the Celestial Country, and seeks to destroy his holy Pilgrims. Many, therefore, that followed after read what was written, and escaped the danger.

They went then till they came to the Delectable Mountains, which Mountains belong to the Lord of that Hill of which we have spoken before; so they went up to the Mountains, to behold the Gardens and Orchards, the Vineyards and Fountains of water; where also they drank, and washed themselves, and did freely eat of the Vineyards. Now there were on the tops of these Mountains Shepherds feeding their flocks, and they stood by the Highway side. The Pilgrims therefore went to them, and leaning upon their staves (as is common with weary Pilgrims, when they stand to talk with any by the way), they asked, Whose Delectable Mountains are these? And whose be the sheep that feed upon them?

SHEPHERDS. These mountains are Immanuel's Land, and they are within sight of his City; and the sheep also are his, and he laid down his life for them (John 10:11).

CHRISTIAN. Is this the way to the Celestial City?

SHEPHERDS. You are just in your way.

CHRISTIAN. How far is it thither?

SHEPHERD. Too far for any but those that shall get thither indeed.

CHRISTIAN. Is the way safe or dangerous?

SHEPHERDS. Safe for those for whom it is to be safe, but transgressors shall fall therein (Hos. 14:9).

CHRISTIAN. Is there in this place any relief for Pilgrims that are weary and faint in the way?

SHEPHERDS. The Lord of these Mountains hath given us a charge not to be forgetful to entertain strangers (Heb. 13:1, 2); therefore the good of the place is even before you.

I saw also in my Dream, that when the Shepherds perceived that they were wayfaring men, they also put questions to them (to which they made answer as in other places), as, Whence came you? and, How got you into the way? and, By what means have you so persevered therein? For but few of them that begin to come hither do shew their face on these Mountains. But when the Shepherds heard their answers, being pleased therewith, they looked very lovingly upon them, and said, Welcome to the Delectable Mountains.

The Shepherds, I say, whose names were Knowledge, Experience, Watchful, and Sincere, took them by the hand, and had them to their Tents, and made them partake of that which was ready at present. They said, moreover, We would that ye should stay here a while, to acquaint with us,[130] and yet more, to solace yourselves with the good of these Delectable Mountains. They then told them, that they were content to stay; and so they went to their rest that night, because it was very late.

Then I saw in my Dream, that in the morning the Shepherds called up Christian and Hopeful to walk with them upon the Mountains; so they went forth with them, and walked a while, having a pleasant prospect on every side. Then said the Shepherds one to another, Shall we shew these Pilgrims some wonders? So when they had concluded to do it, they had them first to the top of a Hill called Error, which was very steep on the farthest side, and bid them look down to the bottom. So Christian and Hopeful looked down, and saw at the bottom several men dashed all to pieces by a fall that they had from the top. Then said Christian, What meaneth this? The Shepherds answered, Have you not heard of them that were made to err, by hearkening to Hymeneus and Philetus (II Tim. 2:17, 18), as concerning the Faith of the Resurrection of the Body? They answered, Yes. Then said the Shepherds, Those that you see lie dashed in pieces at the bottom of this Mountain are they; and they have continued to this day unburied (as you see) for an example to others to take heed how they clamber too high, or how they come too near the brink of this Mountain.

Then I saw that they had them to the top of another Mountain, and the name of that is Caution, and bid them look afar off; which when they did, they perceived, as they thought, several men walking up and down among the Tombs[131] that were there; and they perceived that the men were blind, because they stumbled sometimes upon the Tombs, and because they could not get out from among them. Then said Christian, What means this?

The Shepherds then answered, Did you not see a little below these Mountains a Stile that led into a Meadow, on the left hand of this way? They answered, Yes. Then said the Shepherds, From that Stile there goes a path that leads directly to Doubting Castle, which is kept by Giant Despair; and these men (pointing to them among the Tombs) came once on Pilgrimage, as you do now, even till they came to that same Stile; and because the right way was rough in that place, they chose to go out of it into that Meadow, and there were taken by Giant Despair, and cast into Doubting Castle; where, after they had been awhile kept in the Dungeon, he at last did put out their eyes, and led them among those Tombs, where he has left them to wander to this very day, that the saying of the Wise Man might be fulfilled, He that wandereth out of the way of understanding, shall remain in the congregation of the dead (Prov. 21:16). Then Christian and Hopeful looked one upon another, with tears gushing out, but yet said nothing to the Shepherds.

Then I saw in my Dream, that the Shepherds had them to another place, in a bottom, where was a door in the side of an Hill; and they opened the door, and bid them look in. They looked in, therefore, and saw that within it was very dark and smoky; they also thought that they heard there a lumbring[132] noise as of Fire, and a cry of some tormented, and that they smelt the scent of Brimstone. Then said Christian, What means this? The Shepherds told them, This is a by-way to Hell, a way that Hypocrites go in at; namely, such as sell their Birthright, with Esau; such as sell their Master, with Judas; such as blaspheme the Gospel, with Alexander;[133] and that lie and dissemble, with Ananias and Sapphira his Wife.

Then said Hopeful to the Shepherds, I perceive that these had on them, even every one, a shew of Pilgrimage, as we have now; had they not?

SHEPHERDS. Yes, and held it a long time too.

HOPEFUL. How far might they go on in Pilgrimage in their day, since they notwithstanding were thus miserably cast away?

SHEPHERDS. Some farther, and some not so far as these Mountains.

Then said the Pilgrims one to another, We had need cry to the Strong for strength.

SHEPHERDS. Ay, and you will have need to use it when you have it too.

By this time the Pilgrims had a desire to go forwards, and the Shepherds a desire they should; so they walked together towards the end of the Mountains. Then said the Shepherds one to another, Let us here shew to the Pilgrims the Gates of the Celestial City, if they have skill to look through our Perspective Glass. The Pilgrims then lovingly accepted the motion; so they had them to the top of an high Hill, called Clear, and gave them their Glass to look.

Then they essayed to look, but the remembrance of that last thing that the Shepherds had shewed them made their hands shake, by means of which impediment they could not look steadily through the Glass; yet they thought they saw something like the Gate, and also some of the Glory of the place. Then they went away and sang this song,

> Thus by the Shepherds Secrets are reveal'd,
> Which from all other men are kept conceal'd:
> Come to the Shepherds, then, if you would see
> Things deep, things hid, and that mysterious be.

When they were about to depart, one of the Shepherds gave them a Note of the way. Another of them bid them beware of the Flatterer. The third bid them take heed that they sleep not on the Enchanted Ground. And the fourth bid them Godspeed. So I awoke from my Dream.[134]

And I slept, and Dreamed again, and saw the same two Pilgrims going down the Mountains along the Highway towards the City. Now a little below these Mountains, on the left hand, lieth the Country of Conceit; from which Country there comes into the way in which the Pilgrims walked a little crooked Lane. Here, therefore, they met with a very brisk Lad, that came out of that Country; and his name was Ignorance.[135] So Christian asked him from what parts he came and whither he was going.

IGNORANCE. Sir, I was born in the Country that lieth off there, a little on the left hand, and I am going to the Celestial City.

CHRISTIAN. But how do you think to get in at the Gate, for you may find some difficulty there?

IGNORANCE. As other good people do, said he.

CHRISTIAN. But what have you to shew at that Gate, that may cause that the Gate should be opened to you?

IGNORANCE. I know my Lord's will, and I have been a good liver; I pay every man his own; I Pray, Fast, pay Tithes, and give Alms, and have left my Country for whither I am going.

CHRISTIAN. But thou camest not in at the Wicket-Gate that is at the head of this way; thou camest in hither through that same crooked Lane, and, therefore, I fear, however thou mayest think of thyself, when the reckoning day shall come, thou wilt have laid to thy charge that thou art a Thief and a Robber, instead of getting admittance into the City.

IGNORANCE. Gentlemen, ye be utter strangers to me, I know you not; be content to follow the Religion of your Country, and I will follow the Religion of mine. I hope all will be well. And as for the Gate that you talk of, all the world knows that that is a great way off of our Country. I cannot think that any man in all our parts doth so much as know the way to it, nor need they matter whether they do or no, since we have, as you see, a fine pleasant Green Lane, that comes down from our Country the next way into the way.

When Christian saw that the man was wise in his own conceit, he said to Hopeful whisperingly, There is more hopes of a fool than of him (Prov. 26:12). And said, moreover, When he that is a fool walketh by the way, his wisdom faileth him, and he saith to every one that he is a fool (Eccles. 10:3). What, shall we talk further with him, or outgo him at present, and so leave him to think of what he hath heard already, and then stop again for him afterwards, and see if by degrees we can do any good of him? Then said Hopeful,

Let Ignorance a little while now muse
On what is said, and let him not refuse
Good counsel to embrace, lest he remain
Still ignorant of what's the chiefest gain.
God saith, Those that no understanding have
(Although he made them) them he will not save.

HOPEFUL. He further added, It is not good, I think, to say all to him at once; let us pass him by, if you will, and talk to him anon, even as he is able to bear it.

So they both went on, and Ignorance he came after. Now when they had passed him a little way, they entered into a very dark Lane, where they met a man whom seven Devils had bound with seven strong cords, and were carrying of him back to the Door that they saw in the side of the Hill (Matt. 12:45; Prov. 5:22). Now good Christian began to tremble, and so did Hopeful his Companion; yet as the Devils led away the man, Christian looked to see if he knew him, and he thought it might be one Turn-away that dwelt in the Town of Apostacy. But he did not perfectly see his face, for he did hang his head like a Thief that is found. But being gone past, Hopeful looked after him, and espied on his back a paper with this inscription, Wanton Professor and damnable Apostate. Then said Christian to his fellow, Now I call to remembrance that which was told me of a thing that happened to a good man hereabout. The name of the man was Little-faith, but a good man, and he dwelt in the Town of Sincere. The thing was this: At the entering in of this passage, there comes down from Broad-way Gate, a Lane called Dead Man's Lane; so called because of the Murders that are commonly done there; and this Little-faith, going on Pilgrimage as we do now, chanced to sit down there and slept. Now there happened at that time to come down the Lane from Broad-way Gate, three sturdy Rogues, and their names were Faint-heart, Mistrust, and Guilt (three Brothers), and they espying Little-faith where he was, came galloping up with speed. Now the good man was just awaked from his sleep, and was getting up to go on his Journey. So they came all up to him, and with threatening language bid him stand. At this Little-faith looked as white as a Clout, and had neither power to fight nor fly. Then said Faint-heart, Deliver thy Purse. But he making no haste to do it (for he was loth to lose his Money), Mistrust ran up to him, and thrusting his hand into his Pocket, pulled out thence a bag of Silver. Then he cried out, Thieves, Thieves. With that Guilt, with a great Club that was in his hand, struck Little-faith on the head, and with that blow fell'd him flat to the ground, where he lay bleeding as one that would bleed to death. All this while the Thieves stood by. But at last, they hearing that some were upon the road, and fearing lest it should be one Great-grace that dwells in the City of Good-confidence, they betook themselves to their heels, and left this good man to shift for himself. Now after a while Little-faith came to himself, and getting up made shift to scrabble on his way.[136] This was the story.

HOPEFUL. But did they take from him all that ever he had?

CHRISTIAN. No; the place where his Jewels[137] were they never ransacked, so those he kept still; but as I was told, the good man was much afflicted for his loss, for the Thieves got most of his spending Money. That which they got not (as I said) were Jewels, also he had a little odd Money left, but scarce enough to bring him to his Journey's end (I Pet. 4:18); nay, if I was not misinformed, he was forced to beg as he went, to keep himself alive, for his Jewels he might not sell. But beg, and do what he could, he went (as we say) with many a hungry belly the most part of the rest of the way.

HOPEFUL. But is it not a wonder they got not from him his Certificate, by which he was to receive his admittance at the Celestial Gate?

CHRISTIAN. 'Tis a wonder but they got not that, though they missed it not through any good cunning of his; for he being dismayed with their coming upon him, had neither power nor skill to hide anything; so 'twas more by good Providence than by his endeavour that they missed of that good thing (II Tim. 1:14).

HOPEFUL. But it must needs be a comfort to him that they got not this Jewel from him (II Pet. 1:19).

CHRISTIAN. It might have been great comfort to him, had he used it as he should; but they that told me the story said that he made but little use of it all the rest of the way, and that because of the dismay that he had in their taking away of his Money; indeed he forgot it a great part of the rest of his Journey; and, besides, when at any time it came into his mind, and he began to be comforted therewith, then would fresh thoughts of his loss come again upon him, and those thoughts would swallow up all.

HOPEFUL. Alas, poor man! This could not but be a great grief unto him.

CHRISTIAN. Grief! ay, a grief indeed. Would it not have been so to any of us, had we been used as he, to be robbed, and wounded too, and that in a strange place as he was? 'Tis a wonder he did not die with grief, poor heart! I was told that he scattered almost all the rest of the way with nothing but doleful and bitter complaints; telling also to all that overtook him, or that he overtook in the way as he went, where he was robbed, and how; who they were that did it, and what he lost; how he was wounded, and that he hardly escaped with life.

HOPEFUL. But 'tis a wonder that his necessities did not put him upon selling or pawning some of his Jewels, that he might have wherewith to relieve himself in his Journey.

Christian snibbeth his fellow for unadvised speaking.

CHRISTIAN. Thou talkest like one upon whose head is the Shell to this very day; for what should he pawn them, or to whom should he sell them? In all that Country where he was robbed, his Jewels were not accounted of; nor did he want that relief which could from thence be administered to him. Besides, had his Jewels been missing at the Gate of the Celestial City, he had (and that he knew well enough) been excluded from an Inheritance there; and that would have been worse to him than the appearance and villainy of ten thousand Thieves.

HOPEFUL. Why art thou so tart, my Brother? Esau sold his Birthright, and that for a mess of Pottage (Heb. 12:16), and that Birthright was his greatest Jewel; and if he, why might not Little-faith do so too?

CHRISTIAN. Esau did sell his Birthright indeed, and so do many besides, and by so doing exclude themselves from the chief blessing, as also that caitiff [138] did; but you must put a difference betwixt Esau and Little-faith, and also betwixt their Estates. Esau's Birthright was typical,[139] but Little-faith's Jewels were not so: Esau's belly was his god, but Little-faith's belly was not so: Esau's want lay in his fleshly appetite, Little-faith's did not so. Besides, Esau could see no farther than to the fulfilling of his lusts: For I am at the point to die, said he, and what good will this Birthright do me? (Gen. 25:32.) But Little-faith, though it was his lot to have but a little faith, was by his little faith kept from such extravagancies, and made to see and prize his Jewels more than to sell them, as Esau did his Birthright. You read not anywhere that Esau had faith, no not so much as a little; therefore no marvel if where the flesh only bears sway (as it will in that man where no faith is to resist) if he sells his Birthright, and his soul and all, and that to the Devil of Hell; for it is with such, as it is with the ass, who in her occasions cannot be turned away (Jer. 2:24). When their minds are set upon their lusts, they will have them whatever they cost. But Little-faith was of another temper, his mind was on things Divine; his livelihood was upon things that were Spiritual, and from above; therefore to what end should he that is of such a temper sell his Jewels (had there been any that would have bought them) to fill his mind with empty things? Will a man give a penny to fill his belly with Hay? or can you persuade the Turtle-dove to live upon Carrion like the Crow? Though faithless ones can, for carnal Lusts, pawn or mortgage, or sell what they have, and themselves outright to boot; yet they that have faith, saving faith, though but a little of it, cannot do so. Here, therefore, my Brother, is thy mistake.

HOPEFUL. I acknowledge it; but yet your severe reflection had almost made me angry.

CHRISTIAN. Why, I did but compare thee to some of the Birds that are of the brisker sort, who will run to and fro in trodden paths, with the Shell upon their heads; but pass by that, and consider the matter under debate, and all shall be well betwixt thee and me.

Hopeful swaggers.

HOPEFUL. But, Christian, these three fellows, I am persuaded in my heart, are but a company of Cowards; would they have run else, think you, as they did, at the noise of one that was coming on the road? Why did not Little-faith pluck up a great heart? He might, methinks, have stood one brush[140] with them, and have yielded when there had been no remedy.

CHRISTIAN. That they are Cowards, many have said, but few have found it so in the time of Trial. As for a great heart, Little-faith had none; and I perceive by thee, my Brother, hadst thou been the man concerned, thou art but for a brush, and then to yield. And verily since this is the height of thy stomach, now they are at a distance from us, should they appear to thee as they did to him, they might put thee to second thoughts.

But consider again, they are but journeymen Thieves;[141] they serve under the King of the bottomless Pit, who, if need be, will come to their aid himself, and his voice is as the roaring of a Lion. I myself have been engaged as this Little-faith was, and I found it a terrible thing. These three Villains set upon me, and I beginning like a Christian to resist they gave but a call, and in came their Master: I would, as the saying is, have given my life for a penny; but that, as God would have it, I was clothed with Armour of proof. Ay, and yet though I was so harnessed, I found it hard work to quit myself like a man: no man can tell what in that Combat attends us, but he that hath been in the Battle himself.

HOPEFUL. Well, but they ran, you see, when they did but suppose that one Great-grace was in the way.

CHRISTIAN. True, they have often fled, both they and their Master, when Great-grace hath but appeared; and no marvel, for he is the King's Champion. But I trow[142] you will put some difference between Little-faith and the King's Champion. All the King's Subjects are not his Champions, nor can they, when tried, do such feats of War as he. Is it meet to think that a little child should handle Goliath as David did? Or that there should be the strength of an Ox in a Wren? Some are strong, some are weak; some have great faith, some have little: this man was one of the weak, and therefore he went to the wall.

HOPEFUL. I would it had been Great-grace for their sakes.

CHRISTIAN. If it had been he, he might have had his hands full; for I must tell you, that though Great-grace is excellent good at his Weapons, and has, and can, so long as he keeps them at Sword's point, do well enough with them; yet if they get within him, even Faint-heart, Mistrust, or the other, it shall go hard but they will throw up his heels. And when a man is down, you know what can he do?

Whoso looks well upon Great-grace's face, shall see those scars and cuts there, that shall easily give demonstration of what I say. Yea, once I heard he should say[143] (and that when he was in the Combat), We despaired even of life. How did these sturdy Rogues and their fellows make David groan, mourn, and roar? Yea, Heman[144] and Hezekiah too though Champions in their day, were forced to bestir them when by these assaulted; and yet notwithstanding they had their Coats soundly brushed by them. Peter upon a time would go try what he could do; but though some do say of him that he is the Prince of the Apostles, they handled him so, that they made him at last afraid of a sorry Girl.[145]

Besides their King is at their whistle, he is never out of hearing; and if at any time they be put to the worst, he if possible comes in to help them; and of him it is said, The Sword of him that layeth at him cannot hold: [146] the Spear, the Dart, nor the Habergeon (Job 41:26): he esteemeth Iron as Straw, and Brass as rotten Wood. The Arrow cannot make him fly; Sling-stones are turned with him into Stubble, Darts are counted as Stubble: he laugheth at the shaking of a Spear. What can a man do in this case? 'Tis true, if a man could at every turn have Job's Horse, and had skill and courage to ride him, he might do notable things; for his Neck is clothed with thunder, he will not be afraid of the Grasshopper, the glory of his Nostrils is terrible, he paweth in the Valley, rejoiceth in his strength, and goeth out to meet the armed men (Job 39:19). He mocketh at fear, and is not affrighted, neither turneth back from the Sword. The Quiver rattleth against him, the glittering Spear, and the Shield. He swalloweth the ground with fierceness and rage, neither believeth he that it is the sound of the Trumpet. He saith among the Trumpets, Ha, ha; and he smelleth the Battle afar off, the thundering of the Captains, and the Shoutings.

But for such footmen as thee and I are, let us never desire to meet with an enemy, nor vaunt as if we could do better, when we hear of others that they have been foiled, nor be tickled at the thoughts of our own manhood; for such commonly come by the worst when tried. Witness Peter, of whom I made mention before. He would swagger, ay, he would; he would, as his vain mind prompted him to say, do better, and stand more for his Master than all men; but who so foiled and run down by these Villains as he?

When, therefore, we hear that such Robberies are done on the King's Highway, two things become us to do: First, To go out harnessed and to be sure to take a Shield with us; for it was for want of that, that he that laid so lustily at Leviathan could not make him yield; for indeed if that be wanting he fears us not at all. Therefore he that had skill hath said, Above all take the Shield of faith, wherewith ye shall be able to quench all the fiery darts of the wicked (Eph. 6:16).

'Tis good also that we desire of the King a Convoy, yea that he will go with us himself (Exod. 33:15). This made David rejoice when in the Valley of the Shadow of Death: and Moses was rather for dying where he stood, than to go one step without his God. Oh, my Brother, if he will but go along with us what need we be afraid of ten thousands that shall set themselves against us? But without him, the proud helpers fall under the slain (Ps. 3:5-8; Isa. 10:4; Job 9:10).

I, for my part, have been in the fray before now, and though (through the goodness of him that is best) I am, as you see, alive; yet I cannot boast of my manhood. Glad shall I be, if I meet with no more such brunts, though I fear we are not got beyond all danger. However, since the Lion and the Bear have not as yet devoured me, I hope God will also deliver us from the next uncircumcised Philistine. Then sang Christian,

> Poor Little-faith! Hast been among the Thieves?
> Wast robb'd? Remember this: Whoso believes
> And gets more Faith, shall then a victor be
> Over ten thousand, else scarce over three.

So they went on, and Ignorance followed. They went then till they came at a place where they saw a way put itself into their way, and seemed withal to lie as straight as the way which they should go; and here they knew not which of the two to take, for both seemed straight before them; therefore here they stood still to consider. And as they were thinking about the way, behold a man black of flesh,[147] but covered with a very light Robe, came to them, and asked them why they stood there? They answered they were going to the Celestial City, but knew not which of these ways to take. Follow me, said the man, it is thither that I am going. So they followed him in the way that but now came into the road, which by degrees turned, and turned then so from the City that they desired to go to, that in little time their faces were turned away from it: yet they followed him. But by-and-by, before they were aware, he led them both within the compass of a Net, in which they were both so entangled, that they knew not what to do; and with that the white Robe fell off the black man's back: then they saw where they were. Wherefore there they lay crying some time, for they could not get themselves out.

CHRISTIAN. Then said Christian to his fellow, Now do I see myself in an error. Did not the Shepherds bid us beware of the flatterers? As is the saying of the Wise man, so we have found it this day, A man that flattereth his Neighbour, spreadeth a Net for his feet (Prov. 29:5).

HOPEFUL. They also gave us a Note of directions about the way, for our more sure finding thereof; but therein we have also forgotten to read, and have not kept ourselves from the paths of the destroyer (Ps. 17:4). Here David was wiser than we; for saith he, Concerning the works of men, by the word of thy lips I have kept me from the paths of the destroyer. Thus they lay bewailing themselves in the Net. At last they espied a Shining One coming towards them with a Whip of small cord in his hand. When he was come to the place where they were, he asked them whence they came? and what they did there? They told him that they were poor Pilgrims going to Zion, but were led out of their way by a black man, clothed in white, who bid us, said they, follow him, for he was going thither too. Then said he with the Whip, It is Flatterer, a false Apostle, that hath transformed himself into an Angel of Light (Prov. 29:5; Dan. 11:32; II Cor. 11:13, 14). So he rent the Net, and let the men out. Then said he to them, Follow me, that I may set you in your way again: so he led them back to the way which they had left to follow the Flatterer. Then he asked them, saying, Where did you lie the last night? They said, With the Shepherds upon the Delectable Mountains. He asked them then, If they had not of those Shepherds a Note of direction for the way? They answered, Yes. But did you, said he, when you was at a stand, pluck out and read your Note? They answered, No. He asked them, Why? They said they forgot. He asked, moreover, If the Shepherds did not bid them beware of the Flatterer? They answered, Yes; but we did not imagine, said they, that this fine-spoken man had been he (Rom. 16:18).

Then I saw in my Dream that he commanded them to lie down (Deut. 25:2); which when they did, he chastised them sore, to teach them the good way wherein they should walk (II Chron. 6:26, 27); and as he chastised them he said, As many as I love, I rebuke and chasten; be zealous, therefore, and repent (Rev. 3:19). This done, he bid them go on their way, and take good heed to the other directions of the Shepherds. So they thanked him for all his kindness, and went softly along the right way, singing,

Come hither, you that walk along the way,
See how the Pilgrims fare that go astray;
They catched are in an intangling Net,
'Cause they good Counsel lightly did forget;
'Tis true they rescu'd were, but yet you see
They're scourg'd to boot: Let this your caution be.

Now after a while, they perceived afar off one coming softly and alone all along the Highway to meet them. Then said Christian to his fellow, Yonder is a man with his back toward Zion, and he is coming to meet us.

HOPEFUL. I see him, let us take heed to ourselves now, lest he should prove a Flatterer also. So he drew nearer and nearer, and at last came up unto them. His name was Atheist, and he asked them whither they were going?

CHRISTIAN. We are going to the Mount Zion.

Then Atheist fell into a very great Laughter.

CHRISTIAN. What is the meaning of your Laughter?

ATHEIST. I laugh to see what ignorant persons you are, to take upon you so tedious a Journey, and you are like to have nothing but your travel for your pains.

CHRISTIAN. Why man? Do you think we shall not be received?

ATHEIST. Received! There is no such place as you dream of in all this World.

CHRISTIAN. But there is in the World to come.

ATHEIST. When I was at home in mine own Country, I heard as you now affirm, and from that hearing went out to see, and have been seeking this City this twenty years; but find no more of it than I did the first day I set out (Jer. 22:13;[148] Eccles. 10:15).

CHRISTIAN. We have both heard and believe that there is such a place to be found.

ATHEIST. Had not I when at home believed, I had not come thus far to seek; but finding none (and yet I should, had there been such a place to be found, for I have gone to seek it farther than you), I am going back again, and will seek to refresh myself with the things that I then cast away, for hopes of that which I now see is not.

CHRISTIAN. Then said Christian to Hopeful his fellow, Is it true which this man hath said?

HOPEFUL. Take heed, he is one of the Flatterers; remember what it hath cost us once already for our hearkening to such kind of fellows. What! no Mount Zion! Did we not see from the Delectable Mountains the Gate of the City? Also, are we not now to walk by Faith? (II Cor. 5:7.) Let us go on, said Hopeful, lest the man with the Whip overtake us again. You should have taught me that lesson, which I will round you in the ears[149] withal: Cease, my Son, to hear the instruction that causeth to err from the words of knowledge (Prov. 19:27; Heb. 10:39). I say, my Brother, cease to hear him, and let us believe to the saving of the Soul.

CHRISTIAN. My Brother, I did not put the question to thee for that I doubted of the Truth of our belief myself, but to prove thee, and to fetch from thee a fruit of the honesty of thy heart. As for this man, I know that he is blinded by the god of this World. Let thee and I go on, knowing that we have belief of the Truth, and no lie is of the Truth (I John 2:21).

HOPEFUL. Now do I rejoice in hope of the Glory of God. So they turned away from the man; and he laughing at them went his way.

I saw them in my Dream, that they went till they came into a certain Country, whose air naturally tended to make one drowsy, if he came a stranger into it. And here Hopeful began to be very dull and heavy of sleep; wherefore he said unto Christian, I do now begin to grow so drowsy that I can scarcely hold up mine eyes, let us lie down here and take one nap.

CHRISTIAN. By no means, said the other, lest sleeping we never awake more.

HOPEFUL. Why, my Brother? Sleep is sweet to the labouring man; we may be refreshed if we take a nap.

CHRISTIAN. Do you not remember that one of the Shepherds bid us beware of the Enchanted Ground? He meant by that, that we should beware of sleeping; wherefore let us not sleep as do others, but let us watch and be sober (I Thess. 5:6).

HOPEFUL. I acknowledge myself in a fault, and had I been here alone I had by sleeping run the danger of death. I see it is true that the Wise man saith, Two are better than one. Hitherto hath thy company been my mercy, and thou shalt have a good reward for thy labour.

Now then, said Christian, to prevent drowsiness in this place, let us fall into good discourse.

[This "good discourse" has been omitted, as it is drawn out over several pages and reads like a tract; however, we must not forget that, for the Puritan, *The Pilgrim's Progress* was precisely a "necessary and useful tract," as was said by one of Bunyan's contemporaries. This contemporary, an admirer of a sort, was, nevertheless, seriously worried about "the lightness and laughter which the reading some passages therein occasions in some vain and frothy minds."

Coleridge has said that, occasionally, Bunyan of the Conventicle had the better of Bunyan of Parnassus. For Puritan readers the former's teaching counted far more than the latter's art, however much they may have enjoyed it.]

I then saw in my Dream that Hopeful looked back and saw Ignorance, whom they had left behind, coming after. Look, said he to Christian, how far yonder youngster loitereth behind.

CHRISTIAN. Ay, ay, I see him; he careth not for our company.

HOPEFUL. But I trow it would not have hurt him, had he kept pace with us hitherto.

CHRISTIAN. That's true, but I warrant you he thinketh otherwise.

HOPEFUL. That I think he doth, but, however, let us tarry for him. So they did.

Then Christian said to him, Come away, man; why do you stay so behind?

IGNORANCE. I take my pleasure in walking alone, even more a great deal than in Company, unless I like it the better.

Then said Christian to Hopeful (but softly), Did I not tell you he cared not for our company? But, however, said he, come up, and let us talk away the time in this solitary place. Then directing his speech to Ignorance, he said, Come, how do you? How stands it between God and your Soul now?

IGNORANCE. I hope well; for I am always full of good motions, that come into my mind to comfort me as I walk.

CHRISTIAN. What good motions? pray tell us.

IGNORANCE. Why, I think of God and Heaven.

CHRISTIAN. So do the Devils and damned Souls.

IGNORANCE. But I think of them and desire them.

CHRISTIAN. So do many that are never like to come there. The Soul of the Sluggard desires, and hath nothing (Prov. 13:4).

IGNORANCE. But I think of them, and leave all for them.

CHRISTIAN. That I doubt, for leaving all is an hard matter, yea a harder matter than many are aware of. But why, or by what, art thou persuaded that thou hast left all for God and Heaven?

IGNORANCE. My heart tells me so.

CHRISTIAN. The wise man says, He that trusts his own heart is a fool (Prov. 28:26).

IGNORANCE. This is spoken of an evil heart, but mine is a good one.

CHRISTIAN. But how dost thou prove that?

IGNORANCE. It comforts me in hopes of Heaven.

CHRISTIAN. That may be through its deceitfulness, for a man's heart may minister comfort to him in the hopes of that thing for which he yet has no ground to hope.

IGNORANCE. But my heart and life agree together, and therefore my hope is well grounded.

CHRISTIAN. Who told thee that thy heart and life agree together?

IGNORANCE. My heart tells me so.

CHRISTIAN. Ask my fellow if I be a Thief! [150] Thy heart tells thee so! Except the Word of God beareth witness in this matter, other testimony is of no value.

IGNORANCE. But is it not a good heart that has good thoughts? and is not that a good life that is according to God's Commandments?

CHRISTIAN. Yes, that is a good heart that hath good thoughts, and that is a good life that is according to God's Commandments; but it is one thing indeed to have these, and another thing only to think so.

IGNORANCE. Pray, what count you good thoughts, and a life according to God's Commandments?

CHRISTIAN. There are good thoughts of divers kinds, some respecting ourselves, some God, some Christ, and some other things.

IGNORANCE. What be good thoughts respecting ourselves?

CHRISTIAN. Such as agree with the Word of God.

IGNORANCE. When do our thoughts of ourselves agree with the Word of God?

CHRISTIAN. When we pass the same Judgment upon ourselves which the Word passes: to explain myself, the Word of God saith of persons in a natural condition, There is none righteous (Rom. 3:10), there is none that doeth good. It saith also, That every imagination of the heart of man is only evil, and that continually (Gen. 6:5). And again, The imagination of man's heart is evil from his youth. Now then, when we think thus of ourselves, having sense thereof, then are our thoughts good ones, because according to the Word of God.

IGNORANCE. I will never believe that my heart is thus bad.

CHRISTIAN. Therefore thou never hadst one good thought concerning thyself in thy life. But let me go on: As the Word passeth a Judgment upon our Heart, so it passeth a Judgment upon our Ways; and when our thoughts of our Hearts and Ways agree with the Judgment which the Word giveth of both, then are both good, because agreeing thereto.

IGNORANCE. Make out your meaning.

CHRISTIAN. Why, the Word of God saith that man's ways are crooked ways, not good, but perverse. It saith they are naturally out of the good way, that they have not known it (Ps. 125:5, Prov. 2:15; Rom. 3:12). Now when a man thus thinketh of his ways, I say, when he doth sensibly, and with heart-humiliation thus think, then hath he good thoughts of his own ways, because his thoughts now agree with the Judgment of the Word of God.

IGNORANCE. What are good thoughts concerning God?

CHRISTIAN. Even as I have said concerning ourselves, when our thoughts of God do agree with what the Word saith of him; and that is, when we think of his Being and Attributes as the Word hath taught, of which I cannot now discourse at large: but to speak of him with reference to us, then we have right thoughts of God, when we think that he knows us better than we know ourselves, and can see sin in us when and where we can see none in ourselves; when we think he knows our innmost thoughts, and that our heart with all its depths is always open unto his eyes; also when we think that all our righteousness stinks in his nostrils, and that therefore he cannot abide to see us stand before him in any confidence, even of all our best performances.

IGNORANCE. Do you think that I am such a fool as to think God can see no further than I? or that I would come to God in the best of my performances?

CHRISTIAN. Why, how dost thou think in this matter?

IGNORANCE. Why, to be short, I think I must believe in Christ for Justification.

CHRISTIAN. How! think thou must believe in Christ, when thou seest not thy need of him! Thou neither seest thy original or actual infirmities; but hast such an opinion of thyself, and of what thou doest, as plainly renders thee to be one that did never see a necessity of Christ's personal righteousness to justify thee before God. How then dost thou say I believe in Christ?

IGNORANCE. I believe well enough for all that.

CHRISTIAN. How dost thou believe?

IGNORANCE. I believe that Christ died for sinners, and that I shall be justified before God from the curse, through his gracious acceptance of my obedience to his Law. Or thus, Christ makes my Duties that are religious acceptable to his Father by virtue of his Merits; and so shall I be justified.

CHRISTIAN. Let me give an answer to this Confession of thy Faith.

1. Thou believest with a fantastical Faith,[151] for this Faith is nowhere described in the Word.

2. Thou believest with a false Faith, because it taketh Justification from the personal righteousness of Christ, and applies it to thy own.

3. This Faith maketh not Christ a Justifier of thy person, but of thy actions; and of thy person for thy actions' sake, which is false.

4. Therefore this Faith is deceitful, even such as will leave thee under wrath in the day of God Almighty; for true Justifying Faith puts the soul (as sensible of its lost condition by the law) upon flying for refuge unto Christ's righteousness (which righteousness of his is not an act of grace, by which he maketh for Justification thy obedience accepted with God; but his personal obedience to the Law, in doing and suffering for us what that required at our hands). This righteousness, I say, true Faith accepteth; under the skirt of which the soul being shrouded, and by it presented as spotless before God, it is accepted, and acquit from condemnation.

IGNORANCE. What! would you have us trust to what Christ in his own person has done without us? This conceit would loosen the reins of our lust, and tolerate us to live as we list. For what matter how we live, if we may be Justified by Christ's personal righteousness from all, when we believe it?

CHRISTIAN. Ignorance is thy name, and as thy name is, so art thou; even this thy answer demonstrateth what I say. Ignorant thou art of what Justifying Righteousness is, and as ignorant how to secure thy Soul through the Faith of it from the heavy wrath of God. Yea, thou also art ignorant of the true effects of saving Faith in this Righteousness of Christ, which is to bow and win over the heart to God in Christ, to love his Name, his Word, Ways, and people, and not as thou ignorantly imaginest.

HOPEFUL. Ask him if ever he had Christ revealed to him from Heaven?

IGNORANCE. What! you are a man for revelations! I believe that what both you, and all the rest of you, say about that matter, is but the fruit of distracted brains.

HOPEFUL. Why, man! Christ is so hid in God from the natural apprehensions of all flesh, that he cannot by any man be savingly known, unless God the Father reveals him to them.

IGNORANCE. That is your Faith, but not mine; yet mine I doubt not is as good as yours, though I have not in my head so many whimsies as you.

CHRISTIAN. Give me leave to put in a word: You ought not so slightly to speak of this matter: for this I will boldly affirm (even as my good Companion hath done), that no man can know Jesus Christ but by the revelation of the Father; yea, and Faith too, by which the soul layeth hold upon Christ (if it be right), must be wrought by the exceeding greatness of his mighty power; the working of which Faith, I perceive, poor Ignorance, thou art ignorant of.

Be awakened, then, see thine own wretchedness, and fly to the Lord Jesus; and by his righteousness, which is the righteousness of God (for he himself is God), thou shalt be delivered from condemnation.

IGNORANCE. You go so fast I cannot keep pace with you; do you go on before, I must stay a while behind.

[Christian and Hopeful resume their "good discourse."]

Now I saw in my Dream, that by this time the Pilgrims were got over the Enchanted Ground, and entering into the Country of Beulah[152] (Isa. 62:4; Song of Sol. 2:10-12), whose air was very sweet and pleasant, the way lying directly through it, they solaced themselves there for a season. Yea, here they heard continually the singing of Birds, and saw every day the Flowers appear in the earth, and heard the voice of the Turtle in the land. In this Country the Sun shineth night and day; wherefore this was beyond the Valley of the Shadow of Death, and also out of the reach of Giant Despair, neither could they from this place so much as see Doubting Castle. Here they were within sight of the City they were going to, also here met them some of the inhabitants thereof; for in this land the Shining Ones commonly walked, because it was upon the borders of Heaven. In this land also the contract between the Bride and Bridegroom was renewed; yea here, as the Bridegroom rejoiceth over the Bride, so did their God rejoice over them (Isa. 62:5). Here they had no want of Corn and Wine (Isa. 62:8); for in this place they met with abundance of what they had sought in all their Pilgrimage. Here they heard voices from out of the City, loud voices, saying, Say ye to the daughter of Zion, Behold thy salvation cometh, behold his reward is with him (Isa. 62:11). Here all the inhabitants of the Country called them, The holy People, The redeemed of the Lord, Sought out, etc. (Isa. 62:12).

Now as they walked in this Land, they had more rejoicing than in parts more remote from the Kingdom to which they were bound; and drawing near to the City, they had yet a more perfect view thereof. It was builded of Pearls and Precious Stones, also the Street thereof was paved with Gold; so that by reason of the natural glory of the City, and the reflection of the Sunbeams upon it, Christian with desire fell sick. Hopeful also had a fit or two of the same disease. Wherefore here they lay by it a while, crying out because of their pangs, If you see my Beloved, tell him that I am sick of love (Song of Sol. 5:8).

But being a little strengthened, and better able to bear their sickness, they walked on their way, and came yet nearer and nearer, where were Orchards, Vineyards, and Gardens, and their gates opened into the Highway. Now as they came up to these places, behold the Gardener stood in the way, to whom the Pilgrims said, Whose goodly Vineyards and Gardens are these? He answered, They are the King's, and are planted here for his own delights, and also for the solace of Pilgrims. So the Gardener had them into the Vineyards, and bid them refresh themselves with Dainties (Deut. 23:24). He also shewed them there the King's walks, and the Arbours where he delighted to be; and here they tarried and slept.

Now I beheld in my Dream, that they talked more in their sleep at this time than ever they did in all their Journey; and being in a muse thereabout, the Gardener said even to me, Wherefore musest thou at the matter? It is the nature of the fruit of the Grapes of these Vineyards to go down so sweetly as to cause the lips of them that are asleep to speak.

So I saw that when they awoke, they addressed themselves[153] to go up to the City. But, as I said, the reflection of the Sun upon the City (for the City was pure Gold) was so extremely glorious, that they could not as yet with open face behold it, but through an Instrument made for that purpose (Rev. 21:18; II Cor. 3:18). So I saw that as they went on, there met them two men, in Raiment that shone like Gold, also their faces shone as the light.

These men asked the Pilgrims whence they came? and they told them. They also asked them where they had lodged, what difficulties and dangers, what comforts and pleasures they had met in the way? and they told them. Then said the men that met them, You have but two difficulties more to meet with, and then you are in the City.

Christian then, and his Companion, asked the men to go along with them, so they told them they would. But, said they, you must obtain it by your own Faith. So I saw in my Dream that they went on together till they came within sight of the Gate.

Now I further saw that betwixt them and the Gate was a River, but there was no Bridge to go over, the River was very deep: at the sight, therefore, of this River the Pilgrims were much stounded;[154] but the men that went with them said, You must go through, or you cannot come at the Gate.

The Pilgrims then began to inquire if there was no other way to the Gate; to which they answered, Yes, but there hath not any, save two, to wit, Enoch and Elijah,[155] been permitted to tread that path, since the foundation of the World, nor shall, until the last Trumpet shall sound (I Cor. 15:51, 52). The Pilgrims then, especially Christian, began to despond in his mind, and looked this way and that, but no way could be found by them by which they might escape the River. Then they asked the men if the Waters were all of a depth? They said, No; yet they could not help them in that case, for, said they, you shall find it deeper or shallower, as you believe in the King of the place.

They then addressed themselves to the Water; and entering, Christian began to sink, and crying out to his good friend Hopeful, he said, I sink in deep Waters; the Billows go over my head, all his Waves go over me, Selah.

Then said the other, Be of good cheer, my Brother, I feel the bottom, and it is good. Then said Christian, Ah, my friend, the sorrows of death have compassed me about, I shall not see the land that flows with milk and honey. And with that a great darkness and horror fell upon Christian, so that he could not see before him. Also here he in great measure lost his senses, so that he could neither remember nor orderly talk of any of those sweet refreshments that he had met with in the way of his Pilgrimage. But all the words that he spake still tended to discover that he had horror of mind, and hearty fears that he should die in that River, and never obtain entrance in at the Gate. Here also, as they that stood by perceived, he was much in the troublesome thoughts of the sins that he had committed, both since and before he began to be a Pilgrim. 'Twas also observed that he was troubled with apparitions of Hobgoblins and evil Spirits, for ever and anon he would intimate so much by words. Hopeful therefore here had much ado to keep his Brother's head above water; yea sometimes he would be quite gone down, and then ere a while he would rise up again half dead. Hopeful also would endeavour to comfort him, saying, Brother, I see the Gate, and men standing by it to receive us. But Christian would answer, 'Tis you, 'tis you they wait for, you have been hopeful ever since I knew you. And so have you, said he to Christian. Ah, Brother! said he, surely if I was right, he would now arise to help me; but for my sins he hath brought me into the snare, and hath left me. Then said Hopeful, My Brother, you have quite forgot the Text, where it is said of the wicked, There is no band in their death, but their strength is firm, they are not troubled as other men, neither are they plagued like other men.[156] (Ps. 73:4-5). These troubles and distresses that you go through in these Waters are no sign that God hath forsaken you, but are sent to try you, whether you will call to mind that which heretofore you have received of his goodness, and live upon him in your distresses.

Then I saw in my Dream that Christian was as in a muse a while. To whom also Hopeful added this word, Be of good cheer, Jesus Christ maketh thee whole: and with that Christian brake out with a loud voice, Oh, I see him again, and he tells me, When thou passest through the Waters, I will be with thee; and through the Rivers, they shall not overflow thee (Isa. 43:2). Then they both took courage, and the Enemy was after that as still as a stone,[157] until they were gone over. Christian, therefore, presently found ground to stand upon, and so it followed that the rest of the River was but shallow. Thus they got over. Now, upon the bank of the River on the other side, they saw the two shining men again, who there waited for them; wherefore being come out of the River, they saluted them saying, We are ministering Spirits, sent forth to minister for those that shall be heirs of salvation. Thus they went along towards the Gate. Now you must note that the City stood upon a mighty Hill, but the Pilgrims went up that Hill with ease, because they had these two men to lead them up by the arms; also they had left their mortal Garments behind them in the River, for though they went in with them, they came out without them. They therefore went up here with much agility and speed, though the foundation upon which the City was framed was higher than the Clouds. They therefore went up through the Regions of the Air, sweetly talking as they went, being comforted, because they safely got over the River, and had such glorious Companions to attend them.

The talk that they had with the Shining Ones was about the glory of the place, who told them that the beauty and glory of it was inexpressible. There, said they, is the Mount Zion, the heavenly Jerusalem, the innumerable company of Angels, and the Spirits of just men made perfect (Heb. 12:22-24). You are going now, said they, to the Paradise of God, wherein you shall see the Tree of Life, and eat of the never-fading fruits thereof; and when you come there, you shall have white Robes given you, and your walk and talk shall be every day with the King, even all the days of Eternity (Rev. 2:7; 3:4). There you shall not see again such things as you saw when you were in the lower Region upon the earth, to wit, sorrow, sickness, affliction, and death, for the former things are passed away. (Rev. 21:1; Isa. 57:1, 2; 65:4). You are now going to Abraham, to Isaac, and Jacob, and to the Prophets, men that God hath taken away from the evil to come, and that are now resting upon their beds, each one walking in his righteousness. The men then asked, What must we do in the holy place? To whom it was answered, You must there receive the comfort of all your toil, and have joy for all your sorrow; you must reap what you have sown, even the fruit of all your Prayers and Tears, and sufferings for the King by the way (Gal. 6:7). In that place you must wear Crowns of Gold, and enjoy the perpetual sight and vision of the Holy One, for there you shall see him as he is (I John 3:2). There also you shall serve him continually with praise, with shouting, and thanksgiving, whom you desired to serve in the World, though with much difficulty, because of the infirmity of your flesh. There your eyes shall be delighted with seeing, and your ears with hearing the pleasant voice of the Mighty One. There you shall enjoy your friends again, that are got thither before you; and there you shall with joy receive even every one that follows into the holy place after you. There also you shall be clothed with Glory and Majesty, and put into an equipage fit to ride out with the King of Glory. When he shall come with sound of Trumpet in the Clouds, as upon the wings of the Wind, you shall come with him; and when he shall sit upon the Throne of Judgment, you shall sit by him; yea, and when he shall pass sentence upon all the workers of iniquity, let them be Angels or Men, you also shall have a voice in that Judgment, because they were his and your Enemies. Also when he shall again return to the City, you shall go too, with sound of Trumpet, and be ever with him (I Thess. 4:13-16; Jude 14; Dan. 7:9, 10; I Cor. 6:2, 3).

Now while they were thus drawing towards the Gate, behold a company of the Heavenly Host came out to meet them; to whom it was said by the other two Shining Ones, These are the men that have loved our Lord when they were in the World, and that have left all for his holy Name, and he hath sent us to fetch them, and we have brought them thus far on their desired Journey, that they may go in and look their Redeemer in the face with joy. Then the Heavenly Host, gave a great shout, saying, Blessed are they that are called to the Marriage Supper of the Lamb (Rev. 19:9).

There came out also at this time to meet them several of the King's Trumpeters, clothed in white and shining Raiment, who, with melodious noises and loud, made even the Heavens to echo with their sound. These Trumpeters saluted Christian and his fellow with ten thousand welcomes from the World, and this they did with shouting and sound of Trumpet.

This done, they compassed them round on every side; some went before, some behind, and some on the right hand, some on the left (as 'twere to guard them through the upper Regions), continually sounding, as they went, with melodious noise, in notes on high: so that the very sight was, to them that could behold it, as if Heaven itself was come down to meet them. Thus, therefore, they walked on together; and as they walked, ever and anon these Trumpeters, even with joyful sound, would, by mixing their Music with looks and gestures, still signify to Christian and his Brother, how welcome they were into their company, and with what gladness they came to meet them. And now were these two men as 'twere in Heaven before they came at it, being swallowed up with the sight of the Angels, and with hearing of their melodious notes. Here also they had the City itself in view, and they thought they heard all the Bells therein ring to welcome them thereto. But above all, the warm and joyful thoughts that they had about their own dwelling there, with such company, and that for ever and ever. Oh! by what tongue or pen can their glorious joy be expressed! And thus they came up to the Gate.

Now when they were come up to the Gate, there was written over it in Letters of Gold, Blessed are they that do his Commandments, that they may have right to the Tree of Life, and may enter in through the Gates into the City (Rev. 22:14).

Then I saw in my Dream, that the Shining Men bid them call at the Gate; the which when they did, some from above looked over the Gate, to wit, Enoch, Moses, and Elijah, etc., to whom it was said, These Pilgrims are come from the city of Destruction for the love that they bear to the King of this place: and then the Pilgrims gave in unto them each man his Certificate, which they had received in the beginning; those, therefore, were carried in to the King, who when he had read them, said, Where are the men? To whom it was answered, They are standing without the Gate. The King then commanded to open the Gate, That the righteous nation, said he, that keepeth Truth may enter in (Isa. 26:2).

Now I saw in my Dream that these two men went in at the Gate: and lo, as they entered, they were transfigured, and they had Raiment put on that shone like Gold. There were also that met them with Harps and Crowns, and gave them to them, the Harps to praise withal, and the Crowns in token of honour. Then I heard in my Dream that all the Bells in the City rang for joy, and that it was said unto them, Enter ye into the joy of your Lord. I also heard the men themselves, that they sang with a loud voice, saying, Blessing, Honour, Glory, and Power, be to him that sitteth upon the Throne and to the Lamb for ever and ever (Rev. 5:13, 14).

Now just as the Gates were opened to let in the men, I

looked in after them, and behold the City shone like the Sun; the Streets also were paved with Gold, and in them walked many men, with Crowns on their heads, Palms in their hands, and golden Harps to sing praises withal.

There were also of them that had wings, and they answered one another without intermission, saying, Holy, Holy, Holy, is the Lord. And after that they shut up the Gates. Which when I had seen, I wished myself among them.

Now while I was gazing upon all these things, I turned my head to look back, and saw Ignorance come up to the River side; but he soon got over, and that without half that difficulty which the other two men met with. For it happened that there was then in that place one Vain-hope, a Ferryman, that with his Boat helped him over; so he, as the other, I saw, did ascend the Hill to come up to the Gate, only he came alone; neither did any man meet him with the least encouragement. When he was come up to the Gate, he looked up to the writing that was above, and then began to knock, supposing that entrance should have been quickly administered to him; but he was asked by the men that looked over the top of the Gate, Whence came you? and what would you have? He answered, I have eat and drank in the presence of the King, and he has taught in our Streets. Then they asked him for his Certificate, that they might go in and shew it to the King. So he fumbled in his bosom for one, and found none. Then said they, Have you none? But the man answered never a word. So they told the King, but he would not come down to see him, but commanded the two Shining Ones that conducted Christian and Hopeful to the City, to go out and take Ignorance, and bind him hand and foot, and have him away. Then they took him up, and carried him through the air to the door that I saw in the side of the Hill, and put him in there. Then I saw that there was a way to Hell even from the Gates of Heaven, as well as from the City of Destruction. So I awoke, and behold it was a Dream.

The Conclusion

Now, Reader, I have told my Dream to thee;
See if thou canst interpret it to me,
Or to thyself, or Neighbour; but take heed
Of mis-interpreting; for that, instead

Of doing good, will but thyself abuse:
By mis-interpreting, evil insues.

Take heed also, that thou be not extreme,
In playing with the outside of my Dream:
Nor let my figure or similitude
Put thee into a laughter or a feud;
Leave this for Boys and Fools; but as for thee
Do thou the substance of my matter see.

Put by the Curtains, look within my Veil;
Turn up my Metaphors, and do not fail
There, if thou seekest them, such things to find,
As will be helpful to an honest mind.

What of my dross thou findest there, be bold
To throw away, but yet preserve the Gold.
What if my Gold be wrapped up in Ore?
None throws away the Apple for the Core.
But if thou shalt cast all away as vain,
I know not but 'twill make me Dream again.

THE PILGRIM'S PROGRESS

From This World to That Which is to Come

The Second Part

Delivered Under the Similitude of a Dream

Wherein is Set Forth the Manner
of the Setting Out of Christian's Wife and Children,
Their Dangerous Journey and Safe Arrival
at the Desired Country

I have used similitudes.—Hos. 12:10.

The Author's Way of Sending Forth His Second Part of the "Pilgrim"

Go now my little Book, to every place
Where my first Pilgrim has but shewn his Face:
Call at their door. If any say, Who's there?
Then answer thou, Christiana is here.
If they bid thee Come in, then enter thou,
With all thy Boys; and then, as thou know'st how,
Tell who they are, also from whence they came;
Perhaps they'll know them by their looks or name.
But if they should not, ask them yet again
If formerly they did not entertain
One Christian a Pilgrim? If they say
They did, and were delighted in his Way;
Then let them know that those related were
Unto him, yea, his Wife and Children are.
  Tell them that they have left their House and Home,
Are turned Pilgrims, seek a World to come;
That they have met with Hardships in the way;
That they do meet with Troubles night and day;

That they have trod on Serpents, fought with Devils,
Have also overcome a many evils.
Yea, tell them also of the rest,[1] who have
Of love to Pilgrimage been stout and brave
Defenders of that Way, and how they still
Refuse this World, to do their Father's will.
Go tell them also of those dainty things,
That Pilgrimage unto the Pilgrim brings,
Let them acquainted be, too, how they are
Beloved of their King, under his care;
What goodly Mansions for them he provides,
Tho' they meet with rough Winds and swelling Tides,
How brave a Calm they will enjoy at last,
Who to their Lord and by his ways hold fast.
Perhaps with heart and hand they will embrace
Thee, as they did my Firstling,[2] and will grace
Thee, and thy fellows, with such cheer and fare,
As shew will, they of Pilgrims lovers are.

OBJECTION I

But how if they will not believe of me
That I am truly thine, 'cause some there be
That counterfeit the Pilgrim[3] and his name,
Seek by disguise to seem the very same,
And by that means have wrought themselves into
The hands and houses of I know not who?

ANSWER

'Tis true, some have of late, to counterfeit
My Pilgrim, to their own my Title set;
Yea others half my Name and Title too
Have stitched to their Book, to make them do;
But yet they by their Features do declare
Themselves not mine to be, whose e'er they are.
If such thou meet'st with, then thine only way
Before them all is to say out thy say,
In thine own native language, which no man
Now useth, nor with ease dissemble can.
If after all they still of you shall doubt,
Thinking that you like Gipsies go about
In naughty wise[4] the Country to defile,
Or that you seek good people to beguile

With things unwarrantable; send for me,
And I will testify you Pilgrims be;
Yea, I will testify that only you
My Pilgrims are; and that alone will do.

OBJECTION II

But yet perhaps I may inquire for him,
Of those that wish him damned, life and limb.
What shall I do, when I at such a door
For Pilgrims ask, and they shall rage the more?

ANSWER

Fright not thyself, my Book, for such Bugbears
Are nothing else but ground for groundless fears:
My Pilgrim's Book has travell'd sea and land,
Yet could I never come to understand
That it was slighted, or turn'd out of door
By any Kingdom, were they rich or poor.
In France[5] and Flanders, where men kill each other,
My Pilgrim is esteem'd a Friend, a Brother.
In Holland, too, 'tis said, as I am told,
My Pilgrim is with some worth more than Gold.
Highlanders and Wild Irish can agree
My Pilgrim should familiar with them be.
'Tis in New England[6] under such advance,
Receives there so much loving countenance,
As to be trimm'd, new cloth'd, and deck't with Gems,[7]
That it may shew its features and its limbs,
Yet more, so comely doth my Pilgrim walk
That of him thousands daily sing and talk.
If you draw nearer home, it will appear
My Pilgrim knows no ground of shame or fear;
City and Country will him entertain
With, Welcome, Pilgrim; yea, they can't refrain
From smiling, if my Pilgrim be but by,
Or shews his head in any Company.
Brave Gallants do my Pilgrim hug and love,
Esteem it much, yea, value it above
Things of a greater bulk: yea, with delight,
Say my Lark's leg is better than a Kite.
Young ladies, and young Gentlewomen too,
Do no small kindness to my Pilgrim shew;

Their Cabinets, their Bosoms, and their Hearts
My Pilgrim has, 'cause he to them imparts
His pretty riddles in such wholesome strains,
As yield them profit double to their pains
Of reading. Yea, I think I may be bold
To say some prize him far above their gold.
The very Children that do walk the street,
If they do but my holy Pilgrim meet,
Salute him well, will wish him well, and say,
He is the only Stripling of the Day.
They that have never seen him, yet admire
What they have heard of him, and much desire
To have his company, and hear him tell
Those Pilgrim stories which he knows so well.
Yea, some who did not love him at the first,
But call'd him Fool and Noddy, say they must
Now they have seen and heard him, him commend,
And to those whom they love they do him send.
Wherefore, my Second Part, thou need'st not be
Afraid to shew thy Head; none can hurt thee,
That wish but well to him that went before,
'Cause thou com'st after with a second store
Of things as good, as rich, as profitable,
For Young, for Old, for Stagg'ring, and for Stable.

OBJECTION III

But some there be that say he laughs too loud;
And some do say his Head is in a Cloud.
Some say his Words and Stories are so dark,
They know not how by them to find his mark.

ANSWER

One may (I think) say, Both his laughs and cries
May well be guess'd at by his watery eyes.
Some things are of that nature as to make
One's Fancy chuckle, while his Heart doth ache,
When Jacob saw his Rachel with the sheep,[8]
He did at the same time both kiss and weep.
Whereas some say, A Cloud is in his Head,
That doth but shew how Wisdom's covered
With its own mantles, and to stir the mind
To a search after what it fain would find:

Things that seem to be hid in words obscure,
Do but the Godly mind the more allure;
To study what those sayings should contain
That speak to us in such a Cloudy strain.
  I also know a dark Similitude
Will on the Fancy more itself intrude,
And will stick faster in the Heart and Head,
Than things from Similes not borrowed.
  Wherefore, my Book, let no discouragement
Hinder thy travels. Behold, thou are sent
To Friends, not foes; to Friends that will give place
To thee, thy Pilgrims and thy words embrace.
  Besides, what my first Pilgrim left conceal'd,
Thou my brave Second Pilgrim hast reveal'd;
What Christian left lock't up, and went his way,
Sweet Christiana opens with her Key.

OBJECTION IV

But some love not the method of your first,
Romance they count it, throw't away as dust.
If I should meet with such, what should I say?
Must I slight them as they slight me, or nay?

ANSWER

My Christiana, if with such thou meet,
By all means in all loving wise them greet;
Render them not reviling for revile;
But if they frown, I prithee on them smile;
Perhaps 'tis Nature, or some ill report,
Has made them thus despise, or thus retort.
  Some love no Cheese, some love no Fish, and some
Love not their Friends, nor their own House or Home;
Some start at Pig, slight Chicken, love not Fowl,
More than they love a Cuckoo or an Owl;
Leave such, my Christiana, to their choice,
And seek those who to find thee will rejoice;
By no means strive, but in all humble wise
Present thee to them in thy Pilgrim's guise.
  Go then, my little Book, and shew to all
That entertain, and bid thee welcome shall,
What thou shalt keep close, shut up from the rest,
And wish what thou shalt shew them may be blest

To them for good, nay, make them choose to be
Pilgrims better by far than thee or me.
  Go then, I say, tell all men who thou art,
Say, I am Christiana, and my part
Is now, with my four Sons, to tell you what
It is for men to take a Pilgrim's lot:
  Go also, tell them who and what they be,
That now do go on Pilgrimage with thee;
Say, Here's my Neighbour Mercy, she is one
That has long time with me a Pilgrim gone.
Come see her in her Virgin Face, and learn
'Twixt Idle ones and Pilgrims to discern.
Yea, let young Damsels learn of her to prize
The World which is to come, in any wise.
When little tripping Maidens follow God,
And leave old doting Sinners to his Rod;
'Tis like those days wherein the young ones cried
Hosanah, to whom old ones did deride.[9]
  Next tell them of old Honest, whom you found
With his white hairs treading the Pilgrim's ground.
Yea, tell them how plain-hearted this man was,
How after his good Lord he bare his Cross;
Perhaps with some grey Head this may prevail
With Christ to fall in Love, and Sin bewail.
  Tell them also how Master Fearing went
On Pilgrimage, and how the time he spent
In Solitariness, with Fears and Cries,
And how at last he won the joyful Prize.
He was a good man, though much down in Spirit,
He is a good man, and doth Life inherit.
  Tell them of Master Feeble-mind also,
Who not before, but still behind would go;
Shew them also how he had like been slain,
And how one Great-heart did his life regain.
This man was true of Heart, tho' weak in Grace,
One might true Godliness read in his Face.
  Then tell them of Master Ready-to-halt,
A man with Crutches, but much without fault;
Tell them how Master Feeble-mind and he
Did love, and in opinions much agree.
And let all know, tho' weakness was their chance,
Yet sometimes one could sing, the other dance.

Forget not Master Valiant-for-the-truth,
That Man of courage, though a very Youth.
Tell every one his Spirit was so stout,
No man could ever make him face about,
And how Great-heart and he could not forbear,
But put down Doubting Castle, slay Despair.
Overlook not Master Despondency,
Nor Much-afraid, his Daughter, tho' they lie
Under such Mantles as may make them look
(With some) as if their God had them forsook.
They softly went, but sure, and at the end
Found that the Lord of Pilgrims was their Friend.
When thou hast told the world of all these things,
Then turn about, my Book, and touch these strings,
Which if but touched, will such Music make,
They'll make a Cripple dance, a Giant quake.
These Riddles that lie couch'd within thy breast,
Freely propound, expound; and for the rest
Of thy mysterious lines, let them remain
For those whose nimble Fancies shall them gain.[10]

Now may this little Book a blessing be
To those who love this little Book and me,
And may its Buyer have no cause to say,
His Money is but lost or thrown away;
Yea, may this Second Pilgrim yield that fruit
As may with each good Pilgrim's Fancy suit;
And may it persuade some that go astray,
To turn their Feet and Heart to the right way:

Is the Hearty Prayer

of the Author,

JOHN BUNYAN

The Pilgrim's Progress

THE SECOND PART

Courteous Companions, some time since, to tell you my Dream that I had of Christian the Pilgrim, and of his dangerous Journey toward the Celestial Country, was pleasant to me, and profitable to you. I told you then also what I saw concerning his Wife and Children, and how unwilling they were to go with him on Pilgrimage, insomuch that he was forced to go on his Progress without them; for he durst not run the danger of that destruction which he feared would come by staying with them in the City of Destruction. Wherefore, as I then shewed you, he left them and departed.

Now it hath so happened, through the multiplicity of Business, that I have been much hindered and kept back from my wonted Travels into those parts whence he went, and so could not till now obtain an opportunity to make further inquiry after whom he left behind, that I might give you an account of them. But having had some concerns that way of late, I went down again thitherward. Now having taken up my Lodgings in a Wood about a mile off the place, as I slept I dreamed again.

And as I was in my Dream, behold an aged Gentleman came by where I lay; and because he was to go some part of the way that I was travelling, methought I got up and went with him. So as we walked, and as Travellers usually do, I was as if[11] we fell into discourse, and our talk happened to be about Christian and his Travels; for thus I began with the old man.

Sir, said I, what Town is that there below, that lieth on the left hand of our way?

Then said Mr. Sagacity (for that was his name), It is the City of Destruction, a populous place, but possessed with a very ill-conditioned and idle sort of People.

I thought that was that City, quoth I: I went once myself through that Town, and therefore know that this report you give of it is true.

SAGACITY. Too true, I wish I could speak truth in speaking better of them that dwell therein.

Well, Sir, quoth I, then I perceive you to be a well-meaning man; and so one that takes pleasure to hear and tell of that which is good: pray, did you never hear what happened to a man some time ago in this Town (whose name was Christian) that went on Pilgrimage up towards the higher Regions?

SAGACITY. Hear of him! Ay, and I also heard of the Molestations, Troubles, Wars, Captivities, Cries, Groans, Frights, and Fears that he met with and had in his Journey. Besides, I must tell you, all our Country rings of him; there are but few houses that have heard of him and his doings but have sought after and got the Records of his Pilgrimage; yea, I think I may say that his hazardous Journey has got a many well-wishers to his ways; for though, when he was here, he was Fool in every man's mouth, yet now he is gone, he is highly commended of all. For 'tis said he lives bravely where he is; yea, many of them that are resolved never to run his hazards, yet have their mouths water at his gains.

They may, quoth I, well think, if they think anything that is true, that he liveth well where he is; for he now lives at and in the Fountain of Life, and has what he has without labour and sorrow, for there is no grief mixed therewith.

SAGACITY. Talk! the people talk strangely about him. Some say that he now walks in White (Rev. 3:4; 6:11), that he has a Chain of Gold about his neck, that he has a Crown of Gold, beset with Pearls, upon his head. Others say that the Shining

Ones that sometimes shewed themselves to him in his Journey are become his Companions, and that he is as familiar with them in the place where he is, as here one Neighbour is with another (Zech. 3:7). Besides, 'tis confidently affirmed concerning him, that the King of the place where he is has bestowed upon him already a very rich and pleasant dwelling at Court; and that he every day eateth and drinketh, and walketh, and talketh with him; and receiveth of the smiles and favours of him that is Judge of all there (Luke 14:15). Moreover, it is expected of some, that his Prince, the Lord of that Country, will shortly[12] come into these parts, and will know the reason, if they can give any, why his Neighbours set so little by him, and had him so much in derision when they perceived that he would be a Pilgrim (Jude 14, 15). For they say, that now he is so in the affections of his Prince, and that his Sovereign is so much concerned with the indignities that were cast upon Christian when he became a Pilgrim, that he will look upon all as if done unto himself; and no marvel, for 'twas for the love that he had to his Prince that he ventured as he did (Luke 10:16).

I dare say, quoth I, I am glad on't; I am glad for the poor man's sake, for that he now has rest from his labour (Rev. 14:13), and for that he now reapeth the benefit of his Tears with Joy (Ps. 126:5, 6); and for that he has got beyond the Gun-shot of his Enemies, and is out of the reach of them that hate him. I also am glad for that a rumour of these things is noised abroad in this Country; who can tell but that it may work some good effect on some that are left behind? But pray, Sir, while it is fresh in my mind, do you hear anything of his wife and Children? Poor hearts, I wonder in my mind what they do!

SAGACITY. Who! Christiana and her Sons? They are like to do as well as did Christian himself; for though they all play'd the fool at the first, and would by no means be persuaded by either the tears or entreaties of Christian, yet second thoughts have wrought wonderfully with them; so they have packed up, and are also gone after him.

Better and better, quoth I. But what! Wife and Children and all?

SAGACITY. It is true; I can give you an account of the matter, for I was upon the spot at the instant, and was thoroughly acquainted with the whole affair.

Then, said I, a man it seems may report it for a Truth?

SAGACITY. You need not fear to affirm it, I mean that they are all gone on Pilgrimage, both the good woman and her four Boys. And being we are,[13] as I perceive, going some considerable way together, I will give you an account of the whole of the matter.

This Christiana (for that was her name from the day that she with her Children betook themselves to a Pilgrim's life), after her Husband was gone over the River, and she could hear of him no more, her thoughts began to work in her mind. First, for that she had lost her Husband, and for that the loving bond of that relation was utterly broken betwixt them. For you know, said he to me, Nature can do no less but entertain the living with many a heavy cogitation in the remembrance of the loss of loving Relations. This, therefore, of her husband did cost her many a tear. But this was not all, for Christiana did also begin to consider with herself, whether her unbecoming behaviour towards her Husband was not one cause that she saw him no more, and that in such sort he was taken away from her. And upon this came into her mind by swarms, all her unkind, unnatural, and ungodly carriages to her dear Friend; which also clogged her Conscience, and did load her with guilt. She was, moreover, much broken with calling to remembrance the restless groans, brinish tears, and self-bemoanings of her Husband, and how she did harden her heart against all his entreaties, and loving persuasions (of her and her Sons) to go with him; yea, there was not anything that Christian either said to her, or did before her all the while that his Burden did hang on his back, but it returned upon her like a flash of lightning, and rent the caul of her Heart[14] in sunder. Specially that bitter outcry of his, What shall I do to be saved? did ring in her ears most dolefully.

Then said she to her Children, Sons, we are all undone. I have sinned away your Father, and he is gone: he would have had us with him, but I would not go myself; I also have hindered you of Life. With that the Boys fell all into tears, and cried out to go after their Father. Oh! said Christiana, that it had been but our lot to go with him, then had it fared well with us, beyond what 'tis like to do now; for though I formerly foolishly imagin'd concerning the troubles of your Father, that they proceeded of a foolish Fancy that he had, or for that he was overrun with melancholy Humours; yet now 'twill not out of my mind but that they sprang from another cause, to wit, for that the Light of Light was given him, by the help of which, as I perceive, he has escaped the snares of Death (James 1:23-25). Then they all wept again, and cried out, Oh, woe worth the day.[15]

The next night Christiana had a Dream; and behold she saw as if a broad Parchment was opened before her, in which were recorded the sum of her ways; and the times, as she thought, look'd very black upon her. Then she cried out in her sleep, Lord have Mercy upon me a Sinner (Luke 18:13); and the little Children heard her.

After this she thought she saw two very ill-favoured ones standing by her Bedside, and saying, What shall we do with this Woman? for she cries out for Mercy waking and sleeping; if she be suffered to go on as she begins, we shall lose her as we have lost her Husband. Wherefore we must, by one way or other, seek to take her off from the thoughts of what shall be hereafter, else all the World cannot help it but she will become a Pilgrim.

Now she awoke in a great sweat, also a trembling was upon her, but after a while she fell to sleeping again. And then she thought she saw Christian her Husband in a place of Bliss among many Immortals, with an Harp in his Hand, standing and playing upon it before one that sat on a Throne with a Rainbow about his Head. She saw also as if he bowed his Head with his Face to the pav'd-work[16] that was under the Prince's feet, saying, I heartily thank my Lord and King for bringing of me into this Place. Then shouted a company of them that stood round about, and harped with their Harps; but no man living could tell what they said, but Christian and his Companions (Rev. 14:2, 3).

Next morning, when she was up, had prayed to God, and talked with her Children a while, one knocked hard at the door, to whom she spake out, saying, If thou comest in God's name, come in. So he said, Amen, and opened the Door, and saluted her with Peace be to this house. The which when he had done, he said, Christiana, knowest thou wherefore I am come? Then she blushed and trembled, also her Heart began to wax warm with desires to know whence he came, and what was his errand to her. So he said unto her, My name is Secret; I dwell with those that are high. It is talked of where I dwell, as if thou hadst a desire to go thither; also there is a report that thou art aware of the evil thou hast formerly done to thy Husband, in hardening of thy Heart against his way, and in keeping of these thy Babes in their Ignorance. Christiana, the Merciful One has sent me to tell thee that he is a God ready to forgive, and that he taketh delight to multiply to pardon offences. He would also have thee know that he inviteth thee to come into his Presence, to his Table, and that he will feed thee with the Fat of his House, and with the Heritage of Jacob thy Father.

There is Christian thy Husband that was, with Legions more his Companions, ever beholding that Face that doth minister Life to beholders; and they will all be glad when they shall hear the sound of thy feet step over thy Father's threshold.

Christiana at this was greatly abashed in herself, and bowing her head to the ground, this Visitor proceeded and said, Christiana, here is also a Letter for thee, which I have brought from thy Husband's King. So she took it and opened it, but it smelt after the manner of the best Perfume (Song of Sol. 1:3), also it was written in letters of Gold. The contents of the Letter was, That the King would have her do as did Christian her Husband; for that was the way to come to his City, and to dwell in his Presence with Joy for ever. At this the good Woman was quite overcome; so she cried out to her Visitor, Sir, will you carry me and my Children with you, that we also may go and worship this King?

Then said the Visitor, Christiana, the bitter is before the sweet: thou must through troubles, as did he that went before thee, enter this Celestial City. Wherefore, I advise thee to do as did Christian thy Husband. Go to the Wicket-gate yonder, over the Plain, for that stands in the head of the way up which thou must go, and I wish thee all good speed. Also I advise that thou put this Letter in thy bosom; that thou read therein to thyself and to thy Children, until you have got it by root-of-heart,[17] for it is one of the Songs that thou must sing while thou art in this House of thy Pilgrimage (Ps. 119:54); also this thou must deliver in at the further Gate.

Now I saw in my Dream, that this old Gentleman, as he told me this story, did himself seem to be greatly affected therewith. He moreover proceeded, and said, So Christiana called her Sons together, and began thus to address herself unto them: My Sons, I have, as you may perceive, been of late under much exercise in my Soul about the Death of your Father; not for that I doubt at all of his Happiness, for I am satisfied now that he is well. I have also been much affected with the thoughts of mine own state and yours, which I verily believe is by nature miserable. My carriages also to your Father in his distress, is a great load to my Conscience; for I hardened both my own heart and yours against him, and refused to go with him on Pilgrimage.

The thoughts of these things would now kill me outright but for a Dream which I had last night, and but for the encouragement that this stranger has given me this morning. Come, my Children, let us pack up and be gone to the Gate that leads to the Celestial Country, that we may see your Father, and be with him and his Companions in peace, according to the Laws of that Land.

Then did her Children burst out into tears for joy that the heart of their Mother was so inclined. So their Visitor bid them farewell, and they began to prepare to set out for their Journey.

But while they were thus about to be gone, two of the women that were Christiana's Neighbours came up to her house and knocked at her door. To whom she said as before, If you come in God's name, come in. At this the women were stunned, for this kind of language they used not to hear, or to perceive to drop from the lips of Christiana. Yet they came in: but behold they found the good woman a preparing[18] to be gone from her house.

So they began and said, Neighbour, pray what is your meaning by this?

Christiana answered and said to the eldest of them, whose name was Mrs. Timorous, I am preparing for a journey. (This Timorous was daughter to him that met Christian upon the Hill Difficulty, and would have had him go back for fear of the Lions.)

TIMOROUS. For what Journey, I pray you?

CHRISTIANA. Even to go after my good Husband. And with that she fell a weeping.

TIMOROUS. I hope not so, good Neighbour, pray for your poor Children's sakes, do not so unwomanly cast away yourself.

CHRISTIANA. Nay, my Children shall go with me, not one of them is willing to stay behind.

TIMOROUS. I wonder in my very heart, what or who has brought you into this mind.

CHRISTIANA. Oh, Neighbour, knew you but as much as I do, I doubt not but that you would go with me.

TIMOROUS. Prithee what new knowledge hast thou got, that so worketh off thy mind from thy Friends, and that tempteth thee to go nobody knows where?

CHRISTIANA. Then Christiana replied, I have been sorely afflicted since my Husband's departure from me, but especially since he went over the River. But that which troubleth me most, is my churlish carriages to him when he was under his distress. Besides, I am now as he was then; nothing will serve me but going on Pilgrimage. I was a dreaming last night that I saw him. Oh that my Soul was with him. He dwelleth in the presence of the King of the Country, he sits and eats with him at his table, he is become a Companion of Immortals, and has a House now given him to dwell in, to which the best Palaces on Earth, if compared, seem to me to be but as a Dunghill (II Cor. 5:1-4). The Prince of the Place has also sent for me, with promise of entertainment if I shall come to him; his messenger was here even now, and has brought me a Letter, which invites me to come. And with that she pluck'd out her Letter, and read it, and said to them, What now will you say to this?

TIMOROUS. Oh! the madness that has possessed thee and thy Husband, to run yourselves upon such difficulties! You have heard, I am sure, what your Husband did meet with, even in a manner at the first step that he took on his way, as our Neighbour Obstinate can yet testify, for he went along with him; yea, and Pliable too, until they like wise men were afraid to go any further. We also heard over and above, how he met with the Lions, Apollyon, the Shadow of Death, and many other things. Nor is the danger that he met with at Vanity Fair to be forgotten by thee; for if he, though a Man, was so hard put to it, what canst thou, being but a poor Woman, do? Consider also that these four sweet Babes are thy Children, thy Flesh and thy Bones. Wherefore, though thou shouldst be so rash as to cast away thyself, yet for the sake of the Fruit of thy Body keep thou at home.

But Christiana said unto her, Tempt me not, my neighbour. I have now a price put into mine hand to get gain, and I should be a Fool of the greatest size if I should have no heart to strike in with the opportunity. And for that you tell me of all these Troubles that I am like to meet with in the way, they are so far off from being to me a discouragement, that they shew I am in the right. The bitter must come before the sweet, and that also will make the sweet the sweeter. Wherefore, since you came not to my house in God's name, as I said, I pray you to be gone, and not to disquiet me further.

Then Timorous also revil'd her, and said to her fellow, Come, Neighbour Mercy, let us leave her in her own hands, since she scorns our Counsel and Company. But Mercy was at a stand, and could not so readily comply with her Neighbour, and that for a twofold reason. First, her bowels yearned over Christiana: so she said within herself, If my Neighbour will needs be gone, I will go a little way with her and help her. Secondly, her bowels yearned [19] over her own Soul (for what Christiana had said had taken some hold upon her mind). Wherefore she said within herself again, I will yet have more talk with this Christiana, and if I find Truth and Life in what she shall say, myself with my heart shall also go with her. Wherefore Mercy began thus to reply to her Neighbour Timorous.

MERCY. Neighbour, I did indeed come with you to see Christiana this morning; and since she is, as you see, a taking of her last farewell of her Country, I think to walk this Sun-shine morning a little way with her to help her on the way. But she told her not of her second reason, but kept that to herself.

TIMOROUS. Well, I see you have a mind to go a fooling too, but take heed in time, and be wise: while we are out of danger, we are out; but when we are in, we are in. So Mrs. Timorous returned to her house, and Christiana betook herself to her Journey. But when Timorous was got home to her house, she sends for some of her Neighbours, to wit, Mrs. Bat's-eyes, Mrs. Inconsiderate, Mrs. Light-mind, and Mrs. Know-nothing. So when they were come to her house, she falls to telling of the story of Christiana and of her intended Journey. And thus she began her tale.

TIMOROUS. Neighbours, having had little to do this morning, I went to give Christiana a visit; and when I came at the door, I knocked, as you know 'tis our custom. And she answered, If you come in God's name, come in. So in I went, thinking all was well. But when I came in, I found her preparing herself to depart the Town, she and also her Children.

So I asked her what was her meaning by that? And she told me, in short, that she was now of a mind to go on Pilgrimage, as did her Husband. She told me also a Dream that she had, and how the King of the Country where her Husband was had sent her an inviting Letter to come thither.

Then said Mrs. Know-nothing, And what do you think? will she go?

TIMOROUS. Ay, go she will, whatever come on't; and methinks I know it by this, for that which was my great argument to persuade her to stay at home (to wit, the Troubles she was like to meet with in the way) is one great argument with her to put her forward on her Journey. For she told me in so many words, The bitter goes before the sweet. Yea, and for as much as it so doth, it makes the sweet the sweeter.

MRS. BAT'S-EYES. Oh, this blind and foolish woman, said she, will she not take warning by her Husband's afflictions? For my part, I see, if he was here again, he would rest him content in a whole skin, and never run so many hazards for nothing.

Mrs. Inconsiderate also replied, saying, Away with such Fantastical Fools from the Town! A good riddance, for my part, I say of her. Should she stay where she dwells, and retain this her mind, who could live quietly by her? for she will either be dumpish[20] or unneighbourly, or talk of such matters as no wise body can abide; wherefore, for my part, I shall never be sorry for her departure! let her go, and let better come in her room: 'twas never a good World since these whimsical Fools dwelt in it.

Then Mrs. Light-mind added as followeth: Come, put this kind of talk away. I was yesterday at Madam Wanton's, where we were as merry as the maids. For who do you think should be there, but I and Mrs. Love-the-flesh, and three or four more, with Mr. Lechery, Mrs. Filth, and some others. So there we had music and dancing, and what else was meet to fill up the pleasure, and I dare say[21] my Lady herself is an admirably well-bred Gentlewoman, and Mr. Lechery is as pretty a fellow.

By this time Christiana was got on her way, and Mercy went along with her. So as they went, her children being there also, Christiana began to discourse. And Mercy, said Christiana, I take this as an unexpected favour, that thou shouldst set foot out of doors with me, to accompany me a little in my way.

MERCY. Then said young Mercy (for she was but young), If I thought it would be to purpose to go with you, I would never go near the Town any more.

CHRISTIANA. Well, Mercy, said Christiana, cast in thy lot with me: I well know what will be the end of our Pilgrimage; my Husband is where he would not but be for all the Gold in the Spanish Mines. Nor shalt thou be rejected, though thou goest but upon my Invitation. The King who hath sent for me and my Children is one that delighteth in Mercy.[22] Besides, if thou wilt, I will hire thee, and thou shalt go along with me as my servant; yet we will have all things in common betwixt thee and me, only go along with me.

MERCY. But how shall I be ascertained that I also shall be entertained? Had I this hope but from one that can tell, I would make no stick at all, but would go, being helped by him that can help, though the way was never so tedious.

CHRISTIANA. Well, loving Mercy, I will tell thee what thou shalt do. Go with me to the Wicket-gate, and there I will further inquire for thee; and if there thou shalt not meet with encouragement, I will be content that thou shalt return to thy place. I will also pay thee for thy kindness which thou shewest to me and my Children, in thy accompanying us in our way as thou dost.

MERCY. Then I will go thither, and will take what shall follow, and the Lord grant that my lot may there fall even as the King of Heaven shall have his heart upon me.

Christiana then was glad at her heart, not only that she had a Companion, but also for that she had prevailed with this poor Maid to fall in love with her own Salvation. So they went on together, and Mercy began to weep. Then said Christiana, Wherefore weepeth my Sister so?

MERCY. Alas! said she, who can but lament, that shall but rightly consider what a state and condition my poor Relations are in that yet remain in our sinful Town: and that which makes my grief the more heavy is, because they have no Instructor, nor any to tell them what is to come.

CHRISTIANA. Bowels becometh Pilgrims;[23] and thou dost for thy Friends as my good Christian did for me when he left me; he mourned for that I would not heed nor regard him, but his Lord and ours did gather up his Tears, and put them into his Bottle; and now both I and thou and these my sweet Babes are reaping the fruit and benefit of them. I hope, Mercy, these Tears of thine will not be lost; for the truth hath said, That they that sow in Tears shall reap in Joy, in singing. And he that goeth forth and weepeth, bearing precious seed, shall doubtless come again with rejoicing, bringing his Sheaves with him (Ps. 126:5, 6).

Then said Mercy—

Let the Most Blessed be my guide,
If't be his blessed will,
Unto his Gate, into his Fold,
Up to his Holy Hill.
And let him never suffer me
To swerve or turn aside
From his free grace and holy ways,
Whate'er shall me betide.
And let him gather them of mine,
That I have left behind;
Lord make them pray they may be thine,
With all their heart and mind.

Now my old Friend proceeded and said: But when Christiana came up to the Slough of Despond, she began to be at a stand; for said she, This is the place in which my dear Husband had like to have been smothered with mud. She perceived also, that notwithstanding the command of the King to make this place for Pilgrims good, yet it was rather worse than formerly. So I asked if that was true? Yes, said the Old Gentleman, too true; for that many there be that pretend to be the King's Labourers, and that say they are for mending the King's Highway, that bring dirt and dung instead of stones, and so mar instead of mending. Here Christiana, therefore, with her Boys, did make a stand; but said Mercy, Come, let us venture, only let us be wary. Then they looked well to the steps, and made a shift to get staggeringly over.

Yet Christiana had like to have been in, and that not once nor twice. Now they had no sooner got over, but they thought they heard words that said unto them, Blessed is she that believeth, for there shall be a performance of the things that have been told her from the Lord.

Then they went on again; and said Mercy to Christiana, Had I as good ground to hope for a loving reception at the Wicket-gate as you, I think no Slough of Despond would discourage me.

Well, said the other, you know your sore, and I know mine;

and, good friend, we shall all have enough evil before we come at our Journey's end.

For can it be imagined, that the people that design to attain such excellent Glories as we do, and that are so envied that Happiness as we are; but that we shall meet with what Fears and Scares, with what Trouble and Afflictions they can possibly assault us with that hate us?

And now Mr. Sagacity left me to dream out my Dream by myself. Wherefore methought I saw Christiana and Mercy and the Boys go all of them up to the Gate; to which when they were come, they betook themselves to a short debate about how they must manage their calling at the Gate, and what should be said to him that did open to them. So it was concluded, since Christiana was the eldest, that she should knock for entrance, and that she should speak to him that did open for the rest. So Christiana began to knock, and as her poor Husband did, she knocked and knocked again. But instead of any that answered, they all thought that they heard as if a Dog came barking upon them—a Dog, and a great one too; and this made the Women and Children afraid, nor durst they for a while to knock any more, for fear the Mastiff should fly upon them. Now, therefore, they were greatly tumbled up and down in their minds, and knew not what to do. Knock they durst not, for fear of the Dog; go back they durst not, for fear that the Keeper of that Gate should espy them as they so went, and should be offended with them. At last they thought of knocking again, and knocked more vehemently than they did at the first. Then said the Keeper of the Gate, Who is there? So the Dog left off to bark, and he opened unto them.

Then Christiana made low obeisance, and said, Let not our Lord be offended with his Handmaidens, for that we have knocked at this princely Gate. Then said the Keeper, Whence come ye, and what is that you would have?

Christiana answered, We are come from whence Christian did come, and upon the same Errand as he; to wit, to be, if it shall please you, graciously admitted by this Gate into the way that leads to the Celestial City. And I answer, my Lord, in the next place, that I am Christiana, once the Wife of Christian that now is gotten above.

With that the Keeper of the Gate did marvel, saying, What! Is she become now a Pilgrim, that but a while ago abhorred that life? Then she bowed her head, and said, Yes, and so are these my sweet Babes also.

Then he took her by the hand, and let her in, and said also, Suffer the little Children to come unto me; and with that he shut up the Gate. This done, he called to a Trumpeter that was above, over the Gate, to entertain Christiana with shouting and sound of Trumpet for joy (Luke 15:7). So he obeyed and sounded, and filled the air with his melodious notes.

Now all this while poor Mercy did stand without, trembling and crying for fear that she was rejected. But when Christiana had gotten admittance for herself and her Boys, then she began to make intercession for Mercy.

CHRISTIANA. And she said, My Lord, I have a Companion of mine that stands yet without, that is come hither upon the same account as myself: one that is much dejected in her mind, for that she comes, as she thinks, without sending for, whereas I was sent to by my Husband's King to come.

Now Mercy began to be very impatient, for each minute was as long to her as an hour, wherefore she prevented Christiana from a fuller interceding for her, by knocking at the Gate herself. And she knocked then so loud, that she made Christiana to start. Then said the Keeper of the Gate, Who is there? and said Christiana, It is my Friend.

So he opened the Gate, and looked out; but Mercy was fallen down without in a swoon, for she fainted, and was afraid that no Gate would be opened to her.

Then he took her by the hand, and said, Damsel, I bid thee arise.

Oh, Sir, said she, I am faint; there is scarce life left in me. But he answered, that one once said, When my soul fainted within me, I remembered the Lord, and my prayer came in unto thee, into thy Holy Temple (Jon. 2:7). Fear not, but stand upon thy feet, and tell me wherefore thou art come.

MERCY. I am come for that unto which I was never invited, as my Friend Christiana was. Hers was from the King, and mine was but from her:[24] wherefore I fear I presume.

Did she desire thee to come with her to this Place?

MERCY. Yes; and as my Lord sees, I am come. And if there is any grace or forgiveness of sins to spare, I beseech that I thy poor Handmaid may be partaker thereof.

Then he took her again by the hand, and led her gently in, and said, I pray for all them that believe on me, by what means soever they come unto me. Then said he to those that stood by, Fetch something, and give it to Mercy to smell on, thereby to stay her fainting. So they fetch'd her a bundle of Myrrh, and a while after she was revived.

And now was Christiana and her Boys and Mercy received of the Lord at the head of the way, and spoke kindly unto by him.

Then said they yet further unto him. We are sorry for our sins, and beg of our Lord his Pardon, and further information what we must do.

I grant Pardon, said he, by word and deed; by word, in the promise of forgiveness; by deed, in the way I obtained it. Take the first from my lips with a kiss, and the other as it shall be revealed (Song of Sol. 1:2; John 20:20).

Now I saw in my Dream that he spoke many good words unto them, whereby they were greatly gladdened. He also had them up to the top of the Gate, and shewed them by what deed they were saved; and told them withal that that sight they would have again as they went along in the way, to their comfort.

So he left them a while in a Summer Parlour below, where they entered into talk by themselves; and thus Christiana began: O Lord! how glad am I that we are got in hither.

MERCY. So you well may; but I of all have cause to leap for joy.

CHRISTIANA. I thought one time, as I stood at the Gate (because I had knocked and none did answer), that all our labour had been lost, specially when that ugly Cur made such a heavy barking against us.

MERCY. But my worst fear was after I saw that you were taken into his favour and that I was left behind. Now, thought I, 'tis fulfilled which is written, Two women shall be grinding together, the one shall be taken and the other left (Matt. 24:41). I had much ado to forbear crying out, Undone, undone.

And afraid I was to knock any more; but when I looked up to what was written over the Gate,[25] I took courage. I also thought that I must either knock again or die; so I knocked, but I cannot tell how, for my spirit now struggled betwixt life and death.

CHRISTIANA. Can you not tell how you knock? I am sure your knocks were so earnest that the very sound of them made me start; I thought I never heard such knocking in all my life; I thought you would a come in by violent hands, or a took the Kingdom by storm (Matt. 11:12).

MERCY. Alas, to be in my case, who that so was could but have done so? You saw that the Door was shut upon me, and that there was a most cruel Dog thereabout. Who, I say, that was so faint-hearted as I, that would not have knocked with all their might? But pray, what said my Lord to my rudeness? was he not angry with me?

CHRISTIANA. When he heard your lumbering noise, he gave a wonderful innocent smile; I believe what you did pleased him well enough, for he shewed no sign to the contrary. But I marvel in my heart why he keeps such a Dog; had I known that afore, I fear I should not have had heart enough to a ventured myself in this manner. But now we are in, and I am glad with all my heart.

MERCY. I will ask, if you please, next time he comes down, why he keeps such a filthy Cur in his yard; I hope he will not take it amiss.

Ay, do, said the Children, and persuade him to hang him, for we are afraid he will bite us when we go hence.

So at last he came down to them again, and Mercy fell to the ground on her face before him and worshipped, and said, Let my Lord accept of the sacrifice of Praise which I now offer unto him with the calves of my lips.

So he said unto her, Peace be to thee, stand up. But she continued upon her face, and said, Righteous art thou, O Lord, when I plead with thee, yet let me talk with thee of thy Judgments (Jer. 12:1, 2). Wherefore dost thou keep so cruel a Dog in thy yard, at the sight of which such Women and Children as we are ready to fly from thy Gate for fear?

He answered and said, That Dog has another owner; he also is kept close in another man's ground, only my Pilgrims hear his barking; he belongs to the Castle which you see there at a distance, but can come up to the walls of this place. He has frightened many an honest Pilgrim from worse to better, by the great voice of his roaring. Indeed he that owneth him doth not keep him of any good will to me or mine, but with intent to keep the Pilgrims from coming to me, and that they may be afraid to knock at this Gate for entrance. Sometimes also he has broken out, and has worried some that I love; but I take all at present patiently. I also give my Pilgrims timely help, so they are not delivered up to his power, to do to them what his doggish nature would prompt him to. But what! my purchased one, I trow, hadst thou known never so much beforehand, thou wouldest not have been afraid of a Dog.

The Beggars that go from Door to Door will, rather than they will lose a supposed Alms, run the hazard of the bawling, barking, and biting too of a Dog; and shall a Dog—a Dog in another man's yard, a Dog whose barking I turn to the profit of Pilgrims—keep any from coming to me? I deliver them from the Lions, their Darling from the power of the Dog.

MERCY. Then said Mercy, I confess my ignorance; I spake what I understood not; I acknowledge that thou doest all things well.

CHRISTIANA. Then Christiana began to talk of their Journey, and to inquire after the way. So he fed them, and washed their feet, and set them in the way of his steps, according as he had dealt with her Husband before. So I saw in my Dream that they walk'd on their way, and had the weather very comfortable to them.

Then Christiana began to sing, saying,

Bless'd be the Day that I began[26]
A Pilgrim for to be;
And blessed also be that man
That thereto moved me.
'Tis true, 'twas long ere I began
To seek to live for ever:
But now I run fast as I can;
'Tis better late than never.
Our Tears to Joy, our Fears to Faith,
Are turned, as we see,
Thus our beginning (as one saith),
Shews what our end will be (Matt. 20:6).

Now there was, on the other side of the Wall that fenced in the way up which Christiana and her Companions were to go, a Garden, and that Garden belonged to him whose was that barking Dog, of whom mention was made before. And some of the Fruit-trees that grew in that Garden shot their branches over the Wall; and being mellow, they that found them did gather them up, and oft eat of them to their hurt. So Christiana's Boys, as Boys are apt to do, being pleas'd with the trees, and with the Fruit that did hang thereon, did plash them,[27] and began to eat. Their mother did also chide them for so doing, but still the Boys went on.

Well, said she, my Sons, you transgress, for that Fruit is none of ours; but she did not know that they did belong to the Enemy; I'll warrant you if she had, she would a been ready to die for fear. But that passed, and they went on their way. Now by that they were gone about two bows'-shot from the place that let them into the way, they espied two very ill-favoured ones coming down apace to meet them. With that Christiana and Mercy her friend covered themselves with their Veils, and so kept on their Journey; the Children also went on before, so that at last they met together. Then they that came down to meet them, came just up to the Women as if they would embrace them; but Christiana said, Stand back, or go peaceably by as you should. Yet these two, as men that are deaf, regarded not Christiana's words, but began to lay hands upon them. At that Christiana, waxing very wroth, spurned at them with her feet. Mercy also, as well as she could, did what she could to shift them. Christiana again said to them, Stand back, and be gone, for we have no money to lose, being Pilgrims as ye see, and such too as live upon the Charity of our Friends.

Then said one of the two men, We make no assault upon you for Money, but are come out to tell you, that if you will but grant one small request which we shall ask, we will make Women of you for ever.

CHRISTIANA. Now Christiana imagining what they should mean, made answer again, We will neither hear, nor regard, nor yield to what you shall ask. We are in haste, cannot stay, our business is a business of Life and Death. So again she and her Companions made a fresh essay to go past them, but they letted them in their way.

And they said, We intend no hurt to your lives, 'tis another thing we would have.

CHRISTIANA. Ah, quoth Christiana, you would have us Body and Soul, for I know 'tis for that you are come; but we will die rather upon the spot, than suffer ourselves to be brought into such snares as shall hazard our well-being hereafter. And with that they both shrieked out, and cried, Murder, murder: and so put themselves under those Laws that are provided for the Protection of Women (Deut. 22:25-27). But the men still made their approach upon them, with design to prevail against them: they therefore cried out again.

Now they being, as I said, not far from the Gate in at which they came, their voice was heard from where they were, thither. Wherefore some of the House came out, and knowing that it was Christiana's tongue, they made haste to her relief. But by that they were got within sight of them, the Women were in a very great scuffle, the children also stood crying by. Then did he that came in for their relief call out to the Ruffins,[28] saying, What is that thing that you do? Would you make my Lord's people to transgress? He also attempted to take them, but they did make their escape over the Wall into the Garden of the man to whom the great Dog belonged; so the Dog became their Protector. This Reliever then came up to the Women, and asked them how they did. So they answered, We thank thy Prince, pretty well, only we have been somewhat affrighted; we thank thee also for that thou camest in to our help, for otherwise we had been overcome.

RELIEVER. So after a few more words, this Reliever said as followeth: I marvelled much when you were entertained at the Gate above, being ye knew[29] that ye were but weak Women, that you petitioned not the Lord there for a Conductor; then might you have avoided these troubles and dangers, for he would have granted you one.

CHRISTIANA. Alas! said Christiana, we were so taken with our present blessing, that dangers to come were forgotten by us; besides, who could have thought that so near the King's Palace there should have lurked such naughty ones? Indeed, it had been well for us, had we asked our Lord for one; but since our Lord knew 'twould be for our profit, I wonder he sent not one along with us!

RELIEVER. It is not always necessary to grant things not asked for, lest by so doing they become of little esteem; but when the want of a thing is felt, it then comes under, in the eyes of him that feels it, that estimate that properly is its due, and so consequently will be thereafter used. Had my Lord granted you a Conductor, you would not neither so have bewailed that oversight of yours in not asking for one as now you have occasion to do. So all things work for good, and tend to make you more wary.

CHRISTIANA. Shall we go back again to my Lord, and confess our folly, and ask one?

RELIEVER. Your confession of your folly I will present him with. To go back again you need not; for in all places where you shall come, you will find no want at all, for in every of my Lord's Lodgings which he has prepared for the reception of his Pilgrims, there is sufficient to furnish them against all attempts whatsoever. But, as I said, he will be inquired of by them to do it for them (Ezek. 36:37): and 'tis a poor thing that is not worth asking for. When he had thus said, he went back to his place, and the Pilgrims went on their way.

MERCY. Then said Mercy, What a sudden blank is here! I made account we had now been past all danger, and that we should never see sorrow more.

CHRISTIANA. Thy innocency, my Sister, said Christiana to Mercy, may excuse thee much; but as for me, my fault is so much the greater, for that I saw this danger before I came out of the Doors, and yet did not provide for it where provision might a been had. I am therefore much to be blamed.

MERCY. Then said Mercy, How knew you this before you came from home? Pray open to me this riddle.

CHRISTIANA. Why, I will tell you. Before I set foot out of doors, one night, as I lay in my bed, I had a Dream about this; for methought I saw two men, as like these as ever the world they could look, stand at my bed's feet, plotting how they might prevent my Salvation. I will tell you their very words. They said ('twas when I was in my Troubles), What shall we do with this woman? for she cries out waking and sleeping, for forgiveness: if she be suffered to go on as she begins we shall lose her as we have lost her Husband. This you know might a made me take heed, and have provided when provision might a been had.

MERCY. Well, said Mercy, as by this neglect we have an occasion ministered unto us to behold our own imperfections, so our Lord has taken occasion thereby to make manifest the riches of his Grace. For he, as we see, has followed us with unasked kindness, and has delivered us from their hands that were stronger than we, of his mere good pleasure.

Thus now, when they had talked away a little more time, they drew nigh to an House which stood in the way, which House was built for the relief of Pilgrims: as you will find more fully related in the First Part of these Records of the *Pilgrim's Progress*. So they drew on towards the House (the House of the Interpreter), and when they came to the door, they heard a great talk in the House. They then gave ear, and heard, as they thought, Christiana mentioned by name. For you must know that there went along, even before her, a talk of her and her Children's going on Pilgrimage. And this thing was the more pleasing to them, because they had heard that she was Christian's Wife, that Woman who was some time ago so unwilling to hear of going on Pilgrimage. Thus, therefore, they stood still and heard the good people within commending her, who they little thought stood at the door. At last Christiana knocked as she had done at the Gate before. Now when she had knocked, there came to the door a young Damsel, and opened the door and looked, and behold two Women were there.

DAMSEL. Then said the Damsel to them, With whom would you speak in this place?

CHRISTIANA. Christiana answered, We understand that this is a privileged place for those that are become Pilgrims, and we now at this door are such; wherefore we pray that we may be partakers of that for which we at this time are come; for the day, as thou seest, is very far spent, and we are loth to-night to go any farther.

DAMSEL. Pray, what may I call your name, that I may tell it to my Lord within?

CHRISTIANA. My name is Christiana; I was the Wife of that Pilgrim that some years ago did travel this way, and these be his four Children. This Maiden also is my Companion, and is going on Pilgrimage too.

INNOCENT. Then ran Innocent in (for that was her name), and said to those within, Can you think who is at the door? There is Christiana and her Children and her Companion, all waiting for entertainment here. Then they leaped for joy, and went and told their Master. So he came to the door, and looking upon her, he said, Art thou that Christiana whom Christian the Good man left behind him when he betook himself to a Pilgrim's life?

CHRISTIANA. I am that Woman that was so hard-hearted as to slight my Husband's Troubles, and that left him to go on in his Journey alone, and these are his four Children; but now I also am come, for I am convinced that no way is right but this.

INTERPRETER. Then is fulfilled that which also is written of the man that said to his Son, Go, work to-day in my Vineyard;

and he said to his Father, I will not; but afterwards repented and went (Matt. 21:20).

CHRISTIANA. Then said Christiana, So be it, Amen. God make it a true saying upon me, and grant that I may be found at the last of him in peace, without spot, and blameless.

INTERPRETER. But why standest thou thus at the door? Come in, thou Daughter of Abraham. We were talking of thee but now, for tidings have come to us before how thou art become a Pilgrim. Come, Children, come in; come, Maiden, come in. So he had them all into the House.

So when they were within, they were bidden sit down and rest them; the which when they had done, those that attended upon the Pilgrims in the House came into the Room to see them. And one smiled, and another smiled, and they all smiled for joy that Christiana was become a Pilgrim. They also looked upon the Boys: they stroked them over the faces with the hand, in token of their kind reception of them. They also carried it lovingly to Mercy, and bid them all welcome into their Master's House.

After a while, because Supper was not ready, the Interpreter took them into his significant Rooms, and shewed them what Christian, Christiana's Husband, had seen some time before. Here, therefore, they saw the Man in the Cage, the Man and his Dream, the Man that cut his way through his Enemies, and the Picture of the biggest of them all,[30] together with the rest of those things that were then so profitable to Christian.

This done, and after these things had been somewhat digested by Christiana and her company, the Interpreter takes them apart again, and has them first into a Room where was a Man that could look no way but downwards, with a Muck-rake[31] in his hand. There stood also one over his head with a Celestial Crown in his hand, and proffered him that Crown for his Muck-rake; but the man did neither look up, nor regard, but raked to himself the straws, the small sticks, and dust of the floor.

Then said Christiana, I persuade myself that I know somewhat the meaning of this; for this is a figure of a Man of this World, is it not, good Sir?

INTERPRETER. Thou hast said the right, said he, and his Muck-rake doth shew his carnal mind. And whereas thou seest him rather give heed to rake up straws and sticks and the dust of the floor, than to what he says that calls to him from above, with the Celestial Crown in his hand, it is to shew that Heaven is but as a fable to some, and that things here are counted the only things substantial. Now, whereas it was also shewed thee that the man could look no way but downwards, it is to let thee know that earthly things, when they are with power upon men's minds, quite carry their hearts away from God.

CHRISTIANA. Then said Christiana, Oh! deliver me from this Muck-rake.

INTERPRETER. That prayer, said the Interpreter, has lain by till 'tis almost rusty. Give me not Riches (Prov. 30:8), is scarcely the prayer of one of ten thousand. Straws and sticks and dust, with most, are the great things now looked after.

With that Mercy and Christiana wept, and said, It is, alas! too true.

The Interpreter shows them "some other things that are profitable," and Christiana tells her host "What it was that at first did move her to betake herself to a Pilgrim's life."

In the morning they arose with the Sun, and prepared themselves for their departure; but the Interpreter would have them tarry a while, For, said he, you must orderly go from hence. Then said he to the Damsel that at first opened unto them, Take them and have them into the Garden to the Bath,[32] and there wash them, and make them clean from the soil which they have gathered by travelling. Then Innocent, the Damsel, took them, and had them into the Garden, and brought them to the Bath; so she told them that there they must wash and be clean, for so her Master would have the Women to do that called at his house, as they were going on Pilgrimage. They then went in and washed, yea they and the Boys and all; and they came out of that Bath, not only sweet and clean, but also much enlivened and strengthened in their joints. So when they came in, they looked fairer a deal than when they went out to the washing.

When they were returned out of the Garden from the Bath, the Interpreter took them and looked upon them and said unto them, Fair as the Moon. Then he called for the Seal[33] wherewith they used to be sealed that were washed in his Bath. So the Seal was brought, and he set his Mark upon them, that they might be known in the places whither they were yet to go. Now the Seal was the contents and sum of the Passover which the Children of Israel did eat when they came out from the land of Egypt (Ex. 13:8-10), and the Mark was set between their eyes. This Seal greatly added to their beauty, for it was an ornament to their faces. It also added to their gravity, and made their countenances more like those of Angels.

Then said the Interpreter again to the Damsel that waited upon these Women, Go into the Vestry and fetch out Garments for these people; so she went and fetched out white Raiment,[34] and laid it down before him; so he commanded them to put it on. It was fine linen, white and clean. When the Women were thus adorned, they seemed to be a terror one to the other, for that they could not see that glory each one on herself which they could see in each other. Now, therefore, they began to esteem each other better than themselves. For you are fairer than I am, said one; and you are more comely than I am, said another. The Children also stood amazed to see into what fashion they were brought.

The Interpreter then called for a Man-servant of his, one Great-heart,[35] and bid him take sword and helmet and shield: And take these my Daughters, said he, and conduct them to the house called Beautiful, at which place they will rest next. So he took his Weapons and went before them, and the Interpreter said, God speed. Those also that belonged to the Family sent them away with many a good wish.

[There follows a conversation on "pardon by word and deed."]

Now I saw still in my Dream that they went on until they were come to the place that Simple and Sloth and Presumption lay and slept in, when Christian went by on Pilgrimage. And behold they were hanged up in irons, a little way off on the other side.

MERCY. Then said Mercy to him that was their Guide and Conductor, What are those three men? and for what are they hanged there?

GREAT-HEART. These three men were men of very bad qualities, they had no mind to be Pilgrims themselves, and whosoever they could they hindered. They were for sloth and folly themselves, and whoever they could persuade with, they made so too, and withal taught them to presume that they should do well at last. They were asleep when Christian went by, and now you go by they are hanged.

MERCY. But could they persuade any to be of their opinion?

GREAT-HEART. Yes, they turned several out of the way. There was Slow-pace, that they persuaded to do as they. They also prevailed with one Short-wind, with one No-heart, with one Linger-after-lust, and with one Sleepy-head, and with a young woman, her name was Dull, to turn out of the way and become as they. Besides they brought up an ill report of your Lord, persuading others that he was a Task-master. They also brought up an evil report of the good Land, saying 'twas not half so good as some pretend it was. They also began to vilify his Servants, and to count the very best of them meddlesome, troublesome busybodies. Further, they would call the Bread of God Husks, the Comforts of his Children Fancies, the Travel and Labour of Pilgrims things to no purpose.

CHRISTIANA. Nay, said Christiana, if they were such, they shall never be bewailed by me. They have but what they deserve, and I think it is well that they hang so near the Highway that others may see and take warning. But had it not been well if their crimes had been engraven in some plate of iron or brass, and left here, even where they did their mischiefs, for a caution to other bad men?

GREAT-HEART. So it is, as you well may perceive if you will go a little to the Wall.

MERCY. No, no, let them hang, and their names rot, and their crimes live for ever against them. I think it a high favour that they were hanged afore we came hither, who knows else what they might a done to such poor women as we are?

Thus they went on, till they came at the foot of the Hill Difficulty, where again their good Friend, Mr. Great-heart, took an occasion to tell them of what happened there when Christian himself went by. So he had them first to the Spring. Lo, saith he, this is the Spring that Christian drank of before he went up this Hill, and then 'twas clear and good, but now 'tis dirty[36] with the feet of some that are not desirous that Pilgrims here should quench their thirst (Ezek. 34:18). Therat Mercy said, And why so envious, trow? But, said their Guide, it will do, if taken up, and put into a vessel that is sweet and good; for then the dirt will sink to the bottom, and the water will come out by itself more clear. Thus, therefore, Christiana and her Companions were compelled to do. They took it up, and put it into an earthen pot, and so let it stand till the dirt was gone to the bottom, and then they drank thereof.

Next he shewed them the two by-ways that were at the foot of the Hill, where Formality and Hypocrisy lost themselves. And, said he, these are dangerous Paths. Two were here cast away when Christian came by; and although, as you see, these ways are since stopped up with chains, posts, and a ditch, yet there are that will choose to adventure here, rather than take the pains to go up this Hill.

CHRISTIANA. The way of transgressors is hard (Prov. 13:15). 'Tis a wonder that they can get into those ways without danger of breaking their necks.

GREAT-HEART. They will venture; yea, if at any time any of the King's servants doth happen to see them, and doth call unto them, and tell them that they are in the wrong ways, and do bid them beware the danger, then they will railingly return them answer and say, As for the word that thou hast spoken unto us in the name of the King, we will not harken unto thee; but we will certainly do whatsoever thing goeth out of our own mouths, etc. (Jer. 44:16, 17). Nay, if you look a little farther, you shall see that these ways are made cautionary enough, not only by these posts and ditch and chain, but also by being hedged up; yet they will choose to go there.

CHRISTIANA. They are idle, they love not to take pains, uphill way is unpleasant to them. So it is fulfilled unto them as it is written, The way of the slothful man is a Hedge of Thorns (Prov. 15:19). Yea, they will rather choose to walk upon a Snare than to go up this Hill, and the rest of this way to the City.

The Hill puts the Pilgrims to it.

Then they set forward, and began to go up the Hill, and up the Hill they went; but before they got to the top, Christiana began to pant, and said, I dare say this is a breathing Hill.[37] No marvel if they that love their ease more than their souls choose to themselves a smoother way. Then said Mercy, I must sit down; also the least of the Children began to cry. Come, come, said Great-heart, sit not down here, for a little above is the Prince's Arbour. Then took he the little Boy by the hand, and led him up thereto.

When they were come to the Arbour, they were very willing to sit down, for they were all in a pelting heat.[38] Then said Mercy, How sweet is rest to them that labour (Matt. 11:28) And how good is the Prince of Pilgrims to provide such resting-places for them. Of this Arbour I have heard much, but I never saw it before. But here let us beware of sleeping; for as I have heard, for that it cost poor Christian dear.

Then said Mr. Great-heart to the little ones, Come, my pretty Boys, how do you do? What think you now of going on Pilgrimage? Sir, said the least, I was almost beat out of heart, but I thank you for lending me a hand at my need. And I remember now what my Mother has told me, namely, That the way to Heaven is as up a Ladder, and the way to Hell is as down a Hill. But I had rather go up the Ladder to Life, than down the Hill to Death.

Then said Mercy, But the Proverb is, To go down the Hill is easy. But James said (for that was his name), The day is coming when, in my opinion, going down Hill will be the hardest of all. 'Tis a good Boy, said his Master, thou hast given her a right answer. Then Mercy smiled, but the little boy did blush.

CHRISTIANA. Come, said Christiana, will you eat a bit, a little to sweeten your mouths, while you sit here to rest your legs? For I have here a piece of Pomegranate,[39] which Mr. Interpreter put in my hand, just when I came out of his doors. He gave me also a piece of an Honeycomb, and a little Bottle of Spirits. I thought he gave you something, said Mercy, because he called you aside. Yes, so he did, said the other; but Mercy, it shall still be, as I said it should, when at first we came from home, thou shalt be a sharer in all the good that I have, because thou so willingly didst become my Companion. Then she gave to them, and they did eat, both Mercy and the Boys. And said Christiana to Mr. Great-heart, Sir, will you do as we? But he answered, You are going on Pilgrimage, and presently I shall return; much good may what you have do to you; at home I eat the same every day. Now when they had eaten and drank, and had chatted a little longer, their Guide said to them, The day wears away, if you think good, let us prepare to be going. So they got up to go, and the little Boys went before. But Christiana forgot to take her Bottle of Spirits with her, so she sent her little Boy back to fetch it. Then said Mercy, I think this is a losing place. Here Christian lost his Roll, and here Christiana left her Bottle behind her: Sir, what is the cause of this? So their Guide made answer and said, The cause is sleep or forgetfulness: some sleep when they should keep awake, and some forget when they should remember; and this is the very cause why, often at the resting-places, some Pilgrims in some things come off losers. Pilgrims should watch, and remember what they have already received under their greatest enjoyments; but, for want of doing so, oft-times their Rejoicing ends in Tears, and their Sunshine in a Cloud: witness the story of Christian at this place.

When they were come to the place where Mistrust and Timorous met Christian to persuade him to go back for fear of the Lions, they perceived as it were a Stage, and before it towards the Road a broad plate with a Copy of Verses written thereon; and underneath, the reason of raising up of that Stage in that place rendered. The verses were these:

Let him that sees this Stage take heed
Unto his Heart and Tongue;
Lest if he do not, here he speed
As some have long agone.

The words underneath the Verses were, This Stage was built to punish such upon, who, through timorousness or mistrust, shall be afraid to go farther on Pilgrimage. Also on this Stage both Mistrust and Timorous were burned through the Tongue with an hot Iron, for endeavouring to hinder Christian in his Journey.

Then said Mercy, This is much like to the saying of the Beloved, What shall be given unto thee? or what shall be done unto thee, thou false Tongue? Sharp Arrows of the mighty, with coals of Juniper (Ps. 120:3, 4).

So they went on, till they came within sight of the Lions. Now Mr. Great-heart was a strong man, so he was not afraid of a Lion; but yet, when they were come up to the place where the Lions were, the Boys that went before were glad to cringe behind, for they were afraid of the Lions; so they stepped back, and went behind. At this their guide smiled, and said, How now, my Boys, do you love to go before when no danger doth approach, and love to come behind so soon as the Lions appear?

Now, as they went up, Mr. Great-heart drew his Sword, with intent to make a way for the Pilgrims in spite of the Lions. Then there appeared one that it seems had taken upon him to back the Lions;[40] and he said to the Pilgrims' Guide, What is the cause of your coming hither? Now the name of that man was Grim, or Bloody-man,[41] because of his slaying of Pilgrims, and he was of the race of the Giants.

GREAT-HEART. Then said the Pilgrims' Guide, These Women and Children are going on Pilgrimage, and this is the way they must go, and go it they shall in spite of thee and the Lions.

GRIM. This is not their way, neither shall they go therein. I am come forth to withstand them, and to that end will back the Lions.

Now to say truth, by reason of the fierceness of the Lions, and of the grim carriage of him that did back them, this way had of late lain much unoccupied, and was almost all grown over with Grass.

CHRISTIANA. Then said Christiana, Though the Highways have been unoccupied heretofore, and though the Travellers have been made in time past to walk through by-paths, it must not be so now I am risen, now I am risen a Mother in Israel (Judg. 5:6, 7).

GRIM. Then he swore by the Lions but it should, and therefore bid them turn aside, for they should not have passage there.

But their Guide made first his approach unto Grim, and laid so heavily at him with his sword, that he forced him to retreat.

GRIM. Then said he that attempted to back the Lions, Will you slay me upon mine own ground?

GREAT-HEART. 'Tis the King's Highway that we are in, and in his way it is that thou hast placed thy Lions; but these Women and these Children, though weak, shall hold on their way in spite of thy Lions. And with that he gave him again a downright blow, and brought him upon his knees. With this blow he also broke his Helmet, and with the next he cut off an arm. Then did the Giant roar so hideously that his voice frightened the Women, and yet they were glad to see him lie sprawling upon the ground. Now the Lions were chained, and so of themselves could do nothing. Wherefore when old Grim that intended to back them was dead, Mr. Great-heart said to the Pilgrims, Come, now, and follow me, and no hurt shall happen to you from the Lions. They therefore went on, but the Women trembled as they passed by them; the Boys also looked as if they would die, but they all got by without further hurt.

Now then they were within sight of the Porter's Lodge, and they soon came up unto it; but they made the more haste after this to go thither, because 'tis dangerous travelling there in the Night. So when they were come to the Gate, the Guide knocked, and the Porter cried, Who is there? But as soon as the Guide had said, It is I, he knew his voice, and came down (for the Guide had oft before that come thither as a Conductor of Pilgrims). When he was come down, he opened the Gate, and seeing the Guide standing just before it (for he saw not the women, for they were behind him), he said unto him, How now, Mr. Great-heart? what is your business here so late to-night? I have brought, said he, some Pilgrims hither, where by my Lord's commandment they must lodge. I had been here some time ago, had I not been opposed by the Giant that did use to back the Lions; but I, after a long and tedious combat with him, have cut him off, and have brought the Pilgrims hither in safety.

PORTER. Will you not go in, and stay till morning?

GREAT-HEART. No, I will return to my Lord to-night.

CHRISTIANA. O, Sir, I know not how to be willing you should leave us in our Pilgrimage; you have been so faithful and so loving to us, you have fought so stoutly for us, you have been so hearty in counselling of us, that I shall never forget your favour towards us.

MERCY. Then said Mercy, Oh that we might have thy company to our Journey's end. How can such poor Women as we hold out in a way so full of troubles as this way is, without a Friend and Defender?

JAMES. Then said James, the youngest of the Boys, Pray, Sir, be persuaded to go with us, and help us, because we are so weak, and the way so dangerous as it is.

GREAT-HEART. I am at my Lord's commandment. If he shall allot me to be Your Guide quite through, I will willingly wait upon you. But here you failed at first; for when he bid me come thus far with you, then you should have begged me of him to have gone quite through with you, and he would have granted your request. However, at present I must withdraw; and so, good Christiana, Mercy, and my brave Children, Adieu.

Then the Porter, Mr. Watchful, asked Christiana of her Country, and of her Kindred. And she said, I came from the City of Destruction; I am a Widow woman, and my Husband is dead; his name was Christian the Pilgrim. How, said the

Porter, was he your Husband? Yes, said she, and these are his Children; and this, pointing to Mercy, is one of my Towns-women. Then the Porter rang his bell, as at such times he is wont, and there came to the door one of the Damsels, whose name was Humble-mind. And to her the Porter said, Go tell it within that Christiana, the Wife of Christian, and her Children are come hither on Pilgrimage. She went in therefore and told it. But Oh what a noise for gladness was there within, when the Damsel did but drop that word out of her mouth.

So they came with haste to the Porter, for Christiana stood still at the door. Then some of the most grave said unto her, Come in, Christiana; come in, thou Wife of that good man; come in, thou blessed woman; come in with all that are with thee. So she went in, and they followed her that were her Children and her Companions. Now when they were gone in, they were had into a very large room,[42] where they were bidden to sit down; so they sat down, and the Chief of the house was called to see and welcome the Guests. Then they came in, and understanding who they were, did salute each other with a kiss, and said, Welcome, ye Vessels of the Grace of God, welcome to us, your Friends.

Now because it was somewhat late, and because the Pilgrims were weary with their Journey, and also made faint with the sight of the Fight and of the terrible Lions, therefore they desired as soon as might be to prepare to go to rest. Nay, said those of the Family, refresh yourselves first with a morsel of meat (Ex. 12:3, 8). For they had prepared for them a Lamb (John 1:29), with the accustomed Sauce belonging thereto; for the Porter had heard before of their coming, and had told it to them within. So when they had supped, and ended their Prayer with a Psalm, they desired they might go to rest. But let us, said Christiana, if we may be so bold as to choose, be in that Chamber that was my Husband's[43] when he was here. So they had them up thither, and they all lay in a room. When they were at rest, Christiana and Mercy entered into discourse about things that were convenient.

CHRISTIANA. Little did I think once, that when my Husband went on Pilgrimage I should ever a followed.

MERCY. And you as little thought of lying in his Bed and in his Chamber to rest, as you do now.

CHRISTIANA. And much less did I ever think of seeing his

face with comfort, and of worshipping the Lord the King with him, and yet now I believe I shall.

MERCY. Hark; don't you hear a noise?

CHRISTIANA. Yes; 'tis, as I believe, a noise of Music[44] for joy that we are here.

MERCY. Wonderful! Music in the House, Music in the Heart, and Music also in Heaven, for joy that we are here.

Thus they talked awhile, and then betook themselves to sleep. So in the morning, when they were awake, Christiana said to Mercy:

CHRISTIANA. What was the matter that you did laugh in your sleep to-night? I suppose you were in a Dream.

MERCY. So I was; and a sweet Dream it was; but are you sure I laughed?

CHRISTIANA. Yes, you laughed heartily; but prithee, Mercy, tell me thy dream.

MERCY. I was a-dreaming that I sat all alone in a solitary place, and was bemoaning of the hardness of my Heart.

Now I had not sat there long, but methought many were gathered about me, to see me, and to hear what it was that I said. So they hearkened, and I went on bemoaning the hardness of my heart. At this some of them laughed at me, some called me Fool, and some began to thrust me about. With that, methought I looked up, and saw one coming with Wings towards me. So he came directly to me, and said, Mercy, what aileth thee? Now when he had heard me make my complaint, he said, Peace be to thee. He also wiped mine eyes with his Handkerchief, and clad me in Silver and Gold: he put a Chain about my Neck, and Earrings in mine Ears, and a beautiful Crown upon my Head (Ezek. 16:8-12). Then he took me by the Hand, and said, Mercy, come after me. So he went up, and I followed, till we came at a Golden Gate. Then he knocked; and when they within had opened, the man went in, and I followed him up to a Throne, upon which one sat, and he said to me, Welcome, Daughter. The place looked bright and twinkling like the Stars, or rather like the Sun, and I thought that I saw your Husband there. So I awoke from my Dream. But did I laugh?

CHRISTIANA. Laugh: ay, and well you might, to see yourself so well. For you must give me leave to tell you that I believe it was a good Dream, and that as you have begun to find the first part true, so you shall find the second at last. God speaks once, yea twice, yet man perceiveth it not. In a Dream, in a Vision of the night, when deep sleep falleth upon men, in slumbering upon the bed (Job 33:14, 15). We need not, when abed, lie awake to talk with God. He can visit us while we sleep, and cause us then to hear his voice. Our heart ofttimes wakes when we sleep; and God can speak to that, either by Words, by Proverbs, by Signs and Similitudes, as well as if one was awake.

MERCY. Well, I am glad of my Dream, for I hope ere long to see it fulfilled, to the making of me laugh again.

CHRISTIANA. I think it is now high time to rise, and to know what we must do.

MERCY. Pray, if they invite us to stay a while, let us willingly accept of the proffer. I am the willinger to stay a while here, to grow better acquainted with these Maids. Methinks Prudence, Piety, and Charity have very comely and sober countenances.

CHRISTIANA. We shall see what they will do. So when they were up and ready, they came down. And they asked one another of their rest, and if it was comfortable or not.

MERCY. Very good, said Mercy; it was one of the best night's Lodging that ever I had in my life.

Then said Prudence and Piety, If you will be persuaded to stay here a while, you shall have what the house will afford.

CHARITY. Ay, and that with a very good will, said Charity. So they consented, and stayed there about a month or above, and became very profitable one to another.

[Prudence "catechises" the children.]

Now by that these Pilgrims had been at this place a week, Mercy had a visitor that pretended some good will unto her, and his name was Mr. Brisk.[45] A man of some breeding, and that pretended to Religion, but a man that stuck very close to the World. So he came once or twice or more to Mercy, and offered love unto her. Now Mercy was of a fair countenance, and therefore the more alluring.

Her mind also was, to be always busying of herself in doing, for when she had nothing to do for herself she would be making of Hose and Garments for others, and would bestow them upon them that had need. And Mr. Brisk, not knowing where or how she disposed of what she made, seemed to be greatly taken for that he found her never idle. I will warrant her a good housewife, quoth he to himself.

Mercy then revealed the business to the Maidens that were of the house, and inquired of them concerning him, for they did know him better than she. So they told her that he was a very busy young man, and one that pretended to Religion, but was, as they feared, a stranger to the Power of that which was good.

Nay, then, said Mercy, I will look no more on him, for I purpose never to have a clog to my soul.

Prudence then replied, That there needed no great matter of discouragement to be given to him, her continuing so as she had begun to do for the poor, would quickly cool his courage.

So the next time he comes, he finds her at her old work, a making of things for the poor. Then said he, What, always at it? Yes, said she, either for myself or for others. And what canst thou earn a day? quoth he. I do these things, said she, that I may be rich in Good Works, laying up in store a good Foundation against the time to come, that I may lay hold on Eternal Life. (I Tim. 6:17-19). Why, prithee, what dost thou with them? said he. Clothe the naked, said she. With that his countenance fell. So he forbore to come at her again. And when he was asked the reason why, he said that Mercy was a pretty lass, but troubled with ill conditions.[46]

When he had left her, Prudence said, Did I not tell thee that Mr. Brisk would soon forsake thee? yea, he will raise up an ill report of thee; for notwithstanding his pretence to Religion, and his seeming love to Mercy, yet Mercy and he are of tempers so different, that I believe they will never come together.

MERCY. I might a had[47] Husbands afore now, though I spake not of it to any; but they were such as did not like my Conditions, though never did any of them find fault with my Person. So they and I could not agree.

PRUDENCE. Mercy in our days is little set by any further than as to its Name; the Practice, which is set forth by thy Conditions, there are but few that can abide.

MERCY. Well, said Mercy, if nobody will have me, I will die a Maid, or my Conditions shall be to me as a Husband. For I cannot change my nature, and to have one that lies cross to me in this, that I purpose never to admit of as long as I live. I had a Sister named Bountiful, that was married to one of these churls; but he and she could never agree;

but because my Sister was resolved to do as she had begun, that is, to shew kindness to the poor, therefore her Husband first cried her down at the Cross,[48] and then turned her out of his doors.

PRUDENCE. And yet he was a Professor, I warrant you.

MERCY. Yes, such a one as he was, and of such as he the world is now full; but I am for none of them all.

Now Matthew, the eldest son of Christiana, fell sick, and his sickness was sore upon him, for he was much pained in his Bowels, so that he was with it, at times, pulled as 'twere both ends together. There dwelt also not far from thence, one Mr. Skill, an ancient and well-approved Physician. So Christiana desired it, and they sent for him, and he came. When he was entered the room, and had a little observed the Boy, he concluded that he was sick of the Gripes. Then he said to his Mother, What diet has Matthew of late fed upon? Diet, said Christiana, nothing but that which is wholesome. The Physician answered, This Boy has been tampering with something that lies in his maw[49] undigested, and that will not away without means. And I tell you he must be purged, or else he will die.

SAMUEL. Then said Samuel, Mother, Mother, what was that which my Brother did gather up and eat, so soon as we were come from the Gate that is at the head of this way? You know that there was an Orchard on the left hand, on the other side of the wall, and some of the trees hung over the wall, and my Brother did plash and did eat.

CHRISTIANA. True, my Child, said Christiana, he did take thereof and did eat, naughty Boy as he was. I did chide him, and yet he would eat thereof.

SKILL. I knew he had eaten something that was not wholesome food, and that food, to wit, that Fruit, is even the most hurtful of all. It is the Fruit of Beelzebub's Orchard. I do marvel that none did warn you of it; many have died thereof.

CHRISTIANA. Then Christiana began to cry, and she said, O naughty Boy, and O careless Mother, what shall I do for my Son?

SKILL. Come, do not be too much dejected; the Boy may do well again, but he must purge and vomit.

CHRISTIANA. Pray, Sir, try the utmost of your skill with him whatever it costs.

The Latin I borrow.

SKILL. Nay, I hope I shall be reasonable. So he made him a Purge, but it was too weak. 'Twas said it was made of the Blood of a Goat, the Ashes of a Heifer, and with some of the Juice of Hyssop, etc. (Heb. 10:1-4). When Mr. Skill had seen that that Purge was too weak, he made him one to the purpose, 'twas made *Ex Carne et Sanguine Christi* (John 6:54-57). (You know Physicians give strange Medicines to their Patients.) And it was made up into Pills, with a Promise or two, and a proportionable quantity of Salt (Mark 9:49). Now he was to take them three at a time fasting, in half a quarter of a pint of the Tears of Repentance (Heb. 9:14; Zech. 12:10). When this Potion was prepared and brought to the Boy he was loth to take it, though torn with the Gripes as if he should be pulled in pieces. Come, come, said the Physician, you must take it. It goes against my stomach, said the Boy. I must have you take it, said his Mother. I shall vomit it up again, said the Boy. Pray, Sir, said Christiana to Mr. Skill, how does it taste? It has no ill taste, said the Doctor, and with that she touched one of the Pills with the tip of her tongue. Oh, Matthew, said she, this Potion is sweeter than Honey. If thou lovest thy Mother, if thou lovest thy Brothers, if thou lovest Mercy, if thou lovest thy Life, take it. So with much ado, after a short prayer for the blessing of God upon it, he took it, and it wrought kindly with him. It caused him to purge, it caused him to sleep and rest quietly, it put him into a fine heat and breathing sweat, and did quite rid him of his Gripes.

So in little time he got up and walked about with a staff, and would go from room to room, and talk with Prudence, Piety, and Charity, of his Distemper, and how he was healed.

So when the Boy was healed, Christiana asked Mr. Skill, saying, Sir, what will content you for your pains and care to and of my Child? And he said, You must pay the Master of the College of Physicians, according to rules made in that case and provided (Heb. 13:11-15).

CHRISTIANA. But, Sir, said she, what is this Pill good for else?

SKILL. It is a universal Pill, it is good against all the diseases that Pilgrims are incident to, and when it is well prepared, it will keep good time out of mind.

CHRISTIANA. Pray, Sir, make me up twelve boxes of them, for if I can get these, I will never take other Physic.

SKILL. These Pills are good to prevent diseases, as well as to cure when one is sick. Yea, I dare say it, and stand to it, that if a man will but use this Physic as he should, it will make him live for ever. But, good Christiana, thou must give these Pills no other way but as I have prescribed, for if you do, they will do no good. So he gave unto Christiana Physic for herself and her Boys and for Mercy, and bid Matthew take heed how he ate any more green Plums, and kissed them and went his way.

It was told you before that Prudence bid the Boys, that if at any time they would, they should ask her some Questions that might be profitable, and she would say something to them.

MATTHEW. Then Matthew, who had been sick, asked her, Why, for the most part, Physic should be bitter to our palates?

PRUDENCE. To shew how unwelcome the Word of God and the effects thereof are to a Carnal Heart.

MATTHEW. Why does Physic, if it does good, purge, and cause that we vomit?

PRUDENCE. To shew that the Word, when it works effectually, cleanseth the Heart and Mind. For look, what the one doth to the Body the other doth to the Soul.

MATTHEW. What should we learn by seeing the Flame of our Fire go upwards? and by seeing the Beams and sweet Influences of the Sun strike downwards?

PRUDENCE. By the going up of the Fire we are taught to ascend to Heaven by fervent and hot desires; and by the Sun his sending his Heat Beams and sweet Influences downwards, we are taught that the Saviour of the world, though high, reaches down his Grace and Love to us below.

MATTHEW. Where have the Clouds their water?

PRUDENCE. Out of the Sea.

MATTHEW. What may we learn from that?

PRUDENCE. That Ministers should fetch their Doctrine from God.

MATTHEW. Why do they empty themselves upon the Earth?

PRUDENCE. To shew that Ministers should give out what they know of God to the World.

MATTHEW. Why is the Rainbow caused by the Sun?

PRUDENCE. To shew that the Covenant of God's Grace is confirmed to us in Christ.

MATTHEW. Why do the Springs come from the Sea to us through the Earth?

PRUDENCE. To shew that the Grace of God comes to us through the Body of Christ.

MATTHEW. Why do some of the Springs rise out of the tops of high Hills.

PRUDENCE. To shew that the Spirit of Grace shall spring up in some that are Great and Mighty, as well as in many that are Poor and Low.

MATTHEW. Why doth the Fire fasten upon the Candle wick?

PRUDENCE. To shew that unless Grace doth kindle upon the Heart, there will be no true Light of Life in us.

MATTHEW. Why is the Wick and Tallow and all spent to maintain the light of the Candle?

PRUDENCE. To shew that Body and Soul and all should be at the service of, and spend themselves to maintain in good condition, that Grace of God that is in us.

MATTHEW. Why doth the Pelican pierce her own Breast[50] with her Bill?

PRUDENCE. To nourish her young ones with her Blood, and thereby to shew that Christ the blessed so loveth his young, his people, as to save them from Death by his Blood.

MATTHEW. What may one learn by hearing the Cock to crow?

PRUDENCE. Learn to remember Peter's sin, and Peter's repentance. The Cock's crowing shews also that Day is coming on; let then the crowing of the Cock put thee in mind of that last and terrible Day of Judgement.

Now about this time their month was out, wherefore they signified to those of the house that 'twas convenient for them to up and be going. Then said Joseph to his Mother, It is convenient that you forget not to send to the house of Mr. Interpreter, to pray him to grant that Mr. Great-heart should be sent unto us, that he may be our Conductor the rest of our way. Good Boy, said she, I had almost forgot. So she drew up a Petition, and prayed Mr. Watchful, the Porter, to send it by some fit man to her good Friend Mr. Interpreter; who, when it was come, and he had seen the contents of the Petition, said to the Messenger, Go, tell them that I will send him.

When the Family where Christiana was, saw that they had a purpose to go forward, they called the whole house together, to give thanks to their King for sending to them such profitable Guests as these. Which done, they said to Christiana, And shall we not show thee something, according as our custom is to do to Pilgrims, on which thou mayest meditate when thou art upon the way? So they took Christiana, her Children, and Mercy into the closet, and shewed them one of the Apples that Eve did eat of, and that she also did give to her Husband, and that for the eating of which they both were turned out of Paradise, and asked her what she thought that was? Then Christiana said, 'Tis Food or Poison, I know not which. So they opened the matter to her, and she held up her hands and wondered (Gen. 3:6; Rom. 7:24).

Then they had her to a place, and shewed her Jacob's Ladder. Now at that time there were some Angels ascending upon it. So Christiana looked and looked, to see the Angels go up, and so did the rest of the Company (Gen. 28:12). Then they were going in to another place to shew them something else, but James said to his Mother, Pray bid them stay here a little longer, for this is a curious sight. So they turned again, and stood feeding their eyes with this so pleasant a prospect. After this they had them into a place where did hang up a Golden Anchor, so they bid Christiana take it down, For, said they, you shall have it with you, for 'tis of absolute necessity that you should, that you may lay hold of that within the veil, and stand steadfast, in case you should meet with turbulent weather (John 1:51; Heb. 6:12, 19). So they were glad thereof. Then they took them, and had them to the Mount upon which Abraham our Father had offered up Isaac his Son, and shewed them the Altar, the Wood, the Fire, and the Knife, for they remain to be seen to this very day (Gen. 22). When they had seen it, they held up their hands and blest themselves, and said, Oh, what a man for love to his Master, and for denial to himself, was Abraham. After they had shewed them all these things, Prudence took them into the Dining-room, where stood a pair of excellent Virginals, so she played upon them.

Now about this time one knocked at the door; so the Porter opened, and behold Mr. Great-heart was there; but when he was come in, what joy was there! For it came now fresh again into their minds how but a while ago he had slain old Grim Bloody-man the Giant, and had delivered them from the Lions.

Then said Mr. Great-heart to Christiana and to Mercy, My Lord has sent each of you a Bottle of Wine, and also some parched Corn, together with a couple of Pomegranates. He has also sent the Boys some Figs and Raisins to refresh you in your way.

Then they addressed themselves to their Journey, and Prudence and Piety went along with them. When they came at the gate, Christiana asked the Porter if any of late went by? He said, No, only one some time since, who also told me that of late there had been a great robbery committed on the King's Highway, as you go; but he saith the thieves are taken, and will shortly be tried for their lives. Then Christiana and Mercy were afraid, but Matthew said, Mother, fear nothing, as long as Mr. Great-heart is to go with us and to be our Conductor.

Then said Christiana to the Porter, Sir, I am much obliged to you for all the kindnesses that you have shewed me since I came hither, and also for that you have been so loving and kind to my Children. I know not how to gratify your kindness. Wherefore pray, as a token of my respects to you, accept of this small mite. So she put a gold Angel [51] in his hand, and he made her a low obeisance, and said, Let thy Garments be always white, and let thy Head want no Ointment[52] Let Mercy live and not die, and let not her works be few.[53] And to the Boys he said, Do you fly youthful lusts, and follow after Godliness with them that are grave and wise: so shall you put gladness into your Mother's heart, and obtain praise of all that are sober-minded. So they thanked the Porter and departed.

Now I saw in my Dream that they went forward until they were come to the brow of the Hill, where Piety, bethinking herself, cried out, Alas! I have forgot what I intended to bestow upon Christiana and her Companions; I will go back and fetch it. So she ran and fetched it. While she was gone, Christiana thought she heard, in a Grove a little way off on the right hand, a most curious, melodious note, with words much like these—

Through all my Life thy Favour is
So frankly shew'd to me,
That in thy House for evermore
My dwelling-place shall be.[54]

And listening still she thought she heard another answer it, saying—

For why? The Lord our God is good,
His Mercy is for ever sure;
His Truth at all times firmly stood,
And shall from age to age endure.[55]

So Christiana asked Prudence what 'twas that made those curious notes? They are, said she, our Country Birds; they sing these notes but seldom, except it be at the Spring, when the Flowers appear, and the Sun shines warm, and then you may hear them all day long (Song of Sol. 2:11, 12). I often, said she, go out to hear them, we also ofttimes keep them tame in our house. They are very fine company for us when we are melancholy, also they make the Woods and Groves and Solitary places, places desirous to be in.[56]

By this time Piety was come again; so she said to Christiana, Look here, I have brought thee a scheme of all those things that thou hast seen at our house, upon which thou mayest look when thou findest thyself forgetful, and call those things again to remembrance for thy edification and comfort.

Now they began to go down the Hill into the Valley of Humiliation. It was a steep Hill, and the way was slippery; but they were very careful, so they got down pretty well. When they were down in the Valley, Piety said to Christiana, This is the place where Christian your Husband met with that foul Fiend Apollyon, and where they had that dreadful Fight that they had; I know you cannot but have heard thereof. But be of good courage; as long as you have here Mr. Great-heart to be your Guide and Conductor, we hope you will fare the better. So when these two had committed the Pilgrims unto the conduct of their Guide, he went forward and they went after.

GREAT-HEART. Then said Mr. Great-heart, we need not to be so afraid of this Valley, for here is nothing to hurt us unless we procure it to ourselves. 'Tis true, Christian did here meet with Apollyon, with whom he also had a sore Combat; but that fray was the fruit of those slips that he got in his going down the Hill; for they that get slips there must look for combats here. And hence it is that this Valley has got so hard a name; for the common people when they hear that some frightful thing has befallen such a one in such a place, are of an opinion that that place is haunted with some foul Fiend or evil Spirit: when, alas, it is for the fruit of their doing that such things do befall them there.

This Valley of Humiliation is of itself as fruitful a place as any the Crow flies over; and I am persuaded if we could hit upon it, we might find somewhere hereabouts something that might give us an account why Christian was so hardly beset in this place.

Then James said to his Mother, Lo, yonder stands a Pillar, and it looks as if something was written thereon; let us go and see what it is. So they went, and found there written, Let Christian's slips before he came hither, and the Battles that he met with in this place, be a warning to those that come after. Lo, said their Guide, did not I tell you that there was something hereabouts that would give intimation of the reason why Christian was so hard beset in this place? Then turning himself to Christiana, he said, No disparagement to Christian more than to many others whose hap and lot his was; for 'tis easier going up than down this Hill, and that can be said but of few Hills in all these parts of the world. But we will leave the good man, he is at rest, he also had a brave Victory over his Enemy; let him grant that dwelleth above, that we fare no worse when we come to be tried than he.

But we will come again to this Valley of Humiliation. It is the best and most fruitful piece of ground in all those parts. It is fat ground,[57] and as you see, consisteth much in meadows; and if a man was to come here in the Summer-time, as we do now, if he knew not anything before thereof, and if he also delighted himself in the sight of his eyes, he might see that that would be delightful to him. Behold how green this Valley is, also how beautified with Lilies (Song of Sol. 2:1; James 4:6; I Pet. 5:5). I have also known many labouring men that have got good estates in this Valley of Humiliation (for God resisteth the Proud, but gives more Grace to the Humble), for indeed it is a very fruitful soil, and doth bring forth by handfuls. Some also have wished that the next way to their Father's house were here, that they might be troubled no more with either Hills or Mountains to go over; but the way is the way, and there's an end.

Now as they were going along and talking, they espied a Boy feeding his Father's Sheep. The Boy was in very mean clothes, but of a very fresh and well-favoured countenance, and as he sat by himself, he sung. Hark, said Mr. Great-heart, to what the Shepherd's Boy saith. So they hearkened, and he said,

He that is down needs fear no fall,
He that is low, no pride;
He that is humble, ever shall
Have God to be his Guide (Phil. 4:12, 13).
I am content with what I have,
Little be it, or much:
And Lord, contentment still I crave,
Because thou savest such (Heb. 13:5).
Fulness to such a burden is
That go on Pilgrimage;
Here little, and hereafter Bliss,
Is best from age to age.[58]

Then said their Guide, Do you hear him? I will dare to say that this Boy lives a merrier life, and wears more of that Herb called Heart's-ease in his bosom, than he that is clad in Silk and Velvet; but we will proceed in our discourse.

In this Valley our Lord formerly had his Country-house; he loved much to be here: he loved also to walk these Meadows, for he found the air was pleasant. Besides, here a man shall be free from the noise, and from the hurryings of this life. All states are full of Noise and Confusion, only the Valley of Humiliation is that empty and solitary place. Here a man shall not be so let and hindered [59] in his Contemplation as in other places he is apt to be. This is a Valley that nobody walks in but those that love a Pilgrim's life. And though Christian had the hard hap to meet here with Apollyon, and to enter with him a brisk encounter, yet I must tell you that in former times men have met with Angels here, have found Pearls here, and have in this place found the words of Life (Hos. 12:4, 5).

Did I say our Lord had here in former days his Country-house, and that he loved here to walk? I will add, in this place, and to the people that live and trace these Grounds,[60] he has left a yearly revenue to be faithfully paid them at certain seasons, for their maintenance by the way, and for their further encouragement to go on in their Pilgrimage (Matt. 11:29).

SAMUEL. Now as they went on, Samuel said to Mr. Great-heart, Sir, I perceive that in this Valley my Father and

Apollyon had their Battle, but whereabout was the Fight, for I perceive this Valley is large?

GREAT-HEART. Your Father had that Battle with Apollyon at a place yonder before us, in a narrow passage just beyond Forgetful Green. And indeed that place is the most dangerous place in all these parts. For if at any time the Pilgrims meet with any brunt, it is when they forget what favours they have received, and how unworthy they are of them. This is the place also where others have been hard put to it; but more of the place when we are come to it; for I persuade myself that to this day there remains either some sign of the Battle, or some Monument to testify that such a Battle there was fought.

MERCY. Then said Mercy, I think I am as well in this Valley as I have been anywhere else in all our Journey; the place methinks suits with my spirit. I love to be in such places where there is no rattling with Coaches, nor rumbling with Wheels. Methinks here one may without much molestation be thinking what he is, whence he came, what he has done, and to what the King has called him. Here one may think, and break at heart, and melt in one's spirit, until one's eyes become like the Fishpools of Heshbon (Song of Sol. 7:4). They that go rightly through this Valley of Baca make it a well; the Rain that God sends down from Heaven upon them that are here also filleth the Pools (Ps. 84:5-7). This Valley is that from whence also the King will give to their vineyards (Hos. 2:15), and they that go through it shall sing, as Christian did, for all he met with Apollyon.

GREAT-HEART. 'Tis true, said their Guide, I have gone through this Valley many a time, and never was better than when here.

I have also been a Conduct to several Pilgrims, and they have confessed the same: To this man will I look, saith the King, even to him that is Poor, and of a Contrite Spirit, and that trembles at my Word.

Now they were come to the place where the aforementioned Battle was fought. Then said the Guide to Christiana, her Children, and Mercy, This is the place, on this ground Christian stood, and up there came Apollyon against him. And look, did not I tell you? Here is some of your Husband's Blood upon these stones to this day; behold also how here and there are yet to be seen upon the place some of the shivers of

Apollyon's broken Darts. See also how they did beat the ground with their feet as they fought, to make good their places against each other, how also with their by-blows[61] they did split the very stones in pieces. Verily Christian did here play the man, and shewed himself as stout as could, had he been there, even Hercules himself. When Apollyon was beat, he made his retreat to the next Valley, that is called the Valley of the Shadow of Death, unto which we shall come anon.

Lo, yonder also stands a Monument, on which is engraven this Battle, and Christian's Victory, to his fame throughout all ages. So because it stood just on the way-side before them, they stepped to it and read the writing, which word for word was this,

Hard by here was a Battle fought,
Most strange, and yet most true;
Christian and Apollyon sought
Each other to subdue.
The Man so bravely play'd the Man,
He made the Fiend to fly;
Of which a Monument I stand,
The same to testify.

When they had passed by this place, they came upon the borders of the Shadow of Death; and this Valley was longer than the other; a place also most strangely haunted with evil things, as many are able to testify. But these Women and Children went the better through it because they had day-light, and because Mr. Great-heart was their Conductor.

When they were entered upon this Valley, they thought that they heard a groaning as of dead men, a very great groaning. They thought also they did hear words of Lamentation spoken, as of some in extreme Torment. These things made the Boys to quake, the Women also looked pale and wan; but their Guide bid them be of good comfort.

So they went on a little farther, and they thought that they felt the ground begin to shake under them, as if some hollow place was there; they heard also a kind of a hissing as of Serpents, but nothing as yet appeared. Then said the Boys, Are we not yet at the end of this doleful place? But the Guide also bid them be of good courage, and look well to their feet, lest haply, said he, you be taken in some Snare.

Now James began to be sick, but I think the cause thereof

was fear; so his Mother gave him some of that glass of Spirits that she had given her at the Interpreter's house, and three of the Pills that Mr. Skill had prepared, and the Boy began to revive. Thus they went on till they came to about the middle of the Valley, and then Christiana said, Methinks I see something yonder upon the road before us, a thing of such a shape as I have not seen. Then said Joseph, Mother, what is it? An ugly thing, Child, an ugly thing, said she. But, Mother, what is it like? said he. 'Tis like I cannot tell what, said she. And now it was but a little way off. Then said she, It is nigh.

Well, well, said Mr. Great-heart, Let them that are most afraid keep close to me. So the Fiend came on, and the Conductor met it; but when it was just come to him, it vanished to all their sights. Then remembered they what had been said some time ago, Resist the Devil, and he will fly from you.

They went therefore on, as being a little refreshed; but they had not gone far, before Mercy, looking behind her, saw, as she thought, something most like a Lion, and it came a great padding pace[62] after; and it had a hollow Voice of Roaring, and at every Roar that it gave it made all the Valley echo, and their hearts to ache, save the heart of him that was their Guide. So it came up, and Mr. Great-heart went behind, and put the Pilgrims all before him. The Lion also came on apace, and Mr. Great-heart addressed himself to give him Battle. But when he saw that it was determined that resistance should be made, he also drew back and came no farther (I Pet. 5:8, 9).

Then they went on again, and their Conductor did go before them, till they came at a place where was cast up a Pit the whole breadth of the way, and before they could be prepared to go over that, a great Mist and a Darkness fell upon them, so that they could not see. Then said the Pilgrims, Alas! now what shall we do? But their Guide made answer. Fear not, stand still and see what an end will be put to this also. So they stayed there because their path was marr'd. They then also thought that they did hear more apparently the noise and rushing of the Enemies; the fire also and the smoke of the Pit was much easier to be discerned. Then said Christiana to Mercy, Now I see what my poor Husband went through; I have heard much of this place, but I never was here afore now. Poor man, he went here all alone in the night; he had night almost quite through the way; also these Fiends were busy about him, as if they would have torn him in pieces.

Many have spoken of it, but none can tell what the Valley of the Shadow of Death should mean, until they come in it themselves. The heart knows its own Bitterness, and a stranger intermeddleth not with its Joy. To be here is a fearful thing.

GREAT-HEART. This is like doing business in great Waters, or like going down into the deep; this is like being in the heart of the Sea, and like going down to the bottoms of the Mountains; now it seems as if the Earth with its bars[63] were about us for ever. But let them that walk in Darkness and have no Light, trust in the name of the Lord, and stay upon their God. For my part, as I have told you already, I have gone often through this Valley, and have been much harder put to it than now I am, and yet you see I am alive. I would not boast, for that I am not mine own saviour, but I trust we shall have a good Deliverance. Come, let us pray for Light to him that can lighten our Darkness, and that can rebuke not only these, but all the Satans in Hell.

So they cried and prayed, and God sent Light and Deliverance, for there was now no let in their way—no, not there where but now they were stopped with a Pit. Yet they were not got through the Valley; so they went on still, and behold great stinks and loathsome smells, to the great annoyance of them. Then said Mercy to Christiana, There is not such pleasant being here as[64] at the Gate, or at the Interpreter's, or at the house where we lay last.

Oh, but, said one of the Boys, it is not so bad to go through here as it is to abide here always; and for aught I know, one reason why we must go this way to the house prepared for us is, that our home might be made the sweeter to us.

Well said, Samuel, quoth the Guide, thou hast now spoken like a man. Why, if ever I get out here again, said the Boy, I think I shall prize light and good way better than ever I did in all my life. Then said the Guide, We shall be out by and by.

So on they went, and Joseph said, Cannot we see to the end of this Valley as yet? Then said the Guide, Look to your feet, for you shall presently be among the Snares. So they looked to their feet and went on, but they were troubled much with the Snares. Now when they were come among the Snares, they espied a man cast into the Ditch on the left hand, with his flesh all rent and torn. Then said the Guide, That is one Heedless, that was a-going this way; he has lain there a great while. There was one Take-heed with him when he was taken and slain, but he escaped their hands. You cannot imagine how many are killed hereabout, and yet men are so foolishly venturous as to set out lightly on Pilgrimage, and to come without a Guide. Poor Christian, it was a wonder that he here escaped; but he was beloved of his God, also he had a good heart of his own, or else he could never a done it. Now they drew towards the end of the way, and just there where Christian had seen the Cave when he went by, out thence came forth Maul, a Giant.[65] This Maul did use to spoil young Pilgrims with Sophistry; and he called Great-heart by his name, and said unto him, How many times have you been forbidden to do these things? Then said Mr. Great-heart, What things? What things? quoth the Giant; you know what things; but I will put an end to your trade. But pray, said Mr. Great-heart, before we fall to it, let us understand wherefore we must fight. Now the Women and Children stood trembling, and knew not what to do. Quoth the Giant, You rob the Country, and rob it with the worst of thefts. These are but generals, said Mr. Great-heart; come to particulars, man.

Then said the Giant, Thou practisest the craft of a Kidnapper, thou gatherest up Women and Children, and carriest them into a strange Country, to the weakening of my master's Kingdom. But now, Great-heart replied, I am a servant of the God of Heaven; my business is to persuade sinners to repentance; I am commanded to do my endeavour to turn Men, Women, and Children from darkness to light, and from the power of Satan to God; and if this be indeed the ground of thy quarrel, let us fall to it as soon as thou wilt.

Then the Giant came up, and Mr. Great-heart went to meet him; and as he went he drew his Sword, but the Giant had a Club. So without more ado they fell to it, and at the first blow the Giant struck Mr. Great-heart down upon one of his knees; with that the Women and Children cried out; so Mr. Great-heart, recovering himself, laid about him in full lusty manner, and gave the Giant a wound in his arm; thus he fought for the space of an hour to that height of heat, that the breath came out of the Giant's nostrils as the heat doth out of a boiling Caldron.

Then they sat down to rest them, but Mr. Great-heart betook him to prayer; also the Women and Children did nothing but sigh and cry all the time that the Battle did last.

When they had rested them, and taken breath, they both fell to it again, and Mr. Great-heart, with a full blow, fetched the Giant down to the ground. Nay, hold and let me recover, quoth he. So Mr. Great-heart fairly let him get up. So to it they went again, and the Giant missed but little of all-to-breaking[66] Mr. Great-heart's skull with his Club.

Mr. Great-heart, seeing that, runs to him in the full heat of his spirit, and pierceth him under the fifth rib; with that the Giant began to faint, and could hold up his Club no longer. Then Mr. Great-heart seconded his blow, and smit[67] the head of the Giant from his shoulders. Then the Women and Children rejoiced, and Mr. Great-heart also praised God for the deliverance he had wrought.

Now I saw that they went to the Ascent that was a little way off cast up to be a Prospect for Pilgrims (that was the place from whence Christian had the first sight of Faithful, his Brother); wherefore here they sat down and rested, they also here did eat and drink and make merry, for that they had gotten deliverance from this so dangerous Enemy. As they sat thus and did eat, Christiana asked the Guide if he had caught no hurt in the Battle. Then said Mr. Great-heart, No, save a little on my flesh; yet that also shall be so far from being to my determent,[68] that it is at present a proof of my love to my Master and you, and shall be a means by Grace to increase my reward at last (II Cor. 4).

CHRISTIANA. But were you not afraid, good Sir, when you saw him come out with his club?

GREAT-HEART. It is my duty, said he, to distrust mine own ability, that I may have reliance on him that is stronger than all.

CHRISTIANA. But what did you think when he fetched you down to the ground at the first blow?

GREAT-HEART. Why, I thought, quoth he, that so my Master himself was served, and yet he it was that conquered at the last.

MATTHEW. When you all have thought what you please, I think God has been wonderfully good unto us, both in bringing us out of this Valley, and in delivering us out of the hand of this Enemy; for my part, I see no reason why we should distrust our God any more, since he has now and in such a place as this given us such testimony of his love as this.

Then they got up and went forward. Now a little before them stood an Oak, and under it, when they came to it, they found an old Pilgrim fast asleep; they knew that he was a Pilgrim by his Clothes and his Staff and his Girdle.

So the Guide, Mr. Great-heart, awaked him, and the old Gentleman, as he lifted up his eyes, cried out, What's the matter! who are you? and what is your business here?

GREAT-HEART. Come, man, be not so hot, here is none but Friends; yet the old man gets up and stands upon his guard, and will know of them what they were. Then said the Guide, My name is Great-heart; I am the Guide of these Pilgrims which are going to the Celestial Country.

HONEST. Then said Mr. Honest, I cry you mercy; I fear'd that you had been of the company of those that some time ago did rob Little-faith of his money; but now I look better about me, I perceive you are honester people.

GREAT-HEART. Why, what would or could you a done to a helped yourself, if we indeed had been of that company?

HONEST. Done! why, I would a fought as long as breath had been in me; and had I so done, I am sure you could never have given me the worst on't; for a Christian can never be overcome, unless he shall yield of himself.

GREAT-HEART. Well said, Father Honest, quoth the Guide, for by this I know thou art a cock of the right kind, for thou hast said the truth.

HONEST. And by this also I know that thou knowest what true Pilgrimage is, for all others do think that we are the soonest overcome of any.

GREAT-HEART. Well, now we are so happily met, pray let me crave your name, and the name of the place you came from.

HONEST. My name I cannot, but I came from the Town of Stupidity; it lieth about four degrees beyond the City of Destruction.

GREAT-HEART. Oh! are you that Countryman then? I deem I have half a guess of you; your name is Old Honesty, is it not? So the old Gentleman blushed, and said, Not Honesty in the abstract, but Honest is my name, and I wish that my nature shall agree to what I am called.

HONEST. But, Sir, said the old Gentleman, how could you guess that I am such a man, since I came from such a place?

GREAT-HEART. I had heard of you before, by my Master, for

he knows all things that are done on the Earth; but I have often wondered that any should come from your place, for your Town is worse than is the City of Destruction itself.

HONEST. Yes, we lie more off from the Sun, and so are more cold and senseless; but were a man in a Mountain of Ice, yet if the Sun of Righteousness will arise upon him, his frozen heart shall feel a thaw; and thus it hath been with me.

GREAT-HEART. I believe it, Father Honest, I believe it, for I know the thing is true.

Then the old Gentleman saluted all the Pilgrims with a holy kiss of charity, and asked them of their names, and how they had fared since they set out on their Pilgrimage.

CHRISTIANA. Then said Christiana, My name I suppose you have heard of; good Christian was my Husband, and these four are his Children.

But can you think how the old Gentleman was taken when she told them who she was! He skipped, he smiled, and blessed them with a thousand good wishes, saying:

HONEST. I have heard much of your Husband, and of his Travels and Wars which he underwent in his days. Be it spoken to your comfort, the name of your Husband rings over all these parts of the world; his Faith, his Courage, his Enduring, and his Sincerity under all, has made his name famous. Then he turned him to the Boys, and asked them of their names, which they told him. And then said he unto them, Matthew, be thou like Matthew the Publican, not in vice, but in virtue (Matt. 10:3). Samuel, said he, be thou like Samuel the Prophet, a man of faith and prayer (Ps. 99:6). Joseph, said he, be thou like Joseph in Potiphar's house, chaste, and one that flies from temptation (Gen. 39). And James, be thou like James the Just, and like James the Brother of our Lord (Acts 1:13).

Then they told him of Mercy, and how she had left her Town and her Kindred to come along with Christiana and with her Sons. At that the old honest man said, Mercy is thy name? by Mercy shalt thou be sustained, and carried through all those difficulties that shall assault thee in thy way, till thou shalt come thither where thou shalt look the Fountain of Mercy in the face with comfort.

All this while the Guide, Mr. Great-heart, was very much pleased, and smiled upon his Companion.

Now, as they walked along together, the Guide asked the

old Gentleman if he did not know one Mr. Fearing, that came on Pilgrimage out of his parts?

HONEST. Yes, very well, said he. He was a man that had the root of the matter in him, but he was one of the most troublesome Pilgrims that ever I met with in all my days.

GREAT-HEART. I perceive you knew him, for you have given a very right character of him.

HONEST. Knew him! I was a great Companion of his; I was with him most an end;[69] when he first began to think of what would come upon us hereafter, I was with him.

GREAT-HEART. I was his Guide from my Master's house to the gates of the Celestial City.

HONEST. Then you knew him to be a troublesome one.

GREAT-HEART. I did so, but I could very well bear it, for men of my calling are oftentimes intrusted with the conduct of such as he was.

HONEST. Well, then, pray let us hear a little of him, and how he managed himself under your conduct.

GREAT-HEART. Why, he was always afraid that he should come short of whither he had a desire to go. Everything frightened him that he heard anybody speak of, that had but the least appearance of opposition in it. I hear that he lay roaring at the Slough of Despond for above a month together, nor durst he, for all he saw several go over before him, venture, though they, many of them, offered to lend him their hand. He would not go back again neither. The Celestial City, he said, he should die if he came not to it, and yet was dejected at every difficulty, and stumbled at every Straw that anybody cast in his way. Well, after he had lain at the Slough of Despond a great while, as I have told you, one Sun-shine morning, I do not know how, he ventured, and so got over. But when he was over, he would scarce believe it. He had, I think, a Slough of Despond in his mind, a Slough that he carried everywhere with him, or else he would never have been as he was. So he came up to the Gate, you know what I mean, that stands at the head of this way, and there also he stood a good while before he would adventure to knock. When the Gate was opened he would give back,[70] and give place to others, and say that he was not worthy; for, for all he got before[71] some to the Gate, yet many of them went in before him. There the poor man would stand shaking and shrinking, I dare say it would have pitied one's heart to have seen him, nor would he go back again. At last he took the Hammer[72] that hung on the Gate in his hand, and gave a small Rap or two; then one opened to him, but he shrank back as before. He that opened stepped out after him, and said, Thou trembling one, what wantest thou? With that he fell to the ground. He that spoke to him wondered to see him so faint. So he said to him, Peace be to thee; up, for I have set open the door to thee; come in, for thou art blest. With that he got up, and went in trembling, and when he was in, he was ashamed to shew his face. Well, after he had been entertained there a while, as you know how the manner is, he was bid go on his way, and also told the way he should take. So he came till he came to our house. But as he behaved himself at the Gate, so he did at my Master the Interpreter's door. He lay thereabout in the cold a good while, before he would adventure to call, yet he would not go back, and the nights were long and cold then. Nay, he had a Note of Necessity in his bosom to my Master, to receive him and grant him the comfort of his house, and also to allow him a stout and valiant Conduct because he was himself so chicken-hearted a man; and yet for all that he was afraid to call at the door. So he lay up and down thereabouts till, poor man, he was almost starved.[73] Yea, so great was his Dejection, that though he saw several others for knocking get in, yet he was afraid to venture. At last, I think, I looked out of the window, and perceiving a man to be up and down about the door, I went out to him, and asked what he was; but, poor man, the water stood in his eyes; so I perceived what he wanted. I went therefore in and told it in the house, and we shewed the thing to our Lord. So he sent me out again, to venture him to come in; but I dare say I had hard work to do it. At last he came in, and I will say that for my Lord, he carried it wonderfully lovingly[74] to him. There were but a few good bits at the Table, but some of it was laid upon his trencher. Then he presented the Note, and my Lord looked thereon, and said his desire should be granted. So when he had been there a good while, he seemed to get some heart, and to be a little more comfortable; for my Master, you must know, is one of very tender bowels, specially to them that are afraid; wherefore he carried it so towards him as might tend most to his encouragement. Well, when he had had a sight of the things of the place, and was ready to take his Journey to go to the City, my Lord, as he did to Christian before, gave him a

Bottle of Spirits, and some comfortable things to eat. Thus we set forward, and I went before him; but the man was but of few words, only he would sigh aloud.

When we were come to where the three fellows were hanged, he said that he doubted that that would be his end also. Only he seemed glad when he saw the Cross and the Sepulchre. There, I confess, he desired to stay a little to look, and he seemed for a while after to be a little cheery. When we came at the Hill Difficulty, he made no stick at that, nor did he much fear the Lions, for you must know that his trouble was not about such things as those, his fear was about his acceptance at last.

I got him in at the House Beautiful, I think before he was willing. Also when he was in, I brought him acquainted with the Damsels that were of the place, but he was ashamed to make himself much for company. He desired much to be alone, yet he always loved good talk, and often would get behind the Screen to hear it. He also loved much to see ancient things, and to be pondering them in his mind. He told me afterwards that he loved to be in those two houses from which he came last, to wit, at the Gate, and that of the Interpreter's, but that he durst not be so bold to ask.

When we went also from the House Beautiful, down the Hill into the Valley of Humiliation, he went down as well as ever I saw man in my life; for he cared not how mean he was, so he might be happy at last. Yea, I think there was a kind of sympathy betwixt that Valley and him, for I never saw him better in all his Pilgrimage than when he was in that Valley.

Here he would lie down, embrace the ground, and kiss the very Flowers that grew in this Valley (Lam. 3:27-29). He would now be up every morning by break of day, tracing[75] and walking to and fro in this Valley.

But when he was come to the entrance of the Valley of the Shadow of Death, I thought I should have lost my man; not for that he had any inclination to go back—that he always abhorred; but he was ready to die for fear. Oh, the Hobgoblins will have me, the Hobgoblins will have me, cried he, and I could not beat him out on't. He made such a noise and such an outcry here, that had they but heard him, 'twas enough to encourage them to come and fall upon us.

But this I took very great notice of, that this Valley was as quiet while he went through it as ever I knew it before or since. I suppose these Enemies here had now a special check from our Lord, and a command not to meddle until Mr. Fearing was past over it.

It would be too tedious to tell you of all. We will, therefore, only mention a passage or two more. When he was come at Vanity Fair, I thought he would have fought with all the men in the Fair. I feared there we should both have been knock'd o' the head, so hot was he against their fooleries. Upon the Enchanted Ground he was also very wakeful. But when he was come at the River where was no Bridge, there again he was in a heavy case. Now, now, he said, he should be drowned for ever, and so never see that face with comfort that he had come so many miles to behold.

And here also I took notice of what was very remarkable: the Water of that River was lower at this time than ever I saw it in all my life. So he went over at last, not much above wet-shod. When he was going up to the Gate, Mr. Great-heart began to take his leave of him, and to wish him a good reception above. So he said, I shall, I shall. Then parted we asunder, and I saw him no more.

HONEST. Then it seems he was well at last.

GREAT-HEART. Yes, yes; I never had doubt about him; he was a man of a choice spirit, only he was always kept very low, and that made his life so burdensome to himself, and so troublesome to others (Ps. 88). He was above many tender of sin. He was so afraid of doing injuries to others, that he often would deny himself of that which was lawful because he would not offend (Rom. 14:21; I Cor. 8:13).

HONEST. But what should be the reason that such a good man should be all his days so much in the dark?

GREAT-HEART. There are two sorts of reasons for it. One is, the wise God will have it so; some must pipe and some must weep (Matt. 11:16-18). Now Mr. Fearing was one that played upon this Base; he and his fellows sound the Sackbut,[76] whose notes are more doleful than the notes of other Music are; though indeed some say the Base is the Ground of Music. And for my part, I care not at all for that profession that begins not in heaviness of mind. The first string that the Musician usually touches is the Base, when he intends to put all in tune. God also plays upon this string first, when he sets the soul in tune for himself. Only here was the imperfection of Mr.

Fearing: he could play upon no other Music but this, till towards his latter end.

I make bold to talk thus metaphorically, for the ripening of the Wits of young Readers; and because in the Book of the Revelations, the saved are compared to a company of Musicians that play upon their Trumpets and Harps, and sing their Songs before the Throne (Rev. 8:2; 14:2, 3).

HONEST. He was a very zealous man, as one may see by what relation you have given of him. Difficulties, Lions, or Vanity Fair, he feared not at all. 'Twas only Sin, Death, and Hell that was to him a terror, because he had some doubts about his interest in that Celestial Country.

GREAT-HEART. You say right. Those were the things that were his troublers, and they, as you have well observed, arose from the weakness of his mind thereabout, not from weakness of spirit as to the practical part of a Pilgrim's life. I dare believe that, as the Proverb is, he could have bit a Firebrand, had it stood in his way; but the things with which he was oppressed no man ever yet could shake off with ease.

CHRISTIANA. Then said Christiana, This relation of Mr. Fearing has done me good. I thought nobody had been like me, but I see there was some semblance 'twixt this good man and I, only we differed in two things. His troubles were so great they brake out, but mine I kept within. His also lay so hard upon him, they made him that he could not knock at the houses provided for Entertainment; but my trouble was always such as made me knock the louder.

MERCY. If I might also speak my heart, I must say that something of him has also dwelt in me; for I have ever been more afraid of the Lake and the loss of a place in Paradise than I have been of the loss of other things. Oh, thought I, may I have the happiness to have a habitation there, 'tis enough, though I part with all the world to win it.

MATTHEW. Then said Matthew, Fear was one thing that made me think that I was far from having that within me that accompanies Salvation; but if it was so with such a good man as he, why may it not also go well with me?

JAMES. No fears, no Grace, said James. Though there is not always Grace where there is the fear of Hell, yet to be sure there is no Grace where there is no fear of God.

GREAT-HEART. Well said, James, thou hast hit the mark, for the fear of God is the beginning of Wisdom; and to be sure, they that want the beginning have neither middle nor end. But we will here conclude our discourse of Mr. Fearing, after we have sent after him this farewell.

Well, Master Fearing, thou didst fear
Thy God, and wast afraid
Of doing anything while here
That would have thee betray'd.
And didst thou fear the Lake and Pit?
Would others did so too.
For as for them that want thy wit,
They do themselves undo.

Now I saw that they still went on in their talk; for after Mr. Great-heart had made an end with Mr. Fearing, Mr. Honest began to tell them of another, but his name was Mr. Self-will.[77] He pretended himself to be a Pilgrim, said Mr. Honest, but I persuade myself he never came in at the Gate that stands at the head of the way.

GREAT-HEART. Had you ever any talk with him about it?

HONEST. Yes, more than once or twice; but he would always be like himself, self-willed. He neither cared for man, nor argument, nor yet example; what his mind prompted him to, that he would do, and nothing else could he be got to.

GREAT-HEART. Pray what principles did he hold? for I suppose you can tell.

HONEST. He held that a man might follow the Vices as well as the Virtues of the Pilgrims, and that if he did both he should be certainly saved.

GREAT-HEART. How? If he had said 'tis possible for the best to be guilty of the Vices, as well as to partake of the Virtues of Pilgrims, he could not much have been blamed. For indeed we are exempted from no Vice absolutely, but on condition that we watch and strive. But this I perceive is not the thing; but if I understand you right, your meaning is, that he was of that opinion that it was allowable so to be?

HONEST. Ay, ay, so I mean, and so he believed and practised.

GREAT-HEART. But what Ground had he for his so saying?

HONEST. Why, he said he had the Scripture for his Warrant.

GREAT-HEART. Prithee. Mr. Honest, present us with a few particulars.

HONEST. So I will. He said to have to do with other men's Wives had been practised by David, God's beloved, and therefore he could do it. He said to have more Women than one was a thing that Solomon practised, and therefore he could do it. He said that Sarah and the godly Midwives of Egypt lied, and so did saved Rahab, and therefore he could do it. He said that the Disciples went at the bidding of their Master and took away the owner's Ass, and therefore he could do so too. He said that Jacob got the Inheritance of his Father in a way of Guile and Dissimulation, and therefore he could do so too.

GREAT-HEART. High base! indeed;[78] and you are sure he was of this opinion?

HONEST. I have heard him plead for it, bring Scripture for it, bring Argument for it, etc.

GREAT-HEART. An opinion that is not fit to be with any allowance in the world.

HONEST. You must understand me rightly. He did not say that any man might do this, but that those that had the Virtues of those that did such things might also do the same.

GREAT-HEART. But what more false than such a conclusion? for this is as much as to say, that because good men heretofore have sinned of infirmity, therefore he had allowance to do it of a presumptuous mind. Or if because a Child by the Blast of the Wind, or for that it stumbled at a Stone, fell down and defiled itself in mire, therefore he might wilfully lie down and wallow like a Boar therein. Who could a thought that any one could so far a been blinded by the power of Lust? But what is written must be true, They stumble at the word, being disobedient, whereunto also they were appointed (I Pet. 2:8).

His supposing that such may have the godly man's Virtues who addict themselves to their Vices, is also a delusion as strong as the other. 'Tis just as if the Dog should say, I have or may have the qualities of the Child, because I lick up its stinking Excrements. To eat up the Sin of God's People is no sign of one that is possessed with their Virtues (Hos. 4:8). Nor can I believe that one that is of this opinion can at present have Faith or Love in him. But I know you have made strong objections against him; prithee what can he say for himself?

HONEST. Why, he says, To do this by way of opinion, seems abundance more honest than to do it, and yet hold contrary to it in opinion.

GREAT-HEART. A very wicked answer, for though to let loose the Bridle to Lusts, while our opinions are against such things, is bad; yet to sin and plead a toleration so to do, is worse. The one stumbles Beholders accidentally, the other pleads them into the Snare.

HONEST. There are many of this man's mind that have not this man's mouth, and that makes going on Pilgrimage of so little esteem as it is.

GREAT-HEART. You have said the truth, and it is to be lamented. But he that feareth the King of Paradise shall come out of them all.

CHRISTIANA. There are strange opinions in the world; I know one that said, 'Twas time enough to repent when they come to die.

GREAT-HEART. Such are not over-wise. That man would a been loth, might he have had a Week to run twenty mile in for his life, to have deferred that Journey to the last hour of that Week.

HONEST. You say right, and yet the generality of them that count themselves Pilgrims do indeed do thus. I am, as you see, an old man, and have been a Traveller in this road many a day, and I have taken notice of many things.

I have seen some that have set out as if they would drive all the world afore them, who yet have in few days died as they in the Wilderness, and so never got sight of the Promised Land.

I have seen some that have promised nothing at first setting out to be Pilgrims, and that one would a thought could not have lived a day, that have yet proved very good Pilgrims.

I have seen some that have run hastily forward, that again have after a little time run as fast just back again.

I have seen some who have spoken very well of a Pilgrim's life at first, that after a while have spoken as much against it.

I have heard some, when they first set out for Paradise, say positively there is such a place, who, when they have been almost there, have come back again and said there is none.

I have heard some vaunt what they would do in case they should be opposed, that have even at a false alarm fled Faith, the Pilgrim's way, and all.

Now as they were thus in their way, there came one running to meet them, and said, Gentlemen, and you of the weaker sort, if you love Life shift for yourselves, for the Robbers are before you.

GREAT-HEART. Then said Mr. Great-heart, They be the three that set upon Little-faith heretofore. Well, said he, we are ready for them. So they went on their way. Now they looked at every turning when they should a met with the Villains; but whether they heard of Mr. Great-heart, or whether they had some other game, they came not up to the Pilgrims.

Christiana then wished for an Inn for herself and her Children, because they were weary. Then said Mr. Honest, There is one a little before us, where a very honourable Disciple, one Gaius,[79] dwells (Rom. 16:23). So they all concluded to turn in thither, and the rather because the old Gentleman gave him so good a report. So when they came to the door, they went in, not knocking, for Folks use not to knock at the door of an Inn. Then they called for the Master of the house, and he came to them. So they asked if they might lie there that night?

GAIUS. Yes, Gentlemen, if you be true men, for my house is for none but Pilgrims. Then were Christiana, Mercy, and the Boys the more glad, for that the Innkeeper was a lover of Pilgrims. So they called for Rooms, and he shewed them one for Christiana and her Children and Mercy, and another for Mr. Great-heart and the old Gentleman.

GREAT-HEART. Then said Mr. Great-heart, Good Gaius, what hast thou for Supper? for these Pilgrims have come far to-day and are weary.

GAIUS. It is late, said Gaius, so we cannot conveniently go out to seek food, but such as we have you shall be welcome to, if that will content.

GREAT-HEART. We will be content with what thou hast in the house, forasmuch as I have proved thee, thou art never destitute of that which is convenient.

Then he went down and spake to the Cook, whose name was Taste-that-which-is-good, to get ready Supper for so many Pilgrims. This done, he comes up again, saying, Come, my good Friends, you are welcome to me, and I am glad that I have a house to entertain you; and while Supper is making ready, if you please, let us entertain one another with some good discourse. So they all said, Content.

GAIUS. Then said Gaius, Whose Wife is this aged Matron? and whose Daughter is this young Damsel?

GREAT-HEART. The Woman is the Wife of one Christian, a Pilgrim of former times, and those are his four Children. The Maid is one of her Acquaintance, one that she hath persuaded to come with her on Pilgrimage. The Boys take all after their Father, and covet to tread in his steps; yea, if they do but see any place where the old Pilgrim hath lain, or any print of his foot, it ministereth joy to their hearts, and they covet to lie or tread in the same.

GAIUS. Then said Gaius, Is this Christian's Wife? and are these Christian's Children? I knew your Husband's Father, yea, also his Father's Father. Many have been good of their stock: their Ancestors dwelt first at Antioch (Acts 11:26).[80] Christian's Progenitors (I suppose you have heard your husband talk of them) were very worthy men. They have, above any that I know, shewed themselves men of great Virtue and Courage for the Lord of Pilgrims, his ways, and them that loved him. I have heard of many of your Husband's Relations that have stood all trials for the sake of the Truth. Stephen that was one of the first of the Family from whence your Husband sprang, was knocked on the head with Stones (Acts 7:59, 60). James, another of this Generation, was slain with the edge of the Sword (Acts 12:2). To say nothing of Paul and Peter, men anciently of the Family from whence your Husband came, there was Ignatius who was cast to the Lions, Romanus whose flesh was cut by pieces from his bones, and Polycarp that played the man in the Fire.[81] There was he that was hanged up in a Basket in the Sun for the Wasps to eat,[82] and he whom they put into a Sack and cast him into the Sea to be drowned. 'Twould be impossible utterly to count up all of that Family that have suffered Injuries and Death for the love of a Pilgrim's life. Nor can I but be glad to see that thy Husband has left behind him four such Boys as these. I hope they will bear up their Father's name, and tread in their Father's steps, and come to their Father's end.

GREAT-HEART. Indeed, Sir, they are likely Lads, they seem to choose heartily their Father's ways.

GAIUS. That is it that I said, wherefore Christian's Family is like still to spread abroad upon the face of the ground, and yet to be numerous upon the face of the earth. Wherefore let Christiana look out some Damsels for her Sons, to whom they may be betrothed, etc., that the name of their Father and the house of his Progenitors may never be forgotten in the world.

HONEST. 'Tis pity this Family should fall and be extinct.

GAIUS. Fall it cannot, but be diminished it may; but let

Christiana take my advice, and that's the way to uphold it.

And Christiana, said this Innkeeper, I am glad to see thee and thy friend Mercy together here, a lovely couple. And may I advise, take Mercy into a nearer Relation to thee. If she will, let her be given to Matthew, thy eldest Son, 'tis the way to preserve you a Posterity in the earth. So this match was concluded, and in process of time they were married. But more of that hereafter.

Gaius also proceeded and said, I will now speak on the behalf of Women,[83] to take away their Reproach. For as Death and the Curse came into the world by a Woman, so also did Life and Health: God sent forth his Son, made of a Woman (Gen. 3; Gal. 4). Yea, to shew how much those that came after did abhor the act of their Mother, this sex in the Old Testament coveted Children, if happily this or that Woman might be the Mother of the Saviour of the World.

I will say again, that when the Saviour was come, Women rejoiced in him before either Man or Angel (Luke 2). I read not that ever any Man did give unto Christ so much as one Groat, but the Women followed him and ministered to him of their Substance. 'Twas a woman that washed his Feet with Tears, and a Woman that anointed his Body to the Burial. They were Women that wept when he was going to the Cross, and Women that followed him from the Cross, and that sat by his Sepulchre when he was buried. They were Women that were first with him at his Resurrection-morn, and Women that brought tidings first to his Disciples that he was risen from the Dead (Luke 7:37; 8:2, 3; 23:27; 24:22, 23; John 11:2; 12:3; Matt. 27:55, 56, 61). Women therefore are highly favoured, and shew by these things that they are sharers with us in the Grace of life.

Now the Cook sent up to signify that Supper was almost ready, and sent one to lay the Cloth, the Trenchers, and to set the Salt and Bread in order.

Then said Matthew, The sight of this Cloth and of this forerunner of the Supper, begetteth in me a greater Appetite to my food than I had before.

GAIUS. So let all ministering doctrines to thee in this life beget in thee a greater desire to sit at the Supper of the great King in his Kingdom; for all Preaching, Books, and Ordinances here are but as the laying of the Trenchers, and as setting of Salt upon the Board, when compared with the Feast that our Lord will make for us when we come to his House.

So Supper came up, and first a Heave-shoulder and a Wave-breast [84] were set on the Table before them, to shew that they must begin their meal with Prayer and Praise to God (Lev. 7:32-34; 10:14, 15; Ps. 25:1; Heb. 13:15). The Heave-shoulder David lifted his Heart up to God with, and with the Wave-breast, where his Heart lay, with that he used to lean upon his Harp when he played. These two Dishes were very fresh and good, and they all ate heartily well thereof.

The next they brought up was a Bottle of Wine, red as Blood. So Gaius said to them, Drink freely, this is the Juice of the true Vine that makes glad the heart of God and Man. So they drank and were merry (Deut. 32:14; Judg. 9:13; John 15:1).

The next was a dish of Milk well crumbed. But Gaius said, Let the Boys have that, that they may grow thereby (I Pet. 2:1, 2).

Then they brought up in course a dish of Butter and Honey. Then said Gaius, Eat freely of this, for this is good to cheer up and strengthen your Judgments and Understandings. This was our Lord's dish when he was a Child, Butter and Honey shall he eat, that he may know to refuse the Evil and choose the Good (Isa. 7:15).

Then they brought them up a dish of Apples, and they were very good tasted Fruit. Then said Matthew, May we eat Apples, since they were such, by and with which the Serpent beguiled our first Mother?

Then said Gaius,

Apples were they with which we were beguil'd,
Yet sin, not Apples, hath our souls defil'd.
Apples forbid, if eat, corrupt the Blood;
To eat such when commanded, does us good.
Drink of his flagons, then, thou Church, his Dove,
And eat his Apples, who are sick of Love.

Then said Matthew, I made the scruple because I a while since was sick with eating of Fruit.

GAIUS. Forbidden Fruit will make you sick, but not what our Lord has tolerated.

While they were thus talking, they were presented with

another dish, and 'twas a dish of Nuts (Song of Sol. 6:11). Then said some at the Table, Nuts spoil tender Teeth, specially the Teeth of Children; which when Gaius heard, he said,

> Hard texts are Nuts (I will not call them cheaters)
> Whose Shells do keep their Kernels from the Eaters.
> Ope then the Shells, and you shall have the Meat,
> They here are brought for you to crack and eat.

Then were they very merry, and sat at the Table a long time, talking of many things. Then said the old Gentleman, My good Landlord, while we are cracking your Nuts, if you please, do you open this Riddle:

> A man there was, though some did count him mad,
> The more he cast away the more he had.

Then they all gave good heed, wondering what good Gaius would say; so he sat still a while, and then thus replied:

> He that bestows his Goods upon the Poor.
> Shall have as much again, and ten times more.

Then said Joseph, I dare say, Sir, I did not think you could a found it out.

Oh, said Gaius, I have been trained up in this way a great while, nothing teaches like experience. I have learned of my Lord to be kind, and have found by experience that I have gained thereby. There is that scattereth, yet increaseth, and there is that withholdeth more than is meet, but it tendeth to Poverty. There is that maketh himself Rich, yet hath nothing: there is that maketh himself Poor, yet hath great Riches (Prov. 11:24; 13:7).

Then Samuel whispered to Christiana, his Mother, and said, Mother, this is a very good man's house, let us stay here a good while, and let my Brother Matthew be married here to Mercy before we go any farther.

To which Gaius the Host overhearing said, With a very good will, my Child.

So they stayed there more than a month, and Mercy was given to Matthew to Wife.

While they stayed here, Mercy, as her custom was, would be making Coats and Garments to give to the Poor, by which she brought up a very good report upon the Pilgrims.

But to return again to our Story. After Supper the Lads desired a Bed, for that they were weary with Travelling. Then Gaius called to shew them their chamber, but said Mercy, I will have them to Bed. So she had them to Bed, and they slept well. But the rest sat up all night, for Gaius and they were such suitable Company that they could not tell how to part. Then after much talk of their Lord, themselves, and their Journey, old Mr. Honest, he that put forth the Riddle to Gaius, began to nod. Then said Great-heart, What, Sir, you begin to be drowsy. Come, rub up, now here's a Riddle for you. Then said Mr. Honest, Let's hear it.

Then said Mr. Great-heart:

He that will kill, must first be overcome;
Who live abroad would, first must die at home.

Ha! said Mr. Honest, it is a hard one, hard to expound, and harder to practise. But come, Landlord, said he, I will, if you please, leave my part to you; do you expound it, and I will hear what you say.

No, said Gaius, 'twas put to you, and 'tis expected that you should answer it.

Then said the old Gentleman,

He first by Grace must conquer'd be,
That Sin would mortify;
And who, that lives, would convince me,
Unto himself must die.

It is right, said Gaius, good Doctrine and Experience teaches this. For First, until Grace displays itself, and overcomes the soul with its Glory, it is altogether without heart to oppose Sin. Besides, if Sin is Satan's Cords, by which the soul lies bound, how should it make resistance before it is loosed from that infirmity?

Secondly, nor will any that knows either Reason or Grace believe that such a man can be a living Monument of Grace that is a Slave to his own Corruptions.

And now it comes in my mind, I will tell you a Story worth the hearing. There were two men that went on Pilgrimage, the one began when he was young, the other when he was old. The young man had strong Corruptions to grapple with, the old man's were decayed with the decays of nature. The young man trod his steps as even as did the old one, and was every way as light as he. Who now, or which of them, had their Graces shining clearest, since both seemed to be alike?

HONEST. The young man's, doubtless. For that which heads it against the greatest opposition, gives best demonstration that it is strongest. Specially when it also holdeth pace with that that meets not with half so much, as, to be sure, old age does not.

Besides, I have observed that old men have blessed themselves with this mistake, namely, taking the decays of Nature for a gracious Conquest over Corruptions, and so have been apt to beguile themselves. Indeed, old men that are gracious are best able to give advice to them that are young, because they have seen most of the emptiness of things. But yet, for an old and a young to set out both together, the young one has the advantage of the fairest discovery of a work of Grace within him, though the old man's Corruptions are naturally the weakest.

Thus they sat talking till break of day. Now when the Family was up, Christiana bid her Son James that he should read a Chapter, so he read the 53rd of Isaiah. When he had done, Mr. Honest asked why it was said that the Saviour is said to come out of a dry ground, and also, that he had no form nor comeliness in him?

GREAT-HEART. Then said Mr. Great-heart, To the First I answer, Because the Church of the Jews, of which Christ came, had then lost almost all the Sap and Spirit of Religion. To the Second I say, the words are spoken in the person of the Unbelievers, who because they want that Eye that can see into our Prince's Heart, therefore they judge of him by the meanness of his Outside. Just like those that know not that Precious Stones are covered over with a homely Crust, who, when they have found one, because they know not what they have found, cast it again away, as men do a common Stone.

Well, said Gaius, now you are here, and since, as I know, Mr. Great-heart is good at his Weapons, if you please, after we have refreshed ourselves, we will walk into the Fields to see if we can do any good. About a mile from hence there is one Slay-good, a Giant that doth much annoy the King's Highway in these parts; and I know whereabouts his Haunt is. He is Master of a number of Thieves. 'Twould be well if we could clear these parts of him.

So they consented and went, Mr. Great-heart with his Sword,

Helmet, and Shield, and the rest with Spears and Staves.

When they came to the place where he was, they found him with one Feeble-mind in his hands, whom his Servants had brought unto him, having taken him in the way. Now the Giant was rifling of him, with a purpose, after that, to pick his Bones, for he was of the nature of Flesh-eaters.

Well, so soon as he saw Mr. Great-heart and his Friends at the Mouth of his Cave with their Weapons, he demanded what they wanted?

GREAT-HEART. We want thee; for we are come to revenge the quarrel of the many that thou hast slain of the Pilgrims, when thou hast dragged them out of the King's Highway; wherefore come out of thy Cave. So he armed himself and came out, and to a Battle they went, and fought for above an hour, and then stood still to take wind.

SLAY-GOOD. Then said the Giant, Why are you here on my ground?

GREAT-HEART. To revenge the Blood of Pilgrims, as I also told thee before. So they went to it again, and the Giant made Mr. Great-heart give back; but he came up again, and, in the greatness of his mind, he let fly with such stoutness at the Giant's head and sides, that he made him let his Weapon fall out of his hand. So he smote him and slew him, and cut off his Head, and brought it away to the Inn. He also took Feeble-mind, the Pilgrim, and brought him with him to his Lodgings. When they were come home, they shewed his head to the Family, and then set it up, as they had done others before, for a terror to those that should attempt to do as he hereafter.

Then they asked Mr. Feeble-mind how he fell into his hands?

FEEBLE-MIND. Then said the poor man, I am a sickly man, as you see, and, because Death did usually once a day knock at my door, I thought I should never be well at home; so I betook myself to a Pilgrim's life, and have travelled hither from the Town of Uncertain, where I and my Father were born. I am a man of no strength at all of body, nor yet of mind; but would if I could, though I can but crawl, spend my life in the Pilgrim's way. When I came at the Gate that is at the head of the way, the Lord of that place did entertain me freely, neither objected he against my weakly looks, nor against my feeble mind; but gave me such things that were necessary for my Journey, and bid me hope to the end. When I came to the house of the Interpreter, I received much kindness there, and because the Hill Difficulty was judged too hard for me, I was carried up that by one of his servants. Indeed, I have found much relief from Pilgrims, though none was willing to go so softly as I am forced to do; yet, still as they came on, they bid me be of good cheer, and said that it was the will of their Lord that comfort should be given to the feeble-minded (I Thess. 5:14), and so went on their own pace. When I was come up to Assault Lane, then this Giant met with me, and bid me prepare for an Encounter; but, alas, feeble one that I was, I had more need of a Cordial. So he came up and took me. I conceited[85] he should not kill me. Also, when he had got me into his Den, since I went not with him willingly, I believed I should come out alive again; for I have heard that not any Pilgrim that is taken captive by violent hands, if he keeps heart-whole towards his Master, is, by the Laws of Providence, to die by the hand of the Enemy. Robbed I looked to be, and robbed to be sure I am; but I am, as you see, escaped with Life, for the which I thank my King as Author, and you as the Means. Other brunts I also look for, but this I have resolved on, to wit, to run when I can, to go when I cannot run, and to creep when I cannot go. As to the main, I thank him that loves me, I am fixed. My way is before me, my Mind is beyond the River that has no Bridge, though I am, as you see, but of a feeble Mind.

HONEST. Then said old Mr. Honest, Have you not some time ago been acquainted with one Mr. Fearing, a Pilgrim?

FEEBLE-MIND. Acquainted with him. Yes. He came from the Town of Stupidity, which lieth four degrees to the northward of the City of Destruction, and as many off of where I was born; yet we were well acquainted, for indeed he was mine Uncle, my Father's Brother. He and I have been much of a temper. He was a little shorter than I, but yet we were much of a complexion.

HONEST. I perceive you know him, and I am apt to believe also that you were related one to another; for you have his whitely Look, a Cast like his with your eye, and your Speech is much alike.

FEEBLE-MIND. Most have said so that have known us both, and besides, what I have read in him I have, for the most part, found in myself.

GAIUS. Come, Sir, said good Gaius, be of good cheer, you are welcome to me and to my house, and what thou hast a mind to, call for freely; and what thou wouldst have my servants do for thee, they will do it with a ready mind.

Then said Mr. Feeble-mind, This is unexpected Favour, and as the Sun shining out of a very dark Cloud. Did Giant Slay-good intend me this favour when he stopped me, and resolved to let me go no farther? Did he intend that after he had rifled my Pockets I should go to Gaius mine Host? Yet so it is.

Now just as Mr. Feeble-mind and Gaius were thus in talk, there comes one running and called at the door, and told, that about a mile and a half off there was one Mr. Not-right, a Pilgrim, struck dead upon the place where he was with a Thunderbolt.

FEEBLE-MIND. Alas, said Mr. Feeble-mind, is he slain? He overtook me some days before I came so far as hither, and would be my Company-keeper. He also was with me when Slay-good, the Giant, took me, but he was nimble of his heels and escaped. But it seems he escaped to die, and I was taken to live.

What one would think doth seek to slay outright,
Ofttimes delivers from the saddest plight.
That very Providence whose face is Death,
Doth ofttimes to the lowly Life bequeath.
I taken was, he did escape and flee,
Hands cross'd gives Death to him, and Life to me.

Now about this time Matthew and Mercy were married. Also Gaius gave his Daughter Phœbe to James, Matthew's Brother, to Wife; after which time they yet stayed above ten days at Gaius's house, spending their time and the seasons like as Pilgrims used to do.

When they were to depart, Gaius made them a Feast, and they did eat and drink and were merry. Now the hour was come that they must be gone, wherefore Mr. Great-heart called for a Reckoning. But Gaius told him that at his house it was not the custom for Pilgrims to pay for their Entertainment. He boarded them by the year, but looked for his pay from the good Samaritan, who had promised him, at his return, whatsoever charge he was at with them faithfully to repay him (Luke 10:33-35). Then said Mr. Great-heart to him:

GREAT-HEART. Beloved, thou dost faithfully whatsoever thou dost to the Brethren and to Strangers, which have borne witness of thy Charity before the Church; whom if thou (yet) bring forward on their Journey after a Godly sort, thou shalt do well (III John 6).

Then Gaius took his leave of them all, and of his Children, and particularly of Mr. Feeble-mind. He also gave him something to drink by the way.

Now Mr. Feeble-mind, when they were going out of the door, made as if he intended to linger. The which when Mr. Great-heart espied, he said, Come, Mr. Feeble-mind, pray do you go along with us, I will be your Conductor, and you shall fare as the rest.

FEEBLE-MIND. Alas, I want a suitable Companion; you are all lusty and strong, but I, as you see, am weak. I choose, therefore, rather to come behind, lest by reason of my many Infirmities I should be both a Burden to myself and to you. I am, as I said, a man of a weak and feeble mind, and shall be offended and made weak at that which others can bear. I shall like no Laughing, I shall like no gay Attire, I shall like no unprofitable Questions. Nay, I am so weak a man as to be offended with that which others have a liberty to do. I do not yet know all the truth. I am a very ignorant Christian man. Sometimes, if I hear some rejoice in the Lord, it troubles me because I cannot do so too. It is with me as it is with a weak man among the strong, or as with a sick man among the healthy, or as a Lamp despised (He that is ready to slip with his feet, is as a Lamp despised in the thought of him that is at ease [Job 12:5]), so that I know not what to do.

GREAT-HEART. But, Brother, said Mr. Great-heart, I have it in Commission to comfort the feeble-minded, and to support the weak (I Thess. 5:14). You must needs go along with us; we will wait for you, we will lend you our help, we will deny ourselves of some things both opinionative and practical for your sake, we will not enter into doubtful disputations before you, we will be made all things to you rather than you shall be left behind (Rom. 14; I Cor. 8; 9:22).

Now all this while they were at Gaius's door; and behold as they were thus in the heat of their discourse, Mr. Ready-to-halt came by with his Crutches in his hand, and he also was going on Pilgrimage (Ps. 38:17).

FEEBLE-MIND. Then said Mr. Feeble-mind to him, Man, how camest thou hither? I was but just now complaining that I had not a suitable Companion, but thou art according to my wish. Welcome, welcome, good Mr. Ready-to-halt, I hope thee and I may be some help.

READY-TO-HALT. I shall be glad of thy Company, said the other; and good Mr. Feeble-mind, rather than we will part, since we are thus happily met, I will lend thee one of my Crutches.

FEEBLE-MIND. Nay, said he, though I thank thee for thy good will, I am not inclined to halt before I am lame. Howbeit, I think when occasion is, it may help me against a Dog.

READY-TO-HALT. If either myself or my Crutches can do thee a pleasure, we are both at thy command, good Mr. Feeble-mind.

Thus therefore they went on, Mr. Great-heart and Mr. Honest went before, Christiana and her Children went next, and Mr. Feeble-mind and Mr. Ready-to-halt came behind with his Crutches.

[Great-heart speaks about Christian and Faithful.]

Now by this time they were come within sight of the Town of Vanity, where Vanity Fair is kept (Ps. 12:2). So when they saw that they were so near the Town, they consulted with one another how they should pass through the Town, and some said one thing and some another. At last Mr. Great-heart said, I have, as you may understand, often been a Conductor of Pilgrims through this Town, now I am acquainted with one Mr. Mnason, a Cyprusian[86] by Nation, an old Disciple, at whose house we may lodge. If you think good, said he, we will turn in there.

Content, said old Honest, Content, said Christiana, Content, said Mr. Feeble-mind, and so they said all. Now, you must think, it was eventide by that they got to the outside of the Town, but Mr. Great-heart knew the way to the old man's house. So thither they came; and he called at the door, and the old man within knew his tongue so soon as ever he heard it; so he opened, and they all came in. Then said Mnason, their Host, How far have you come to-day? so they said, From the house of Gaius our Friend. I promise you, said he, you have gone a good stitch; you may well be a weary, sit down. So they sat down.

GREAT-HEART. Then said their Guide, Come, what cheer, Sirs? I dare say you are welcome to my Friend.

MNASON. I also, said Mr. Mnason, do bid you welcome, and whatever you want, do but say, and we will do what we can to get it for you.

HONEST. Our great want a while since was Harbour [87] and good Company, and now I hope we have both.

MNASON. For Harbour, you see what it is, but for good Company, that will appear in the trial.

GREAT-HEART. Well, said Mr. Great-heart, will you have the Pilgrims up into their Lodgings?

MNASON. I will, said Mr. Mnason. So he had them to their respective places; and also shewed them a very fair Dining-room, where they might be, and sup together, until time was come to go to Rest.

Now when they were set in their places, and were a little cheery after their Journey, Mr. Honest asked his Landlord if there were any store of good people in the Town?

MNASON. We have a few, for indeed they are but a few when compared with them on the other side.

HONEST. But how shall we do to see some of them? for the sight of good men to them that are going on Pilgrimage is like to the appearing of the Moon and the Stars to them that are sailing upon the Seas.

Then Mr. Mnason stamped with his foot,[88] and his daughter Grace came up; so he said unto her, Grace, go you tell my Friends, Mr. Contrite, Mr. Holy-man, Mr. Love-saint, Mr. Dare-not-lie, and Mr. Penitent, that I have a Friend or two at my house that have a mind this evening to see them.

So Grace went to call them, and they came; and after Salutation made, they sat down together at the Table.

Then said Mr. Mnason, their landlord, My Neighbours, I have, as you see, a Company of Strangers come to my house; they are Pilgrims; they come from afar, and are going to Mount Zion. But who, quoth he, do you think this is? pointing with his finger to Christiana. It is Christiana, the Wife of Christian, that famous Pilgrim who, with Faithful his Brother, were so shamefully handled in our Town. At that they stood amazed, saying, We little thought to see Christiana, when Grace came to call us, wherefore this is a very comfortable surprise. Then they asked her of her welfare, and if these young men were her Husband's Sons? And when she had told them they were, they said, The King whom you love and serve, make you as your Father, and bring you where he is in Peace.

HONEST. Then Mr. Honest (when they were all sat down) asked Mr. Contrite and the rest in what posture their Town was at present?

CONTRITE. You may be sure we are full of hurry in Fair-time. 'Tis hard keeping our hearts and spirits in any good order when we are in a cumbered condition.[89] He that lives in such a place as this is, and that has to do with such as we have, has need of an Item[90] to caution him to take heed every moment of the day.

HONEST. But how are your Neighbours for quietness?

CONTRITE. They are much more moderate now [91] than formerly. You know how Christian and Faithful were used at our Town; but of late, I say, they have been far more moderate. I think the blood of Faithful lieth with load upon them till now, for since they burned him they have been ashamed to burn any more. In those days we were afraid to walk the Streets, but now we can shew our heads. Then the name of a Professor was odious, now, specially in some parts of our Town (for you know our Town is large), Religion is counted honourable.

[Mr. Great-heart tells of the events of the pilgrimage. The Pilgrims stay "in this Fair a great while," grow "acquainted with the good people of the Town," and do them "what service they could." Great-heart and some townsmen defeat a "Monster" (the Church of Rome) that had carried away the children of the town. At last the Pilgrims resume their journey.]

I saw now that they went on till they came at the River that was on this side of the Delectable Mountains. To the River where the fine Trees grow on both sides, and whose Leaves, if taken inwardly, are good against Surfeits (Ps. 23), where the Meadows are green all the year long, and where they might lie down safely.

By this River side, in the Meadow, there were Cotes and Folds for Sheep, an House built for the nourishing and bringing up of those Lambs, the Babes of those Women that go on Pilgrimage. Also there was here one that was intrusted with them, who could have Compassion, and that could gather these Lambs with his Arm and carry them in his Bosom, and that could gently lead those that were with young (Heb. 5:2; Isa. 40:11). Now, to the care of this Man Christiana admonished her four Daughters to commit their little ones, that by these Waters they might be housed, harboured, suckered, and nourished, and that none of them might be lacking in time to come. This Man, if any of them go astray or be lost, he will bring them again: he will also bind up that which was broken, and will strengthen them that are sick (Jer. 23:4; Ezek. 34:11-16). Here they will never want Meat and Drink and Clothing, here they will be kept from Thieves and Robbers, for this Man will die before one of those committed to his trust shall be lost. Besides, here they shall be sure to have good Nurture and Admonition, and shall be taught to walk in right paths, and that you know is a Favour of no small account (John 10:16). Also here, as you see, are delicate Waters, pleasant Meadows, dainty Flowers, variety of Trees, and such as bear wholesome Fruit—Fruit not like that that Matthew eat of, that fell over the Wall out of Beelzebub's Garden, but Fruit that procureth Health where there is none, and that continueth and increaseth it where it is.

So they were content to commit their little ones to him; and that which was also an encouragement to them so to do, was, for that all this was to be at the Charge of the King, and so was an Hospital for young Children[92] and Orphans.

Now they went on; and when they were come to By-path Meadow, to the Stile over which Christian went with his Fellow Hopeful, when they were taken by Giant Despair and put into Doubting Castle, they sat down and consulted what was best to be done; to wit, now they were so strong, and had got such a man as Mr. Great-heart for their Conductor, whether they had not best make an attempt upon the Giant, demolish his Castle, and if there were any Pilgrims in it, to set them at liberty before they went any farther. So one said one thing, and another said the contrary. One questioned if it was lawful to go upon unconsecrated ground, another said they might provided their end was good, but Mr. Great-heart said, Though that Assertion offered last cannot be universally true, yet I have a Commandment to resist Sin, to overcome Evil, to fight the good Fight of Faith, and I pray, with whom should I fight this good Fight, if not with Giant Despair? I will therefore attempt the taking away of his Life, and the demolishing of Doubting Castle. Then said he, who will go with me? Then said old Honest, I will. And so will we too, said Christiana's four Sons, Matthew, Samuel, James, and Joseph, for they were young men and strong (I John 2:13, 14). So they left the Women in the Road, and with them Mr. Feeble-mind and Mr. Ready-to-halt, with his Crutches, to be their Guard, until they came back; for in that place, though Giant Despair dwelt so near, they keeping in the Road, a little Child might lead them (Isa. 11:6).

So Mr. Great-heart, old Honest, and the four young men went to go up to Doubting Castle to look for Giant Despair. When they came at the Castle gate, they knocked for entrance with an unusual Noise. At that the old Giant comes to the Gate, and Diffidence, his Wife, follows. Then said he, Who and what is he that is so hardy as after this manner to molest the Giant Despair? Mr. Great-heart replied, It is I, Great-heart, one of the King of the Celestial Country's Conductors of Pilgrims to their place, and I demand of thee that thou open thy Gates for my Entrance. Prepare thyself also to fight, for I am come to take away thy Head, and to demolish Doubting Castle.

Now Giant Despair, because he was a Giant, thought no man could overcome him; and again, thought he, since heretofore I have made a Conquest of Angels, shall Great-heart make me afraid? So he harnessed himself and went out. He had a Cap of Steel upon his Head, a Breast-plate of Fire girded to him, and he came out in Iron Shoes, with a great Club in his Hand. Then these six men made up to him, and beset him behind and before. Also when Diffidence, the Giantess, came up to help him, old Mr. Honest cut her down at one Blow. Then they fought for their Lives, and Giant Despair was brought down to the Ground, but was very loth to die. He struggled hard, and had, as they say, as many Lives as a Cat, but Great-heart was his Death, for he left him not till he had severed his Head from his Shoulders.

Then they fell to demolishing Doubting Castle, and that, you know, might with ease be done since Giant Despair was dead. They were seven days in destroying of that; and in it of Pilgrims they found one Mr. Despondency, almost starved to Death, and one Much-afraid, his Daughter; these two they saved alive. But it would a made you a-wondered to have seen the dead Bodies that lay here and there in the Castle-yard, and how full of dead men's Bones the Dungeon was.

When Mr. Great-heart and his Companions had performed this exploit, they took Mr. Despondency and his Daughter, Much-afraid, into their protection, for they were honest people though they were Prisoners in Doubting Castle to that Tyrant Giant Despair. They, therefore, I say, took with them the Head of the Giant (for his Body they had buried under a heap of Stones), and down to the Road and to their Companions they came, and shewed them what they had done. Now when Feeble-mind and Ready-to-halt saw that it was the Head of Giant Despair indeed, they were very jocund and merry. Now Christiana, if need was, could play upon the Viol, and her Daughter Mercy upon the Lute; so since they were so merry disposed, she played them a Lesson,[93] and Ready-to-halt would dance. So he took Despondency's Daughter named Much-afraid by the hand, and to dancing they went in the Road. True, he could not dance without one Crutch in his hand, but I promise you he footed it well. Also the Girl was to be commended, for she answered the Music handsomely.

As for Mr. Despondency, the Music was not much to him, he was for feeding rather than dancing, for that he was almost starved. So Christiana gave him some of her Bottle of Spirits for present relief, and then prepared him something to eat; and in little time the old Gentleman came to himself, and began to be finely revived.

Now I saw in my Dream, when all these things were finished, Mr. Great-heart took the Head of Giant Despair, and set it upon a Pole by the Highway side, right over against the Pillar that Christian erected for a Caution to Pilgrims that came after, to take heed of entering into his grounds.

Then he writ under it upon a Marble stone these verses following—

This is the Head of him, whose Name only
In former times did Pilgrims terrify.
His Castle's down, and Diffidence his Wife
Brave Master Great-heart has bereft of Life.
Despondency, his Daughter Much-afraid,
Great-heart for them also the Man has play'd.

Who hereof doubts, if he'll but cast his eye
Up hither, may his scruples satisfy:
This Head also, when doubting Cripples dance,
Doth show from Fears they have Deliverance.

When these men had thus bravely shewed themselves against Doubting Castle, and had slain Giant Despair, they went forward, and went on till they came to the Delectable Mountains, where Christian and Hopeful refreshed themselves with the varieties of the place. They also acquainted themselves with the Shepherds there, who welcomed them, as they had done Christian before, unto the Delectable Mountains.

Then said the Shepherds, This is a comfortable Company. You are welcome to us, for we have comfort for the feeble as for the strong. Our Prince has an eye to what is done to the least of these (Matt. 25:40), therefore Infirmity must not be a block to our Entertainment. So they had them to the Palace door,[94] and then said unto them, Come in, Mr. Feeble-mind, Come in, Mr. Ready-to-halt, Come in, Mr. Despondency, and Mrs. Much-afraid, his Daughter. These, Mr. Great-heart, said the Shepherds to the Guide, we call in by name, for that they are most subject to draw back, but as for you and the rest that are strong, we leave you to your wonted Liberty. Then said Mr. Great-heart, This day I see that Grace doth shine in your Faces, and that you are my Lord's Shepherds indeed; for that you have not pushed these diseased neither with Side nor Shoulder, but have rather strewed their way into the Palace with Flowers, as you should (Ezek. 34:21).

So the feeble and weak went in, and Mr. Great-heart and the rest did follow. When they were also set down, the Shepherds said to those of the weakest sort, What is it that you would have? for, said they, all things must be managed here to the supporting of the weak, as well as the warning of the unruly.

So they made them a Feast of things easy of Digestion, and that were pleasant to the Palate, and nourishing; the which when they had received, they went to their Rest, each one respectively unto his proper place. When Morning was come, because the Mountains were high, and the day clear, and because it was the custom of the Shepherds to shew to the Pilgrims, before their departure, some Rarities, therefore, after they were ready, and had refreshed themselves, the

Shepherds took them out into the Fields, and shewed them first what they had shewn to Christian before.

Then they had them to some new places. The first was Mount Marvel, where they looked, and beheld a man at a distance that tumbled the Hills about with Words. Then they asked the Shepherds what that should mean? So they told them, that that man was the Son of one Great-grace, of whom you read in the First Part of the Records of the *Pilgrim's Progress*. And he is set there to teach Pilgrims how to believe down, or to tumble out of their ways, what Difficulties they shall meet with, by Faith (Mark 11:23, 24). Then said Mr. Great-heart, I know him, he is a man above many.

Then they had them to another place called Mount Innocent, and there they saw a man clothed all in White, and two men, Prejudice and Ill-will, continually casting Dirt upon him. Now behold the Dirt whatsoever they cast at him would in a little time fall off again, and his Garment would look as clear as if no Dirt had been cast thereat.

Then said the Pilgrims, What means this? The Shepherds answered, This man is named Godly-man, and this Garment is to shew the Innocency of his Life. Now those that throw Dirt at him are such as hate his well-doing, but, as you see, the Dirt will not stick upon his Clothes, so it shall be with him that liveth truly innocently in the World. Whoever they be that would make such men dirty, they labour all in vain; for God, by that a little time is spent, will cause that their Innocence shall break forth as the Light, and their Righteousness as the Noon-day.

Then they took them, and had them to Mount Charity, where they shewed them a man that had a bundle of cloth lying before him, out of which he cut Coats and Garments for the Poor that stood about him; yet his Bundle or Roll of Cloth was never the less.

Then said they, What should this be? This is, said the Shepherds, to shew you, that he that has a heart to give of his Labour to the Poor, shall never want wherewithal. He that watereth shall be watered himself. And the Cake that the Widow gave to the Prophet did not cause that she had ever the less in her Barrel.

They had them also to a place where they saw one Fool and one Want-wit washing of an Ethiopian[95] with intention to make him white, but the more they washed him the blacker he was. They then asked the Shepherds what that should mean. So they told them, saying, Thus shall it be with the vile person. All means used to get such an one a good name shall in conclusion tend but to make him more abominable. Thus it was with the Pharisees, and so shall it be with all Hypocrites.

Then said Mercy, the Wife of Matthew, to Christiana, her Mother, Mother, I would, if it might be, see the Hole in the Hill, or that commonly called the By-way to Hell. So her Mother brake her mind to the Shepherds. Then they went to the Door. It was in the side of a Hill, and they opened it, and bid Mercy hearken awhile. So she hearkened, and heard one saying, Cursed be my Father for holding of my feet back from the way of Peace and Life; and another said, Oh that I had been torn in pieces before I had, to save my Life, lost my Soul; and another said, If I were to live again, how would I deny myself, rather than come to this place. Then there was as if the very Earth had groaned and quaked under the feet of this young Woman for fear. So she looked white, and came trembling away, saying, Blessed be he and she that is delivered from this place.

Now when the Shepherds had shewed them all these things, then they had them back to the Palace, and entertained them with what the house would afford. But Mercy being a young and breeding Woman, longed for something that she saw there, but was ashamed to ask. Her Mother-in-law then asked her what she ailed, for she looked as one not well. Then said Mercy, There is a Looking-glass[96] hangs up in the Dining-room, off of which I cannot take my mind; if therefore I have it not, I think I shall miscarry. Then said her Mother, I will mention thy wants to the Shepherds, and they will not deny it thee. But she said, I am ashamed that these men should know that I longed. Nay, my Daughter, said she, it is no Shame, but a Virtue, to long for such a thing as that. So Mercy said, Then, Mother, if you please, ask the Shepherds if they are willing to sell it.

Now the Glass was one of a thousand. It would present a man, one way, with his own Feature exactly, and turn it but another way and it would shew one the very Face and Similitude of the Prince of Pilgrims himself. Yea, I have talked with them that can tell, and they have said that they have seen the very Crown of Thorns upon his Head by looking in that Glass (James 1:23); they have therein also seen the Holes in his Hands, in his Feet, and his Side. Yea, such an excellency is there in that Glass, that it will shew him to one where they have a mind to see him, whether living or dead, whether in Earth or Heaven, whether in a state of Humiliation or in his Exaltation, whether coming to Suffer or coming to Reign (I Cor. 13:12; II Cor. 3:18).

Christiana therefore went to the Shepherds apart (now the names of the Shepherds are Knowledge, Experience, Watchful, and Sincere), and said unto them, There is one of my Daughters, a breeding Woman, that I think doth long for something she hath seen in this house, and she thinks she shall miscarry if she should by you be denied.

EXPERIENCE. Call her, call her; she shall assuredly have what we can help her to. So they called her, and said to her, Mercy, what is that thing thou wouldest have? Then she blushed, and said, The great Glass that hangs up in the Dining-room. So Sincere ran and fetched it, and with a joyful consent it was given her. Then she bowed her head, and gave thanks, and said, By this I know that I have obtained favour in your eyes.

They also gave to the other young Women such things as they desired, and to their Husbands great Commendations for that they joined with Mr. Great-heart to the slaying of Giant Despair and the demolishing of Doubting Castle.

About Christiana's Neck the Shepherds put a Bracelet, and so they did about the Necks of her four Daughters, also they put Earrings in their Ears, and Jewels on their Foreheads.

When they were minded to go hence, they let them go in peace, but gave not to them those certain Cautions which before were given to Christian and his Companion. The reason was, for that these had Great-heart to be their Guide, who was one that was well acquainted with things, and so could give them their Cautions more seasonably, to wit, even then when the Danger was nigh the approaching.

What Cautions Christian and his Companions had received of the Shepherds, they had also lost by that the time was come that they had need to put them in practice. Wherefore here was the advantage that this Company had over the other.

When they were gone from the Shepherds, they quickly

came to the place where Christian met with one Turn-away, that dwelt in the town of Apostacy. Wherefore of him Mr. Great-heart, their Guide, did now put them in mind, saying, This is the place where Christian met with one Turn-away, who carried with him the character of his Rebellion at his back. And this I have to say concerning this man, he would hearken to no counsel, but once a falling, persuasion could not stop him.

When he came to the place where the Cross and the Sepulchre was, he did meet with one that did bid him look there; but he gnashed with his teeth, and stamped, and said he was resolved to go back to his own Town (Heb. 10:26-29). Before he came to the Gate, he met with Evangelist, who offered to lay hands on him to turn him into the way again. But this Turn-away resisted him, and having done much despite unto him, he got away over the Wall, and so escaped his hand.

Then they went on; and just at the place where Little-faith formerly was robbed, there stood a man with his Sword drawn, and his Face all bloody. Then said Mr. Great-heart, What art thou? The man made answer, saying, I am one whose name is Valiant-for-truth. I am a Pilgrim, and am going to the Celestial City. Now, as I was in my way, there were three men did beset me and propounded unto me these three things: 1. Whether I would become one of them? 2. Or go back from whence I came? 3. Or die upon the place? To the first I answered, I had been a true man a long season, and therefore it could not be expected that I now should cast in my Lot with Thieves (Prov. 1:10-14). Then they demanded what I would say to the second. So I told them that the place from whence I came, had I not found Incommodity there, I had not forsaken it at all; but finding it altogether unsuitable to me, and very unprofitable for me, I forsook it for this way. Then they asked me what I said to the third. And I told them, My life cost more dear far than that I should lightly give it away. Besides, you have nothing to do thus to put things to my Choice, wherefore at your Peril be it if you meddle. Then these three, to wit Wild-head, Inconsiderate, and Pragmatic, drew upon me, and I also drew upon them.

So we fell to it, one against three, for the space of above three hours. They have left upon me, as you see, some of the marks of their Valour, and have also carried away with them some of mine. They are but just now gone. I suppose they might, as the saying is, hear your Horse dash, and so they betook them to flight.

GREAT-HEART. But here was great odds, three against one.

VALIANT-FOR-TRUTH. 'Tis true, but little or more are nothing to him that has the Truth on his side. Though an Host should encamp against me, said one, my heart shall not fear; though War should rise against me, in this will I be confident, etc. (Ps. 27:3). Besides, saith he, I have read in some Records, that one man has fought an Army; and how many did Samson slay with the Jaw-bone of an Ass? [97]

GREAT-HEART. Then said the Guide, Why did you not cry out, that some might a come in for your succour?

VALIANT-FOR-TRUTH. So I did, to my King, who I knew could hear, and afford invisible help, and that was sufficient for me.

GREAT-HEART. Then said Great-heart to Mr. Valiant-for-truth, Thou hast worthily behaved thyself. Let me see thy Sword. So he shewed it him. When he had taken it in his hand, and looked thereon a while, he said, Ha, it is a right Jerusalem Blade (Isa. 2:3).

VALIANT-FOR-TRUTH. It is so. Let a man have one of these Blades, with a Hand to wield it and Skill to use it, and he may venture upon an Angel with it. He need not fear its holding, if he can but tell how to lay on. Its edges will never blunt. It will cut flesh and bones and soul and spirit and all (Ephes. 6:12-17; Heb. 4:12).

GREAT-HEART. But you fought a great while; I wonder you were not weary.

VALIANT-FOR-TRUTH. I fought till my Sword did cleave to my Hand (II Sam. 23:10); and when they were joined together, as if a Sword grew out of my Arm, and when the Blood ran through my Fingers, then I fought with most courage.

GREAT-HEART. Thou hast done well. Thou hast resisted unto Blood, striving against Sin. Thou shalt abide by us, come in and go out with us, for we are thy Companions.

Then they took him and washed his Wounds, and gave him of what they had to refresh him, and so they went on together. Now as they went on, because Mr. Great-heart was delighted in him (for he loved one greatly that he found to be a man of his hands),[98] and because there were with his Company them that were feeble and weak, therefore he questioned with him about many things; as, first, what Countryman he was?

VALIANT-FOR-TRUTH. I am of Dark-land, for there I was born, and there my Father and Mother are still.

GREAT-HEART. Dark-land, said the Guide, doth not that lie upon the same Coast with the City of Destruction?

VALIANT-FOR-TRUTH. Yes, it doth. Now that which caused me to come on Pilgrimage was this: We had one Mr. Tell-true came into our parts, and he told it about what Christian had done that went from the City of Destruction, namely, how he had forsaken his Wife and Children, and had betaken himself to a Pilgrim's life. It was also confidently reported how he had killed a Serpent [99] that did come out to resist him in his Journey, and how he got through to whither he intended. It was also told what Welcome he had at all his Lord's Lodgings, especially when he came to the Gates of the Celestial City, for there, said the man, he was received with sound of Trumpet by a company of Shining Ones. He told it also, how all the Bells in the City did ring for joy at his reception, and what Golden Garments he was clothed with, with many other things that now I shall forbear to relate. In a word, that man so told the story of Christian and his Travels, that my heart fell into a burning haste to be gone after him, nor could Father or Mother stay me: so I got from them, and am come thus far on my way.

GREAT-HEART. You came in at the Gate, did you not?

VALIANT-FOR-TRUTH. Yes, yes; for the same man also told us that all would be nothing if we did not begin to enter this way at the Gate.

GREAT-HEART. Look you, said the Guide to Christiana, the Pilgrimage of your Husband, and what he has gotten thereby, is spread abroad far and near.

VALIANT-FOR-TRUTH. Why, is this Christian's wife?

GREAT-HEART. Yes, that it is, and these are also her four Sons.

VALIANT-FOR-TRUTH. What, and going on Pilgrimage too?

GREAT-HEART. Yes, verily they are following after.

VALIANT-FOR-TRUTH. It glads me at heart. Good man, how joyful will he be when he shall see them that would not go with him, yet to enter after him in at the Gates into the City.

GREAT-HEART. Without doubt it will be a comfort to him; for next to the joy of seeing himself there, it will be a joy to meet there his Wife and his Children.

VALIANT-FOR-TRUTH. But now you are upon that, pray let me

hear your opinion about it. Some make a question, Whether we shall know one another when we are there?

GREAT-HEART. Do you think they shall know themselves then, or that they shall rejoice to see themselves in that Bliss? and if they think they shall know and do these, why not know others, and rejoice in their Welfare also?

Again, since Relations are our second self, though that state will be dissolved there, yet why may it not be rationally concluded that we shall be more glad to see them there than to see they are wanting?

VALIANT-FOR-TRUTH. Well, I perceive whereabouts you are as to this. Have you any more things to ask me about my beginning to come on Pilgrimage?

GREAT-HEART. Yes. Were your Father and Mother willing that you should become a Pilgrim?

VALIANT-FOR-TRUTH. Oh, no. They used all means imaginable to persuade me to stay at home.

GREAT-HEART. What could they say against it?

VALIANT-FOR-TRUTH. They said it was an idle life, and if I myself were not inclined to Sloth and Laziness, I would never countenance a Pilgrim's condition.

GREAT-HEART. And what did they say else?

VALIANT-FOR-TRUTH. Why, they told me that it was a dangerous way; yea, the most dangerous way in the World, said they, is that which the Pilgrims go.

GREAT-HEART. Did they shew wherein this way is so dangerous?

VALIANT-FOR-TRUTH. Yes, and that in many particulars.

GREAT-HEART. Name some of them.

VALIANT-FOR-TRUTH. They told me of the Slough of Despond, where Christian was well nigh smothered. They told me that there were Archers standing ready in Beelzebub-castle to shoot them that should knock at the Wicket-gate for entrance. They told me also of the Wood and dark Mountains, of the Hill Difficulty, of the Lions, and also of the three Giants, Bloody-man, Maul, and Slay-good. They said, moreover, that there was a foul Fiend haunted the Valley of Humiliation, and that Christian was by him almost bereft of Life. Besides, say they, you must go over the Valley of the Shadow of Death, where the Hobgoblins are, where the Light is Darkness, where the way is full of Snares, Pits, Traps, and Gins. They told me also of Giant Despair, of Doubting Castle, and of the ruin that the Pilgrims met with there. Further, they said I must go over the Enchanted Ground, which was dangerous. And that, after all this, I should find a River, over which I should find no Bridge, and that that River did lie betwixt me and the Celestial Country.

GREAT-HEART. And was this all?

VALIANT-FOR-TRUTH. No. They also told me that this way was full of Deceivers, and of persons that laid await there, to turn good men out of the Path.

GREAT-HEART. But how did they make that out?

VALIANT-FOR-TRUTH. They told me that Mr. Worldly Wiseman did there lie in wait to deceive. They also said that there was Formality and Hypocrisy continually on the road. They said also that By-ends, Talkative, or Demas would go near to gather me up, that the Flatterer would catch me in his Net, or that with green-headed Ignorance I would presume to go on to the Gate, from whence he always was sent back to the Hole that was in the side of the Hill, and made to go the By-way to Hell.

GREAT-HEART. I promise you this was enough to discourage, but did they make an end here?

VALIANT-FOR-TRUTH. No, stay. They told me also of many that had tried that way of old, and that had gone a great way therein, to see if they could find something of the Glory there that so many had so much talked of from time to time; and how they came back again, and befooled themselves for setting a foot out of doors in that Path, to the satisfaction of all the Country. And they named several that did so, as Obstinate and Pliable, Mistrust and Timorous, Turn-away and old Atheist, with several more, who, they said, had some of them gone far to see if they could find, but not one of them found so much advantage by going as amounted to the weight of a Feather.

GREAT-HEART. Said they anything more to discourage you?

VALIANT-FOR-TRUTH. Yes. They told me of one Mr. Fearing who was a Pilgrim, and how he found this way so solitary that he never had comfortable hour therein. Also that Mr. Despondency had like to have been starved therein; yea, and also, which I had almost forgot, that Christian himself, about whom there has been such a noise, after all his ventures for a Celestial Crown, was certainly drowned in the black River, and never went foot farther, however it was smothered up.

GREAT-HEART. And did none of these things discourage you!

VALIANT-FOR-TRUTH. No, they seemed but as so many nothings to me.

GREAT-HEART. How came that about?

VALIANT-FOR-TRUTH. Why, I still believed what Mr. Tell-true had said, and that carried me beyond them all.

GREAT-HEART. Then this was your Victory, even your Faith.

VALIANT-FOR-TRUTH. It was so; I believed, and therefore came out, got into the Way, fought all that set themselves against me, and by believing am come to this place.

Who would True valour see,
Let him come hither;
One here will constant be,
Come Wind, come Weather.
There's no Discouragement
Shall make him once relent
His first avow'd intent
To be a Pilgrim.
Who so beset him round
With dismal Stories
Do but themselves confound,
His Strength the more is;
No Lion can him fright,
He'll with a Giant fight,
But he will have a right
To be a Pilgrim.
Hobgoblin nor foul Fiend
Can daunt his spirit;
He knows he at the end
Shall Life inherit.
Then Fancies fly away.
He'll fear not what men say,
He'll labour night and day
To be a Pilgrim.[100]

By this time they were got to the Enchanted Ground, where the air naturally tended to make one drowsy, and that place was all grown over with Briars and Thorns, excepting here and there where was an Enchanted Arbour, upon which if a man sits, or in which if a man sleeps, 'tis a question, say some, whether ever he shall rise or wake again in this world. Over this Forest, therefore, they went, both one with another, and Mr. Great-heart went before for that he was the

Guide, and Mr. Valiant-for-truth he came behind, being there a Guard for fear lest peradventure some Fiend or Dragon or Giant or Thief should fall upon their Rear, and so do mischief. They went on here each man with his Sword drawn in his hand, for they knew it was a dangerous place. Also they cheered up one another as well as they could; Feeble-mind, Mr. Great-heart commanded should come up after him, and Mr. Despondency was under the eye of Mr. Valiant.

Now they had not gone far, but a great Mist and a Darkness fell upon them all, so that they could scarce for a great while see the one the other. Wherefore they were forced for some time to feel for one another by Words, for they walked not by Sight.

But any one must think that here was but sorry going for the best of them all, but how much worse for the Women and Children, who both of feet and heart were but tender. Yet so it was, that through the encouraging words of him that led in the front, and of him that brought them up behind, they made a pretty good shift to wag along.

The way also was here very wearisome through Dirt and Slabbiness.[101] Nor was there on all this ground so much as one Inn or Victualling-house, therein to refresh the feebler sort. Here, therefore, was grunting and puffing and sighing. While one tumbleth over a Bush, another sticks fast in the Dirt; and the Children, some of them, lost their Shoes in the Mire. While one cries out, I am down; and another, Ho, where are you? and a third, The Bushes have got such fast hold on me, I think I cannot get away from them.

Then they come at an Arbour, warm, and promising much refreshing to the Pilgrims; for it was finely wrought above head, beautified with Greens,[102] furnished with Benches and Settles. It also had in it a soft Couch whereon the weary might lean. This you must think, all things considered, was tempting, for the Pilgrims already began to be foiled with the badness of the way, but there was not one of them that made so much as a motion to stop there. Yea, for aught I could perceive, they continually gave so good heed to the advice of their Guide, and he did so faithfully tell them of Dangers, and of the nature of Dangers, when they were at them, that usually when they were nearest to them they did most pluck up their spirits, and hearten one another to deny the Flesh. This Arbour was called the Slothful's Friend, on purpose to allure, if it might be, some of the Pilgrims there to take up their Rest when weary.

I saw then in my Dream that they went on in this their solitary ground, till they came to a place at which a man is apt to lose his way. Now though when it was light their Guide could well enough tell how to miss those ways that led wrong, yet in the dark he was put to a stand; but he had in his Pocket a Map of all ways leading to or from the Celestial City; wherefore he struck a Light (for he never goes also without his Tinder-box)[103] and takes a view of his Book or Map,[104] which bids him be careful in that place to turn to the right-hand way. And had he not here been careful to look in his Map, they had all, in probability, been smothered in the Mud, for just a little before them, and that at the end of the cleanest way too, was a Pit, none knows how deep, full of nothing but Mud, there made on purpose to destroy the Pilgrims in.

Then thought I with myself, who that goeth on Pilgrimage but would have one of these Maps about him, that he may look when he is at a stand, which is the way he must take?

They went on, then, in this Enchanted Ground till they came to where there was another Arbour, and it was built by the Highway side. And in that Arbour there lay two men whose names were Heedless and Too-bold. These two went thus far on Pilgrimage, but here being wearied with their Journey, they sat down to rest themselves, and so fell fast asleep. When the Pilgrims saw them, they stood still, and shook their heads, for they knew that the sleepers were in a pitiful case. Then they consulted what to do, whether to go on and leave them in their sleep, or to step to them and try to awake them. So they concluded to go to them and awake them, that is, if they could; but with this caution, namely, to take heed that themselves did not sit down nor embrace the offered benefit of that Arbour.

So they went in and spake to the men, and called each by his name (for the Guide it seems did know them), but there was no voice nor answer. Then the Guide did shake them, and do what he could to disturb them. Then said one of them, I will pay you when I take my Money. At which the Guide shook his Head. I will fight so long as I can hold my Sword in my hand, said the other. At that one of the Children laughed.

Then said Christiana, What is the meaning of this? The Guide said, They talk in their Sleep. If you strike them, beat them, or whatever else you do to them, they will answer you after this fashion; or as one of them said in old time, when the Waves of the Sea did beat upon him, and he slept as one upon the Mast of a Ship, When I awake I will seek it again (Prov. 23:34, 35). You know when men talk in their Sleeps they say anything, but their words are not governed either by Faith or Reason. There is an incoherency in their words now, as there was before betwixt their going on Pilgrimage and sitting down here. This then is the mischief on't, when heedless ones go on Pilgrimage 'tis twenty to one but they are served thus. For this Enchanted Ground is one of the last Refuges that the Enemy to Pilgrims has; wherefore it is, as you see, placed almost at the end of the Way, and so it standeth against us with the more advantage. For when, thinks the Enemy, will these Fools be so desirous to sit down as when they are weary? and when so like to be weary as when almost at their Journey's end? Therefore it is, I say, that the Enchanted Ground is placed so nigh to the Land Beulah, and so near the end of their Race. Wherefore, let Pilgrims look to themselves, lest it happen to them as it has done to these, that, as you see, are fallen asleep, and none can wake them.

Then the Pilgrims desired with trembling to go forward; only they prayed their Guide to strike a Light, that they might go the rest of their way by the help of the Light of a Lanthorn. So he struck a Light, and they went by the help of that through the rest of this way, though the darkness was very great (II Pet. 1:19).

But the Children began to be sorely weary, and they cried out unto him that loveth Pilgrims to make their way more comfortable. So by that they had gone a little farther, a Wind arose that drove away the Fog, so the Air became more clear.

Yet they were not off (by much) of the Enchanted Ground, only now they could see one another better, and the way wherein they should walk.

Now when they were almost at the end of this ground, they perceived that a little before them was a solemn Noise, as of one that was much concerned. So they went on and looked before them; and behold they saw, as they thought, a man upon his Knees, with Hands and Eyes lifted up, and speaking, as they thought, earnestly to one that was above. They drew nigh, but could not tell what he said; so they went softly till he had done. When he had done, he got up and began to run towards the Celestial City. Then Mr. Great-heart called after him, saying, Soho, Friend, let us have your Company, if you go, as I suppose you do, to the Celestial City. So the man stopped, and they came up to him. But so soon as Mr. Honest saw him, he said, I know this man. Then said Mr. Valiant-for-truth, Prithee, who is it? 'Tis one, said he, who comes from whereabouts I dwelt, his name is Stand-fast, he is certainly a right good Pilgrim.

So they came up one to another; and presently Stand-fast said to old Honest, Ho, Father Honest, are you there? Ay, said he, that I am, as sure as you are there. Right glad am I, said Mr. Stand-fast, that I have found you on this Road. And as glad am I, said the other, that I espied you upon your Knees. Then Mr. Stand-fast blushed, and said, But why, did you see me? Yes, that I did, quoth the other, and with my heart was glad at the sight. Why, what did you think? said Stand-fast. Think, said old Honest, what should I think? I thought we had an honest man upon the Road, and therefore should have his Company by and by. If you thought not amiss how happy am I, but if I be not as I should, I alone must bear it. That is true, said the other, but your fear doth further confirm me that things are right betwixt the Prince of Pilgrims and Your Soul, for he saith, Blessed is the man that feareth always.[105]

VALIANT-FOR-TRUTH. Well, but Brother, I pray thee tell us what was it that was the cause of thy being upon thy Knees even now? Was it for that some special mercy laid obligations upon thee, or how?

STAND-FAST. Why we are, as you see, upon the Enchanted Ground, and as I was coming along, I was musing with myself of what a dangerous Road the Road in this place was, and how many that had come even thus far on Pilgrimage had here been stopped and been destroyed. I thought also of the manner of the Death with which this place destroyeth men. Those that die here, die of no violent Distemper. The Death which such die is not grievous to them, for he that goeth away in a sleep begins that Journey with Desire and Pleasure; yea, such acquiesce in the will of that Disease.

HONEST. Then Mr. Honest, interrupting of him, said, Did you see the two men asleep in the Arbour?

STAND-FAST. Ay, ay, I saw Heedless and Too-bold there, and for aught I know, there they will lie till they rot (Prov. 10:7). But let me go on in my Tale. As I was thus musing, as I said, there was one in very pleasant attire, but old, who presented herself unto me, and offered me three things—to wit, her Body, her Purse, and her Bed. Now the truth is, I was both a-weary and sleepy: I am also as poor as a Howlet, and that perhaps the Witch knew. Well, I repulsed her once and twice, but she put by my repulses, and smiled. Then I began to be angry, but she mattered that nothing at all. Then she made offers again, and said, if I would be ruled by her, she would make me great and happy, for, said she, I am the Mistress of the World, and men are made happy by me. Then I asked her name, and she told me it was Madam Bubble.[106] This set me further from her, but she still followed me with Enticements. Then I betook me, as you saw, to my Knees, and with hands lifted up and cries, I pray'd to him that had said he would help. So just as you came up, the Gentlewoman went her way. Then I continued to give thanks for this my great Deliverance, for I verily believe she intended no good, but rather sought to make stop of me in my Journey.

HONEST. Without doubt her Designs were bad. But stay, now you talk of her, methinks I either have seen her or have read some story of her.

STAND-FAST. Perhaps you have done both.

HONEST. Madam Bubble, is she not a tall, comely Dame, something of a swarthy Complexion?

STAND-FAST. Right, you hit it, she is just such an one.

HONEST. Doth she not speak very smoothly, and give you a Smile at the end of a Sentence?

STAND-FAST. You fall right upon it again, for these are her very Actions.

HONEST. Doth she not wear a great Purse by her side, and is not her hand often in it fingering her Money, as if that was her heart's delight?

STAND-FAST. 'Tis just so. Had she stood by all this while, you could not more amply have set her forth before me, nor have better described her Features.

HONEST. Then he that drew her picture was a good Limner, and he that wrote of her said true.

GREAT-HEART. This woman is a Witch, and it is by virtue of her Sorceries that this ground is enchanted. Whoever doth lay his Head down in her Lap had as good lay it down upon that Block over which the Axe doth hang; and whoever lay their Eyes upon her Beauty are counted the Enemies of God (James 4:4; I John 2:15). This is she that maintaineth in their splendour all those that are the Enemies of Pilgrims. Yea, this is she that hath bought off many a man from a Pilgrim's Life. She is a great Gossiper; she is always, both she and her Daughters, at one Pilgrim's heels or another, now commending and then preferring the excellencies of this Life. She is a bold and impudent Slut, she will talk with any man. She always laugheth poor Pilgrims to scorn, but highly commends the rich. If there be one cunning to get Money in a place, she will speak well of him from house to house. She loveth Banqueting and Feasting mainly well, she is always at one full Table or another. She has given it out in some places that she is a Goddess, and therefore some do worship her. She has her times and open places of Feasting[107], and she will say and avow it that none can shew a good comparable to hers. She promiseth to dwell with Children's Children, if they will but love and make much of her. She will cast out of her Purse Gold like Dust, in some places, and to some persons. She loves to be sought after, spoken well of, and to lie in the Bosoms of Men. She is never weary of commending her Commodities, and she loves them most that think best of her. She will promise to some Crowns and Kingdoms if they will but take her advice, yet many has she brought to the Halter, and ten thousand times more to Hell.

STAND-FAST. Oh, said Stand-fast, what a mercy is it that I did resist her, for whither might she a drawn me?

GREAT-HEART. Whither? nay, none but God knows whither. But, in general, to be sure, she would a drawn thee into many foolish and hurtful Lusts, which drown men in Destruction and Perdition (I Tim. 6:9).

'Twas she that set Absalom against his Father, and Jeroboam against his Master. 'Twas she that persuaded Judas to sell his Lord, and that prevailed with Demas to forsake the godly Pilgrim's Life. None can tell of the Mischief that she doth. She makes variance betwixt Rulers and Subjects, betwixt Parents and Children, 'twixt Neighbour and Neighbour, 'twixt a Man and his Wife, 'twixt a Man and Himself, 'twixt the Flesh and the Heart. Wherefore, good Master Stand-fast, be as your name is, and when you have done all, stand.

At this Discourse there was among the Pilgrims a mixture of Joy and Trembling, but at length they brake out, and sang—

What danger is the Pilgrim in,
How many are his Foes,
How many ways there are to sin,
No living mortal knows.
Some of the Ditch shy are, yet can
Lie tumbling in the Mire;
Some, though they shun the Frying-pan,
Do leap into the Fire.

After this I beheld until they were come unto the Land of Beulah, where the Sun shineth Night and Day. Here, because they were weary, they betook themselves awhile to rest. And because this Country was common for Pilgrims, and because the Orchards and Vineyards that were here belonged to the King of the Celestial Country, therefore they were licensed to make bold with any of his things. But a little while soon refreshed them here; for the Bells did so ring, and the Trumpets continually sound so melodiously, that they could not sleep; and yet they received as much refreshing as if they had slept their sleep never so soundly. Here also all the noise of them that walked the Streets was, More Pilgrims are come to Town. And another would answer, saying, And so many went over the Water, and were let in at the Golden Gates to-day. They would cry again, There is now a Legion of Shining Ones just come to Town, by which we know that there are more Pilgrims upon the road, for here they come to wait for them, and to comfort them after all their Sorrow. Then the Pilgrims got up and walked to and fro; but how were their Ears now filled with Heavenly Noises, and their eyes delighted with Celestial Visions! In this Land they heard nothing, saw nothing, felt nothing, smelt nothing, tasted nothing, that was offensive to their Stomach or Mind; only when they tasted of the Water of the River over which they were to go, they thought that tasted a little bitterish to the Palate, but it proved sweeter when 'twas down.

In this place there was a Record kept of the names of them that had been Pilgrims of old and a History of all the famous Acts that they had done. It was here also much discoursed how the River to some had had its flowings, and what ebbings it has had while others have gone over. It has been, in a manner, dry for some, while it has overflowed its banks for others.

In this place the Children of the Town would go into the King's Gardens and gather Nosegays for the Pilgrims, and bring them to them with much affection. Here also grew Camphire, with Spikenard and Saffron, Calamus and Cinnamon, with all its Trees of Frankincense, Myrrh, and Aloes, with all chief Spices. With these the Pilgrims' Chambers were perfumed while they stayed here, and with these were their Bodies anointed, to prepare them to go over the River when the time appointed was come.

Now while they lay here and waited for the good hour, there was a noise in the Town that there was a Post come from the Celestial City, with matter of great importance, to one Christiana, the Wife of Christian the Pilgrim. So inquiry was made for her, and the house was found out where she was. So the Post presented her with a letter, the contents whereof was, Hail, good Woman, I bring thee Tidings that the Master calleth for thee, and expecteth that thou shouldest stand in his presence, in Clothes of Immortality, within this ten days.

When he had read this Letter to her, he gave her therewith a sure token that he was a true Messenger, and was come to bid her make haste to be gone. The token was an Arrow with a point sharpened with Love, let easily into her heart, which by degrees wrought so effectively with her, that at the time appointed she must be gone.

When Christiana saw that her time was come, and that she was the first of this Company that was to go over, she called for Mr. Great-heart, her guide, and told him how matters were. So he told her he was heartily glad of the News, and could have been glad had the Post come for him. Then she bid that he should give advice how all things should be prepared for her journey. So he told her, saying, Thus and thus it must be, and we that survive will accompany you to the Riverside.

Then she called for her Children, and gave them her Blessing, and told them that she yet read with comfort the Mark that was set in their Foreheads, and was glad to see them with her there, and that they had kept their Garments so white. Lastly, she bequeathed to the Poor that little she had, and commanded her Sons and her Daughters to be ready against the Messenger should come for them.

When she had spoken these words to her Guide and to her

Children, she called for Mr. Valiant-for-truth, and said unto him, Sir, you have in all places shewed yourself true-hearted, be faithful unto Death, and my King will give you a Crown of Life. I would also entreat you to have an eye to my Children, and if at any time you see them faint, speak comfortably to them. For my Daughters, my Sons' Wives, they have been faithful, and a fulfilling of the Promise upon them will be their end. But she gave Mr. Stand-fast a Ring.

Then she called for old Mr. Honest, and said of him, Behold an Israelite indeed, in whom is no Guile. Then said he, I wish you a fair day when you set out for Mount Zion, and shall be glad to see that you go over the River dry-shod. But she answered, Come wet, come dry, I long to be gone, for however the Weather is in my Journey, I shall have time enough when I come there to sit down and rest me and dry me.

Then came in that good man, Mr. Ready-to-halt, to see her. So she said to him, Thy Travel hither has been with difficulty, but that will make thy Rest the sweeter. But watch and be ready, for at an hour when you think not, the Messenger may come.

After him came in Mr. Despondency and his Daughter, Much-afraid, to whom she said, You ought with thankfulness for ever to remember your Deliverance from the hands of Giant Despair and out of Doubting Castle. The effect of that Mercy is, that you are brought with safety hither. Be ye watchful and cast away Fear, be sober and hope to the end.

Then she said to Mr. Feeble-mind, Thou wast delivered from the mouth of Giant Slay-good, that thou mightest live in the Light of the Living for ever, and see thy King with comfort. Only I advise thee to repent thee of thine aptness to fear and doubt of his goodness before he sends for thee, lest thou shouldest, when he comes, be forced to stand before him for that fault with blushing.

Now the day drew on that Christiana must be gone. So the Road was full of People to see her take her Journey. But behold all the Banks beyond the River were full of Horses and Chariots, which were come down from above to accompany her to the City Gate. So she came forth and entered the River, with a beckon of Farewell to those that followed her to the Riverside. The last word she was heard to say here was, I come, Lord, to be with thee and bless thee.

So her Children and Friends returned to their place, for

that those that waited for Christiana had carried her out of their sight. So she went and called, and entered in at the Gate with all the Ceremonies of Joy that her Husband Christian had done before her.

At her departure her Children wept, but Mr. Great-heart and Mr. Valiant played upon the well-tuned Cymbal and Harp for Joy. So all departed to their respective places.

In process of time there came a Post to the Town again, and his business was with Mr. Ready-to-halt. So he inquired him out, and said to him, I am come to thee in the name of him whom thou hast loved and followed, though upon Crutches; and my Message is to tell thee that he expects thee at his Table to sup with him in his Kingdom the next day after Easter; wherefore prepare thyself for this Journey.

Then he also gave him a Token that he was a true Messenger, saying, I have broken thy golden bowl, and loosed thy silver cord (Eccles. 12:6).

After this Mr. Ready-to-halt called for his fellow Pilgrims, and told them, saying, I am sent for, and God shall surely visit you also. So he desired Mr. Valiant to make his Will. And because he had nothing to bequeath to them that should survive him but his Crutches and his good Wishes, therefore thus he said, These Crutches I bequeath to my Son that shall tread in my steps, with a hundred warm wishes that he may prove better than I have done.

Then he thanked Mr. Great-heart for his Conduct and Kindness, and so addressed himself to his Journey. When he came at the Brink of the River he said, Now I shall have no more need of these Crutches, since yonder are Chariots and Horses for me to ride on. The last words he was heard to say were, Welcome, Life. So he went his way.

After this Mr. Feeble-mind had Tidings brought him that the Post sounded his Horn at his Chamber-door. Then he came in and told him, saying, I am come to tell thee that thy Master has need of thee, and that in very little time thou must behold his Face in Brightness. And take this as a Token of the Truth of my Message, Those that look out at the Windows shall be darkened (Eccles. 12:3).

Then Mr. Feeble-mind called for his Friends, and told them what Errand had been brought unto him, and what Token he had received of the Truth of the Message. Then he said, Since I have nothing to bequeath to any, to what purpose should I make a Will? As for my feeble mind, that I will leave behind me, for that I have no need of that in the place whither I go. Nor is it worth bestowing upon the poorest Pilgrim; wherefore, when I am gone, I desire that you, Mr. Valiant, would bury it in a Dunghill. This done, and the day being come in which he was to depart, he entered the River as the rest. His last words were, Hold out, Faith and Patience. So he went over to the other side.

When days had many of them passed away, Mr. Despondency was sent for. For a Post was come, and brought this Message to him, Trembling man, these are to summon thee to be ready with thy King by the next Lord's day, to shout for Joy for thy Deliverance from all thy Doubtings.

And, said the Messenger, that my Message is true take this for a Proof; so he gave him the Grasshopper to be a Burden unto him (Eccles. 12:5). Now Mr. Despondency's Daughter, whose name was Much-afraid, said, when she heard what was done, that she would go with her Father. Then Mr. Despondency said to his Friends, Myself and my Daughter, you know what we have been, and how troublesomely we have behaved ourselves in every Company. My Will and my Daughter's is, that our Desponds and slavish Fears be by no man ever received from the day of our Departure for ever, for I know that after my Death they will offer themselves to others. For, to be plain with you, they are Ghosts, the which we entertained when we first began to be Pilgrims, and could never shake them off after; and they will walk about and seek entertainment of the Pilgrims, but for our sakes shut ye the doors upon them.

When the time was come for them to depart, they went to the Brink of the River. The last words of Mr. Despondency were, Farewell Night, welcome Day. His Daughter went through the River singing, but none could understand what she said.

Then it came to pass a while after, that there was a Post in the town that inquired for Mr. Honest. So he came to his house where he was, and delivered to his hand these lines, Thou art commanded to be ready against this day seven night to present thyself before thy Lord at his Father's house. And for a token that my Message is true, All thy Daughters of Music shall be brought low (Eccles. 12:4). Then Mr. Honest called for his Friends, and said unto them, I die, but shall make no Will. As for my honesty, it shall go with me; let him that comes after be told of this. When the day that he was to be gone was come, he addressed himself to go over the River. Now the River at that time overflowed the Banks in some places, but Mr. Honest in his lifetime had spoke to one Good-conscience to meet him there, the which he also did, and lent him his hand, and so helped him over. The last words of Mr. Honest were, Grace reigns. So he left the World.

After this it was noised abroad that Mr. Valiant-for-truth was taken with a Summons by the same Post as the other, and had this for a Token that the Summons was true, That his Pitcher was broken at the Fountain (Eccles. 12:6). When he understood it, he called for his Friends, and told them of it. Then said he, I am going to my Father's, and though with great difficulty I am got hither, yet now I do not repent me of all the Trouble I have been at to arrive where I am. My Sword I give to him that shall succeed me in my Pilgrimage, and my Courage and Skill to him that can get it. My Marks and Scars I carry with me, to be a witness for me that I have fought his Battles who now will be my Rewarder. When the day that he must go hence was come, many accompanied him to the Riverside, into which as he went he said, Death, where is thy Sting? And as he went down deeper he said, Grave, where is thy Victory? So he passed over, and all the Trumpets sounded for him on the other side.

Then there came forth a Summons for Mr. Stand-fast (this Mr. Stand-fast was he that the rest of the Pilgrims found upon his Knees in the Enchanted Ground), for the Post brought it him open in his hands. The contents whereof were, that he must prepare for a Change of Life, for his Master was not willing that he should be so far from him any longer. At this Mr. Stand-fast was put into a muse. Nay, said the Messenger, you need not doubt of the truth of my Message, for here is a Token of the Truth thereof, Thy Wheel is broken at the Cistern (Eccles. 12:6). Then he called to him Mr. Great-heart who was their Guide, and said unto him, Sir, although it was not my hap to be much in your good Company in the days of my Pilgrimage, yet since the time I knew you, you have been profitable to me. When I came from home, I left behind me a Wife and five small Children, let me entreat you at your return (for I know that you will go and return to your Master's house, in hopes that you may yet be a Conductor to more of the holy Pilgrims), that you send to my Family, and let them be acquainted with all that hath and shall happen unto me. Tell them, moreover, of my happy Arrival to this place, and of the present late blessed condition that I am in. Tell them also of Christian and Christiana his Wife, and how she and her Children came after her Husband. Tell them also of what a happy end she made, and whither she is gone. I have little or nothing to send to my Family, except it be Prayers and Tears for them; of which it will suffice if thou acquaint them, if peradventure they may prevail.

When Mr. Stand-fast had thus set things in order, and the time being come for him to haste him away, he also went down to the River. Now there was a great Calm at that time in the River; wherefore Mr. Stand-fast, when he was about half-way in, stood a while, and talked to his Companions that had waited upon him thither. And he said:

This River has been a Terror to many, yea, the thoughts of it also have often frightened me. But now methinks I stand easy, my Foot is fixed upon that upon which the Feet of the Priests that bare the Ark of the Covenant stood while Israel went over this Jordan (Jos. 3:17). The Waters indeed are to the Palate bitter and to the Stomach cold, yet the thoughts of what I am going to, and of the Conduct that waits for me on the other side, doth lie as a glowing Coal at my Heart.

I see myself now at the end of my Journey, my toilsome days are ended. I am going now to see that Head that was crowned with Thorns, and that Face that was spit upon for me.

I have formerly lived by Hearsay and Faith, but now I go where I shall live by sight, and shall be with him in whose Company I delight myself.

I have loved to hear my Lord spoken of, and wherever I have seen the print of his Shoe in the Earth, there I have coveted to set my Foot too.

His name has been to me as a Civet-box,[108] yea, sweeter than all Perfumes. His Voice to me has been most sweet, and his Countenance I have more desired than they that have most desired the Light of the Sun. His word I did use to gather for my Food, and for Antidotes against my Faintings. He has held me, and I have kept me from mine iniquities, yea, my Steps hath he strengthened in his Way.

Now while he was thus in Discourse, his Countenance changed, his strong man bowed under him, and after he had said, Take me, for I come unto thee, he ceased to be seen of them.

But glorious it was to see how the open Region was filled with Horses and Chariots, with Trumpeters and Pipers, with Singers and Players on stringed Instruments, to welcome the Pilgrims as they went up, and followed one another in at the beautiful Gate of the City.

As for Christian's Children, the four Boys that Christiana brought with her, with their Wives and Children, I did not stay where I was till they were gone over. Also, since I came away, I heard one say that they were yet alive, and so would be for the Increase of the Church in that place where they were for a time.

Shall it be my Lot to go that way again, I may give those that desire it an account of what I here am silent about: meantime, I bid my Reader Adieu.

FINIS

most desired the Light of the Sun. His word I did use to gather for my Food, and for Antidotes against my Faintings. He has held me, and I have kept me from mine Iniquities; yea, my Steps hath he strengthened in his Way.

Now while he was thus in Discourse, his Countenance changed, his strong man bowed under him, and after he had said, Take me, for I come unto thee, he ceased to be seen of them.

But glorious it was to see how the open Region was filled with Horses and Chariots, with Trumpeters and Pipers, with Singers and Players on stringed Instruments, to welcome the Pilgrims as they went up, and followed one another in at the beautiful Gate of the City.

As for Christian's Children, the four Boys that Christiana brought with her, with their Wives and Children, I did not stay where I was till they were gone over. Also since I came away, I heard one say that they were yet alive, and so would be for the Increase of the Church in that place where they were for a time.

Shall it be my Lot to go that way again, I may give those that desire it an Account of what I here am silent about; mean time I bid my Reader Adieu.

Notes

INTRODUCTION

1. *The Poor Husbandman,* F. J. Powicke, ed., Manchester Univ. Press, 1926, p. 24.
2. *Grace Abounding,* § 8.
3. *A New and Authentic Account of the Life and Death of Mr. John Bunyan . . . Written by a Friend to the Cause of Religion,* printed for Alex. Hogg, at the King's Arm, Paternoster Row, London, p. 26.
4. *The Holy War; An Advertisement to the Reader.*
5. Harold Golder, "John Bunyan's Hypocrisy," *North American Rev.,* 1926; "Bunyan's Valley of the Shadow," *Modern Philology,* 1929; "Bunyan and Spenser," *P.M.L.A.,* 1930; "Bunyan's Giant Despair," *J.E.G.P.,* 1931; James Blanton Wharey, *A Study of Bunyan's Allegories, with Special Reference to Deguilville's Pilgrimage of Man,* Baltimore, 1904.
6. John Geree, *The Character of an Old English Puritane,* London, 1646, p. 2.
7. See G. R. Owst, *Preaching in Medieval England,* Cambridge, 1926; *Literature and Pulpit in Medieval England,* Cambridge, 1933.
8. William Haller, *The Rise of Puritanism,* Columbia Univ. Press, 1938 (Harper Torchbooks, 1957), p. 145.
9. See C. S. Lewis's remarks about Seneca in his *Allegory of*

Love, Oxford Univ. Press, 1936, p. 689, and indeed all the chapter on allegory. Cf. E. M. W. Tillyard, *The English Epic and Its Background,* London, 1954, pp. 134-45.
10. Geree, op. cit., p. 6.
11. Q. D. Leavis, *Fiction and the Reading Public,* London, 1932.
12. I am indebted for some suggestions to Henri Gouhier's article "Intrigue et action," *Mélanges Georges Jamati,* Paris, 1956.
13. *John Bunyan,* London, 1954, p. 14.
14. "Bunyan's Mr. Ignorance," *M.L.R.,* 1949, Vol. XLIV, p. 483.
15. See Hardin Craig, *Literary Study and the Scholarly Profession,* Univ. of Washington Press, 1944.
16. This is not a literal quotation. See Leibniz's letter to Rémond, January 10, 1714.
17. C. H. Firth, *Essays, Historical and Literary,* Oxford Univ. Press, 1938.
18. "Give me a ballad, a news-book, George on Horseback or Bevis of Southampton," *A Few Sighs from Hell, Works,* Offor's ed. Vol. III, p. 711.
19. See Jacques Blondel's perceptive remark in *Allégorie et réalisme dans le Pilgrim's Progress,* a small brochure (47 pages), Archives des Lettres Modernes, December 1959, p. 29.
20. S. T. Coleridge, *Notes on English Divines,* Derwent Coleridge's ed., 2 vols., London, 1853, Vol. I, p. 343.
21. Jer. 13:16.
22. See Charles Feidelson's analysis of American Puritanism, in his remarkable book on *Symbolism and American Literature,* Univ. of Chicago Press, 1953 (and Phoenix Books, 1959).
23. See Friedrich Heiler, *Prayer: A Study in the History and Psychology of Religion,* Oxford Univ. Press, 1932 (and Galaxy Books, 1958).
24. *Works,* Boston and New York, 1909, Vol. X, p. 234.
25. Introduction to *The Pilgrim's Progress,* Rinehart, 1949, p. xii.
26. *Dark Conceit: The Making of Allegory,* Northwestern Univ. Press, and Faber, London, 1959, p. 109.
27. Luke 14:26.
28. Isa. 64:6.
29. Although, later, when he refers to Christian before he met Evangelist, Bunyan calls him Graceless.
30. Ps. 38:4.
31. G. M. Trevelyan, *Clio, A Muse, and Other Essays,* London, 1930, p. 52.
32. *Grace Abounding,* §§ 133 ff.
33. "Culpabilité tragique et culpabilité biblique," *Revue d'Hist. et de Philosophie Religieuses,* 1953, p. 298.

34. *Saved by Grace, Works,* Vol. I, p. 342.
35. *A Few Sighs from Hell, Works,* Vol. III, p. 720.
36. *I and Thou* (1937), Scribner's, p. 53.
37. See some penetrating remarks in Rosemary Freeman, *English Emblem Books,* London, 1948.

THE HEAVENLY FOOTMAN

1. The title was probably suggested by the words of Jeremiah "If thou hast run with the footmen, and they have wearied thee, then how canst thou contend with horses? And if in the land of peace, wherein thou trustedst, they wearied thee, then how wilt thou do in the swelling of Jordan?" (Jer. 12:5.) *The Heavenly Footman* was first published in 1698 by Charles Doe.
2. *He hath turned up their heels,* i.e., knocked them down.
3. *Francis Spira.* See Note 33, *The Pilgrim's Progress,* First Part. Part.
4. *A professor.* One who makes open declaration of his religion.
5. *One runs a-quaking, another a-ranting.* One follows the teaching of the Quakers; another that of the Ranters. The Ranters believed in the divine immanence, denied the Church and the Scripture, and listened only to the Christ within their heart.
6. *Runs after the Baptism.* Believes in adult baptism but not in infant baptism.
7. *Much in studying of.* Cf. the next sentence, *let thy study be,* etc., study in the now archaic sense of thought, meditation.
8. *Light into any lane.* Enter by chance.
9. *If such an opinion . . . be but cried up,* i.e., extolled. *To cry up;* to proclaim a thing to be excellent; to exalt in public estimation by loud praise.
10. *Painted.* Colored so as to look what they are not. Lydgate: "Ffor all thy peynted wordys swete, my staff in soth I wyl not lete."
11. *Sink-souls.* This vigorous compound word was probably coined by Bunyan.
12. *Knock off.* Desist; cease.
13. *Way-mark.* Cf. Jer. 31:21. "Set thee up waymarks . . . set thine heart toward the highway."
14. *A spurt.* A short spell; a brief period.
15. *Beat out of wind.* Rendered breathless.
16. *Froward.* Perverse.
17. *Peevish.* Headstrong; perverse.
18. *A seldom work.* Cf. Shakespeare's "seldom pleasure," in *Sonnets,* 52.

19. *Starting-holes.* Places of refuge.
20. *Out of fit.* This expression has puzzled several editors; George Offor's emendation, *out of sight,* makes no sense and Henry Stebbing's *till my children are out* is little better. *Out of fit* (see *O.E.D.*) meant fitted out, settled in life.
21. *Get thy will tipt with the heavenly grace.* Get it strengthened, as an arrow is strengthened by the addition of a metal tip.
22. *Confederation.* Altered to *consideration* both by Stebbing and Offor. The meaning that Mabel Peacock has suggested "combination, or connection, of ideas" is not in the *O.E.D.*
23. *Scrubbed.* Mean; worthless. See Note 104, *The Pilgrim's Progress,* First Part.
24. *Befool.* Treat as a fool.
25. *While.* Until.
26. *They shall ride.* They shall be carried.
27. *All them jostles.* Both Stebbing and Offor have corrected Bunyan's grammar (*all these jostles*).
28. *Young striplings of Jesus that began to strip but the other day. Striplings;* young men. *To strip;* to take off one's clothes in preparation for a contest. Bunyan refers to young men who have laid aside every sin and mean to win the heavenly race.
29. *To pick up here and there a lock of wool that hangeth by the way-side.* This image brings us a whiff of rural life in the seventeenth and, indeed, even in the early nineteenth century. It was usual for the housewives to collect the loose tufts of wool left by the flocks on the pasture grounds, and to spin them into mop yarn or into finer thread.
30. *Flaggering. To flagger* obviously means *to flag,* but it is very unusual.

THE PILGRIM'S PROGRESS [*The First Part*]

1. A metaphor derived from spinning. Like the wool or flax on the distaff when the spinner takes hold of an end and draws it toward her, twisting it between her finger and thumb to make a continuous thread.
2. The toad was believed to have a stone in its head, fraught with great magical virtues.
3. *By pins and loops.* Ex. 26:5; 27:19.
4. The allusions are to the Passover and various Levitical sacrifices: Lev. 16:3, 14, 15; Isa. 10; 19:2-9, 22:19; Ex. 29:15-32.
5. Lev. 14:4-39; Ex. 12:7, 8.
6. The Puritans advocated a figurative interpretation of certain books in the Bible.
7. The reference is to the silver shrines made for the Ephesian Diana (Acts 19:24).

8. Bunyan's first wife brought him a book in dialogue form, Arthur Dent's *Plain Mans Path-way to Heaven,* which exercised a great influence upon him. The phrase in parentheses remains obscure.
9. *He that taught us first to Plow.* Cf. Isa. 28:24, 26.
10. *In this plight.* The whole passage consisting of this paragraph and the next first appeared in the second edition.
11. *His Relations.* His family.
12. *Tophet.* Hell.
13. *I am sure.* This parenthesis is found only in the first edition.
14. *Take a fancy by the end.* The image is from spinning, as in line 31 of the author's "Apology."
15. The representation of despair in the guise of an allegorical slough suggested itself quite naturally to Bunyan. Cf. *Grace Abounding,* §§ 82, 220.
16. Bunyan's own spelling was "Dispond."
17. *The steps.* Bunyan's heading, "The Promises" (originally a marginal note), alludes to such Biblical texts as foreshadow salvation by faith.
18. *These sixteen hundred years.* The years elapsed since the proclamation of the Gospel. *The Pilgrim's Progress* was written in the 1670's.
19. *Mr. Worldly Wiseman.* All the account of Christian's conversation with this gentleman, first appeared in the second edition. See my *John Bunyan: The Man and His Works* and Sharrock's note, p. 314 in the Clarendon edition.
20. *The Bond woman which now is, and is in bondage with her children.* A misquotation from Gal. 4:25—"This Agar . . . answereth to Jerusalem which now is, and [Agar, not Jerusalem] is in bondage with her [Agar's own] children."
21. *Truly, said Christian.* This speech, the four following, and the fifth as far as *in no wise are cast out* were added to the second edition.
22. *There is no betterment 'twixt him and myself.* Christian means "I am just as bad as he; there is no difference for the better."
23. In the sixteenth and the seventeenth century, "dump" was used in serious prose. E.g., J. Hooker: "They were in a great dumpe and perplexitie."
24. *Butt down upon this.* Lead to or issue into another road.
25. *Excellent.* Fine. Frequently used in this sense by Bunyan.
26. *One of a thousand.* This portrait of the ideal pastor reminds one of "holy Mr. Gifford, whose doctrine, by God's Grace, was much for my stability" (*Grace Abounding,* § 117). John Gifford was the first minister of the Bedford independent

church. The minister of Christ is always a prominent person in *The Pilgrim's Progress* and plays an essential part in Christian's conversion and guidance (cf. Evangelist, the Interpreter, the Shepherds of the Delectable Mountains). Bunyan's work mirrors the life of the Puritan community. Preaching the Word was almost as important as the Word itself. In *The Parable of the Sower and the Seed* (1621) Thomas Taylor says "Faith is by hearing, and salvation by faith." For further information about Bunyan's emblematic pictures, and the English emblem writers generally, consult Rosemary Freeman, *English Emblem Books,* London, 1948, And Roger Sharrock, "Bunyan and the English Emblem Writers," *R.E.S.,* April 1945.

27. *This parlour is the heart of a man.* This image, which was first used by Catholic emblem writers on the Continent, was frequently adapted in English by Protestant authors.
28. *The Governor of them.* Their tutor. Cf. Gal. 4:12.
29. Coleridge considered this one of the few instances of faulty allegory in the book. See Coleridge, *Literary Remains* (1836-1839), III, 402.
30. *A Fire burning against a wall.* Another Catholic image adapted by the Protestant emblem writers; but it seems that the image came to Bunyan almost spontaneously. Cf. *Grace Abounding,* § 111: "You are very hot for mercy, but I will cool you; this frame shall not last always. Many have been as hot as you for a spurt, but I have quenched their zeal." Also, *Saved by Grace, Works,* I, 351: "those that will cast water themselves upon those sparks which Christ labours to kindle in them."
31. *In a muse,* in the first edition; *in a maze,* in the second and third.
32. *The Three.* Sharrock says rightly that they seem to be the saints rather than the Trinity; however Bunyan may have had in mind Enoch, Moses, and Elijah, who "looked over the gate" of the Heavenly City when Christian and Hopeful called at the gate.
33. Whoever was the prototype of the *Man in an Iron Cage* does not matter; the apostate was as common a figure in Puritan circles as in Puritan homiletic literature. Let us only mention that Bunyan was terribly impressed by the *Relation of the Fearful State of Francis Spira.* See *Grace Abounding,* § 163, and *The Barren Fig Tree, Works,* III, p. 582.
34. *Professor.* One who makes open declaration of his religion.
35. Cf. Beaumont and Fletcher, *Four Plays in One:* "Stay, clouds, ye *rack* too fast."
36. *As Christian came up with the Cross, his Burden loosed from*

off his shoulders. Cf. *Heavenly Footman:* "The cross is the standing way-mark by which all that go to glory must pass by."

37. *Every Fatt must stand upon his own bottom.* A *fatt;* a vat. This proverbial expression means "Everybody must look to himself."
38. *Ordinances.* The sacraments.
39. *As for this Coat.* See above: "the second stript him of his Rags, and clothed him with Change of Raiment."
40. *A wide field, full of dark Mountains.* A field means a stretch of open country. See Introduction, page 13.
41. *What's the matter you run the wrong way?* There is an ellipsis of *that.* What is the matter *that* you run, etc.
42. *A couple of Lions.* The lions symbolize civil and ecclesiastical persecution.
43. *His foolish fact.* From *factum* (*facere*); a thing done; an act.
44. *If happily he might find.* That is to say if by hap, or by chance.
45. *Doleful creatures.* See Isa. 13:21.
46. *Shift them.* Get them out of the way.
47. *A very stately Palace . . . the name whereof was Beautiful.* The Palace Beautiful represents church fellowship. Cf. Spenser's "House of Holiness," *Faerie Queene,* Bk. I, Canto x, Stanzas 12, 19, 20.
48. *Fear not the Lions, for they are chained.* When Bunyan became a member of Bedford independent church, in 1653, penal laws against nonconformists were not enforced.
49. *I lost my evidence.* Evidence of election.
50. As regards the place held by women in *The Pilgrim's Progress* and in Puritan communities, see my *Bunyan,* pp. 201-3, 64, 193, and William Haller, op. cit., Ch. iii, "The Calling of the Saints."
51. *He had stript himself of his glory,* etc. See II Cor. 8:9; and Phil. 2:7.
52. The references are to St. Paul. "The sword of the Spirit, which is the Word of God," "the shield of faith," "the helmet of the hope of salvation," "the breastplate of righteousness." Eph. 6:13-17; I Thess. 5:8.
53. *Moses' Rod.* See Ex. 4:2-4, 17; 7:10, 17.
54. *Jael.* See Judg. 4:21.
55. *Gideon.* See Judg. 7:16-22.
56. *Shamgar.* See Judg. 15:15.
57. *David.* See I Sam. 17:49, 50.
58. *The Man of Sin.* See II Thess. 2:3-8.
59. *The Delectable Mountains.* One of the expressions with which

Bunyan has enriched the English language, but the landscape itself is reminiscent of that in Solomon's Song, 4:6; 7:12.

60. *A loaf of Bread, a bottle of Wine, and a cluster of Raisins.* See II Sam. 16:1.

61. *Apollyon.* A translation of the Hebrew word *Abaddon* (destruction); refers to the personified destroyer. See Rev. 11:11; Job 26:6; 28:22. Cf. "His feet were as the feet of a bear, and his mouth as the mouth of a lion" (Rev. 13:2). "His scales are his pride, shut up together as with a close seal" (Job 41:15).

62. *I have let myself.* I have *hired* myself.

63. *The King's Highway.* Num. 21:22 (22 and not 17 as found in several editions)—"Let me pass through thy land; we will not turn into the fields, or into the vineyards . . . but we will go along by the king's highway."

64. *Strodled.* This provincial but vigorous form is to be found in the first edition. It has been retained in preference to *straddled,* which appeared in later editions.

65. On the fight with Apollyon, and Apollyon as an example of artistic creation, see my *Bunyan* pp. 176-7. Also pp. 174, 175. Cf. Spenser's dragon, *Faerie Queene,* Bk. I, Canto xi.

66. *Brast.* The reading of the first edition. *Burst* appeared in later editions.

67. *The leaves of the Tree of Life.* Cf. *Faerie Queene,* Bk. I, Canto xi, Stanza 48.

68. *No other affront from Apollyon,* no other hostile encounter with Apollyon.

69. *Children of them that brought up an evil report.* See Num. 13. In order to understand the allusion read all the chapter, or at least, 16-32.

70. *Satyrs.* Isa. 13:21—"Owls shall dwell there and satyrs shall dance there." In the English Bible the word *satyr* is applied to the hairy demons or monsters of Semitic superstitions, supposed to inhabit deserts (*O.E.D.*).

71. *Grievous blasphemies.* See *Grace Abounding,* § 97; and Introduction, p. 17.

72. *I will fear none ill.* From Thomas Sternhold's version of Ps. 23: "Yea though I walke in vaile of death, Yet will I fear none ill."

73. As Sharrock has remarked, the reference to "the weakness of Roman Catholic power could hardly have been made after the Declaration of Indulgence of 1672 and probably not after the Treaty of Dover of 1670 and the ascendancy of the Cabal." *The Pilgrim's Progress,* Sharrock's edition, p. 324, note.

74. *The Avenger of blood.* See Deut. 19:4-6.

75. *Overrun.* Outrun.

76. *Leered away*. Walked stealthily or with averted looks; slunk away; sneaked away. Cf. *Grace Abounding*, § 144.
77. *Slave*. "Whosoever committeth sin is the slave of sin" (John 8:34).
78. *A deadly twitch back*. Bunyan wishes thus to represent the dualistic nature of man, and the struggle between the flesh and the spirit.
79. *Moses*. On the old Adam and the laws of Moses in Puritan rhetoric, see William Haller, op. cit., Ch. iv.
80. The sleep of the lions is the allegorical representation of a lull in persecution.
81. *Pretty*. The Old English *praettig* meant *cunning, artful; pretty* came to mean *fine*. Here Bunyan opposes the proper, pleasing appearance to the ugly inner reality.
82. *Unreasonable with his Servants*. Bunyan has said, in *Christian Behaviour*, that masters must give their servants "the same bread of God" that is given to the children of the household. *Works*, II, 559.
83. It has been shown (see, for instance, Canon Venables's edition, revised by Mabel Peacock, Oxford, 1925) that Bunyan had good patristic precedent (of which he was ignorant) for this moralization of the Levitical ordinance. Cf. *Grace Abounding*, § 71.
84. *You lie at the catch*, i.e., are on the watch for an opportunity to catch something, especially, to catch a person's words, finding fault (*O.E.D.*).
85. *This sight and sense of things*. Bunyan uses the word *sight* as it was frequently used in the sixteenth century. It meant *knowledge; insight*. (See *O.E.D.*)
86. *Peevish*. Probably meaning *perverse; headstrong; capricious*. (See *O.E.D.*)
87. *Stumble the World*. Puzzle; embarrass; nonplus (See *O.E.D.*) *Stumble* was altered to *puzzle* in the second and later editions. An unfelicitous change!
88. *Peace be to your helpers*. See I Chron. 12:18.
89. *Run that you may obtain it*. See Introduction, p. 22, and *The Heavenly Footman*.
90. *Set your faces like a flint*, i.e., firmly, steadfastly (proverbial).
91. *Will strain hard but they will kill you*. Elliptical and archaic. "They will strain hard and will not be content unless they kill you."
92. *Vanity Fair*. An interesting example of a picture whose symbolism is all the more vigorous because of its graphic realism (Bunyan knew the great annual fair at Stourbridge near Cambridge). As C. S. Lewis puts it in *The Allegory of Love:* "It is a mischievous error to suppose that in an allegory the

author is 'really' talking about the thing symbolized and not at all about the thing that symbolizes; the very essence of the art is to talk about both."

93. *Legion.* The context makes it clear that Bunyan misunderstood the word and thought it was one of the scriptural names of the Devil. The reference is to Mark 5:9; Luke 8:30.
94. *Bedlams.* Madmen.
95. *Outlandish-men.* Foreigners; as in Neh. 12:26.
96. *The language of Canaan.* The reference is to Isa. 19:18.
97. *Barbarians.* The reference is to I Cor. 14:11.
98. *The carriages of the men,* i.e., their behavior.
99. *To let them in their Journey.* To hinder them. Cf. "I'll make a ghost of him that lets me," *Hamlet,* Act I, Scene 4.
100. *Let fly at them.* Abused them.
101. *The best on't.* The best of it. *On* was very often used for *of.*
102. *Pickthank.* A flatterer.
103. *Sins are all Lords and Great ones.* On Bunyan's social thought see my *Bunyan,* pp. 282-304; also pp. 45, 208.
104. *A sorry Scrub.* A mean fellow. Cf. Fielding, *Tom Jones,* Bk. viii, Ch. iv—"He is an arrant scrub, I assure you."
105. *A chariot and a couple of Horses.* See the ascension of Elijah, II Kings 2:11.
106. *By-Ends.* A *by-end* is a secret, selfish purpose. "Are there not many by-ends in duties?"—Flavel, *Touchstone of Sincerity,* p. 36. This character has grown little by little in Bunyan's hands. It was not until the second edition that By-ends acquired his juicy genealogy, and not until the third edition that he reflected in the minds of his friends as in a hall of mirrors. By-ends is a hypocrite and a "man of latitude." On this character and Bunyan's controversy with Edward Fowler, whom he called "a glorious Latitudinarian," see my *Bunyan,* pp. 99-103; 207-8.
107. *How to carry it to all.* How to behave.
108. *To jump in my Judgment.* To fall in with.
109. *At a clap.* At one stroke.
110. *A Tradesman.* In some respects By-ends foreshadows Mr. Badman.
111. *Disserting.* This reading makes better sense than the *dissenting* of the third edition, but neither is satisfactory.
112. *Witches.* The word was both masculine and feminine. See below, *Simon the Witch.*
113. *Hamor and Shechem.* See Gen. 34.
114. *Judas the Devil.* See John 6:70, 71.
115. *A delicate Plain called Ease. Delicate* is here equivalent to *pleasant.* Cf. Cowper, "Retired Cat," line 60—"Cried Puss:

'Oh! what a delicate retreat! I will resign myself to rest.'"

116. *I will shew you a thing.* See I Sam. 14:12.
117. *One of his Majesty's Judges,* i.e., St. Paul. "Demas hath forsaken me, having loved this present world" (II Tim. 4:10).
118. *A Woman transformed into the shape of a Pillar.* It was believed that the pillar of Lot's wife could still be seen. "At the right side of the Dead Sea the wife of Lot still stands in likeness of a salt stone"—Sir John Maundeville's *Travels,* Ch. ix.
119. *Sell all.* Cf. Matt. 13:44—the parable of the treasure hidden in the field.
120. *By-path Meadow.* This is Hawthorne's comment: "An American would never understand the passage about Christian and Hopeful going astray along a by-path into the ground of Giant Despair, from there being no stiles or by-paths in our country" *(English Note-books,* I, 147). It is quoted in the Venables-Peacock edition.
121. *Eminent,* and not *imminent* as found in many editions. *Eminent* and *imminent* were often confused (as were the Medieval Latin *eminens* and *imminens*).
122. *Doubting Castle.* As Sharrock rightly remarks, "doubts as to whether they have been predestined for salvation, not a sceptical attitude to the dogmas of religion." The account of the Pilgrims' imprisonment, which was very short in the first edition, was considerably enlarged in the second so as to include the counsels of Mrs. Diffidence and the Giant's treatment of the prisoners. As regards Bunyan's sense of sin and despair, see Introduction, and *Grace Abounding,* §§ 132-87.
123. *He fell into one of his Fits.* It is said that despair comes and goes in fits, hence Giant Despair's fits.
124. *Sun-shine,* as in the early editions, and not *sun-shiny.* The adjectival use of *sun-shine* was usual. Cf. "a sunshine day," Henry VI, Third Part, Act II, Scene 1; and Milton's "sunshine holiday," "L'Allegro," line 95.
125. *To kill body and soul at once.* Cf. *Justification by an Imputed Righteousness, Works,* I, 315.
126. *Swound.* Swoon.
127. *Den.* See heading, "The Gaol," p. 66.
128. *A Key.* Compare this concrete realization of a Biblical metaphor ("The keys of the kingdom of heaven" [Matt. 16:19]) with the fits of Giant Despair. Cf. also St. Peter's deliverance from prison (Acts 12:10).
129. *Consented to erect.* Agreed to erect.
130. *To acquaint with us.* This is the reading of the first edition. This active use of *acquaint* was usual.
131. *Among the Tombs.* Cf. Prov. 21:16—"The man that wandereth

out of the way of understanding shall remain in the congregation of the dead." Bunyan also alludes to this text in *Grace Abounding,* § 187.

132. *Lumbring.* The first edition reading is perfectly correct. Bunyan made no mistake whatever; *lumbring* was a synonym of *rumbling*—from *lumber,* as in "One other Person . . . heard the Noise [of an earthquake], but judged it to be an odd Lumber above Stairs" (a 1750 example given by Smith in *Phil. Trans.,* XLVI, 729 and quoted by the *O.E.D.*).
133. *Alexander.* See II Tim. 4:14—"Alexander the coppersmith did me much evil: the Lord reward him according to his works."
134. *So I awoke from my Dream.* See John Brown, *John Bunyan* (1885), pp. 262 *ff.* Roger Sharrock's *John Bunyan,* and his introduction to *The Pilgrim's Progress;* also my *Bunyan.*
135. *A very brisk Lad . . . his name was Ignorance.* By far the most interesting study of Ignorance is Maurice Hussey's, *M.L.R.,* 1949.
136. *To scrabble on his way. Scrabble* is here equivalent to *struggle along.* The usage is now rare. The *O.E.D.* quotes this passage and one from *Grace Abounding.*
137. *His Jewels.* His saving faith.
138. *Caitiff.* A poor wretch, or a villain. In early use the two meanings are often inseparable. The word "often implies a mixture of wickedness and misery" (*O.E.D.*).
139. *Esau's Birthright was typical,* i.e., symbolical. The Puritans called a system of correspondences between the Old Testament and the New, *typology.* Certain episodes in the Old Testament were held to foreshadow certain occurrences in the New. Adam and David were *types* of Christ; the deliverance from Egypt prefigured the deliverance of the Church from the Antichrist.
140. *Brush.* Chiefly, a short but smart encounter (*O.E.D.*).
141. *Journeymen Thieves.* Thieves who did not rob on their own account but served under a master thief.
142. *I trow.* I believe.
143. *He should say.* He was reported to have said.
144. *Heman.* The psalmist, grandson of the Prophet Samuel. In the third edition *Heman* was altered to *Haman,* whose unwonted presence among the champions of faith startled Southey and other editors.
145. *A sorry Girl.* "But a certain maid beheld him [Peter] . . . and said, This man was also with him [Jesus]. And he denied him, saying, Woman, I know him not" (Luke 22:56-57).
146. The first edition has no pointing after *hold.* See Sharrock's comment, op. cit., p. 335.
147. *A man black of flesh.* This incident has caused a good deal of controversy and puzzled many commentators. I believe that

Mr. Sharrock's new interpretation (Op. cit., p. 335) is the right one.

148. *Jer. 22:13.* It should be *Jer. 22:12* (George Offor's suggestion).
149. *I will round you in the ears,* i.e., whisper (Middle English *rounen;* Old English *rūnian*).
150. *Ask my fellow if I be a Thief!* An old proverb, 1539 (*O.E.D.*).
151. *A fantastical Faith.* A faith whose seat is merely in the fantasy or imagination.
152. *Country of Beulah.* "Thou shalt be called Hephzi-bah [my delight is in her], and thy land Beulah [married]" (Isa. 62:4).
153. *They addressed themselves,* i.e., prepared themselves.
154. *Stounded.* Astounded.
155. *Enoch and Elijah.* God "took" Enoch, and Elijah "went up by a whirlwind into heaven."
156. *Where it is said of the wicked. There is no band in their death,* etc. Cf. Mr. Badman. Mr. Badman died "as quietly as a lamb."
157. *The Enemy was after that as still as a stone.* See Ex. 15:16.

THE PILGRIM'S PROGRESS: THE SECOND PART

1. *Rest,* not *next* (Sharrock's correction).
2. *My Firstling.* The First Part of *The Pilgrim's Progress.*
3. *That counterfeit the Pilgrim.* The immediate success of *The Pilgrim's Progress* encouraged imitators and forgers to capitalize on the popularity of Bunyan's allegory. In 1683, a certain T. S., whom we can now identify as Thomas Sherman, a General Baptist, published a second part to *The Pilgrim's Progress.* He was no ordinary forger, but a holy man who did not wear his saintliness so graciously as Bunyan. He objected to Bunyan's humor and to his racy and homely style. Sherman wanted to suppress the laugh that the story sometimes gave rise to. He also regretted the lack of emphasis on the organized life of the Church, and he wrote his own book in "serious and spiritual phrases."
4. *In naughty wise.* In a scandalous fashion.
5. *In France.* The earliest French edition that we know was published in Amsterdam in 1685.
6. *New England.* The earliest known American edition was published in Boston in 1681.
7. *Trimm'd, new cloth'd, and deck't with Gems.* The reference is to the fine, bound copies of the early American editions.
8. "It came to pass, when Jacob saw Rachel the daughter of Laban his mother's brother, and the sheep of Laban . . . Jacob kissed Rachel and lifted up his voice and wept" (Gen. 29:10, 11).
9. See Matt. 21:15, 16.

10. *Shall them gain,* i.e., gain their meaning.
11. *I was as if.* It seemed to me that.
12. *Will shortly,* i.e., at the Day of Judgment.
13. *And being we are,* i.e., since we are. This form was usual: "Being God is of universal knowledge" (Bishop Pearson, *Exposition of the Creed* [1669]).
14. *The caul of her Heart.* A *caul* (*O.E.D.*) is any investing membrane or structure, one of the membranes of the brain, for example. The *caul of the heart* is apparently the *pericardium;* the phrase is also used figuratively (see Hosea 13:8; cf. Joel 2:13).
15. *Woe worth the day.* Ezek. 30:2—"Howl ye, Woe worth the day!"—i.e., woe be to the day.
16. *The pav'd-work.* Ex. 24:10—"under his feet as it were a paved work of a sapphire stone."
17. *Root-of-heart.* Bunyan has combined or confused two expressions: *by rote* and *by heart. By rote* (by routine; by the mere exercise of memory) is thought to derive from the Old French *route* (way).
18. *The good woman a preparing,* i.e., was in process of, in course of.
19. *Her bowels yearned.* Cf. I Kings 3:26.
20. *Dumpish.* Melancholy.
21. *I dare say.* I make bold to say; I have no hesitation in saying.
22. *One that delighteth in Mercy.* Bunyan always liked a pun!
23. *Bowels becometh Pilgrims. Bowels* is here equivalent to *compassion.*
24. *Hers was from the King, and mine was but from her.* Mercy has received no personal call, but has been moved by Christian's example. This and several other instances show that Bunyan's experience as a minister had enlarged his human horizon and modified his early certainties. The theology of the Second Part is more liberal and social. Whereas Christian had to fight his fights alone, Christiana goes in company. In the house of the Interpreter, there was no one but the host when Christian called there, whereas there is now a large household, etc. See Introduction.
25. *What was written over the Gate.* "Knock, and it shall be opened unto you" (Matt. 7:7).
26. *Bless'd be the Day that I began.* This and the other lyrics in the Second Part constituted hidden propaganda for congregational singing.
27. *Did plash them.* Beat them to bring down the fruit.
28. *Ruffins,* and not *ruffians* as in most modern editions. *Ruffin* is the name of a fiend (*O.E.D.*).
29. *Being ye knew.* Since ye knew.

30. *The Picture of the biggest of them all,* i.e., the picture of Evangelist.
31. *A Man . . . with a Muck-rake.* This is one of Bunyan's most famous emblematic images. Arthur Dent, from whom Bunyan learned so much, speaks of "the gripple muck-rakers" (*Plain Mans Pathway to Heaven*). The metaphor was traditional with reference to avarice.
32. *The Bath.* Adult baptism. This passage is a concession to those among Bunyan's coreligionists who insisted on the necessity of adult baptism. Bunyan has expressed his ideas about baptism most clearly in *A Confession of My Faith and a Reason of My Practice* (1672). He distinguished between John's baptism, which was the baptism of the body, and Christ's baptism, which was the baptisms of souls. John's water-baptism was to last only until Christ's fire-baptism. Neither Christ nor Paul had baptized. Bunyan, like his master John Gifford, disliked controversy about secondary questions and "externalls." Faith in Christ and holiness of life—those were the essentials. "I will not let water-baptism be the rule, the door, the bolt, the bar, the wall of division between the righteous and the righteous" (*Works,* II, 629).
33. *The Seal.* Cf. Eph. 1:13—"In whom also after that ye believed, ye were sealed with that holy Spirit of promise."
34. *White Raiment.* Cf. Rev. 19:8—"And to her was granted that she should be arrayed in fine linen, clean and white: for the fine linen is the righteousness of saints." See also Rev. 19:14.
35. *Great-heart.* The minister, both as guide of his brethren and as *miles Christi.* See Introduction.
36. *Now 'tis dirty.* "The river of life is pure and clear as crystal. Is the doctrine offered to thee so? Or is it muddy and mixed with the doctrines of men? . . . What water is fouled is not the water of life, or at least not in its clearness." *Works,* III, 559.
37. *A breathing Hill,* i.e., one that is hard to climb, taxing the breath.
38. *A pelting heat.* Excessive heat; cf. *pelting rain.*
39. *A piece of Pomegranate.* See Deut. 8:8; Song of Sol. 4:13.
40. *Back the Lions.* Encourage them.
41. *Grim, or Bloody-man.* The lions symbolize the penal laws against nonconformists, and Grim stands for the civil power that enforces them. When Faithful passed, the lions were asleep, i.e., there was a short suspension of prosecution; but from 1681 to 1684, there was a renewal of persecution.
42. *They were had into a very large room.* Again an instance of Bunyan's emphasis on the communal life of the Saints. This episode represents the reception of new members of the

Church, and the partaking together of the Holy Communion ("a lamb").

43. *That Chamber that was my Husband's.* The name of it was *Peace.*
44. *A noise of Music.* A company of musicians. Cf. Shakespeare, *Henry IV,* Second Part, Act II, Scene 4: "See if thou canst find out Sneak's noise."
45. *Mr. Brisk.* Bunyan's use of the adjective *brisk* (cf., in the First Part, *a very brisk Lad . . . Ignorance*) makes clear the depreciatory connotation of the word. Cf. Samuel Butler, *Characters and Passages from Note-books* (Cambridge Univ. Press, 1908, p. 201): "A Brisk man—Pert . . . has nothing in him that is properly his own but confidence."
46. *Ill conditions. Conditions* is here equivalent to *characteristic attributes, qualities.* The *O.E.D.* quotes the Hayward translation of Giovanni Biondi's *Eromena* (1632): "Excellency of judgement . . . more . . . than any other condition whatsoever."
47. *I might a had.* I might have had.
48. *Cried her down at the Cross.* This refers to an old custom. A husband who refused to be answerable for his wife's debts had the fact published at the market cross.
49. *Maw.* Cf. Deut. 18:3—"They shall give unto the priest the shoulder, and the two cheeks, and the maw." The episode of Matthew's illness was selected by Alfred Noyes as an example of Bunyan's bad taste. The allegory is indeed crude but the humorous realism of the picture is a redeeming feature.
50. *Why doth the Pelican pierce her own Breast.* Bunyan refers to a traditional belief, which was not confined to the unlearned.
51. *A gold Angel.* An ancient gold coin.
52. *Let thy Garments,* etc. See Eccles. 9:8.
53. *Let Mercy live,* etc. Adapted from Moses' prayer for Reuben, Deut. 33:6.
54. This stanza is from Sternhold's version of Ps. 23:6.
55. From the Sternhold's version of Ps. 100:5.
56. *Desirous to be in.* Desirable to be in. The use of *desirous* for *desirable* was not unusual.
57. *Fat ground.* Cf. I Chron. 4:40—"fat pasture and good."
58. Bunyan was not a felicitous poet, but these lines are among the best he wrote.
59. *So let and hindered.* A familiar quotation from the collect for the fourth Sunday in Advent: "Through our sins and wickedness we are sore let and hindered in running the race that is set before us." *Hinder* and *let* were synonymous.
60. *Live and trace these Grounds. Trace* is equivalent here to *tread.*

61. *By-blows.* Side blows.
62. *Padding pace.* Running with steady, dull-sounding steps.
63. *The Earth with its bars.* Cf. Jonah 2:6—"the earth with her bars was about me for ever."
64. *There is not such pleasant being here as,* etc., i.e., it is not so pleasant to be here.
65. *Maul, a Giant.* The Roman Church.
66. *All-to-breaking. All* emphasized the particle combined with a verb, especially the prefix *to* (*asunder*). *All-to-broken* is thus equivalent to *quite broken in pieces. All-to* was extended to other verbs as the equivalent of *wholly, completely.* Bunyan wrote elsewhere in *The Pilgrim's Progress,* "she all-to-be fooled me."
67. *Smit.* Smote.
68. *Being to my determent.* Being a deterring circumstance.
69. *Most an end. On* end; almost uninterruptedly.
70. *He would give back,* i.e., draw back.
71. *For all he got before.* Although he got before.
72. *The Hammer.* An iron hammer, suspended by a chain, was often used as a knocker.
73. *Almost starved.* Dying a lingering death, as from hunger, cold, grief, or slow disease. The meaning of *starved* was extensive.
74. *He carried it wonderfully lovingly.* He behaved with wonderful love. Cf., below, *he carried it so towards him,* etc.
75. *Tracing.* Treading.
76. *Sackbut.* A bass trumpet with a slide like a trombone.
77. *Self-will.* A Ranter or Antinomian. The elect cannot sin. See *Grace Abounding* §§ 21 and 24, and § 45—"These [the Ranters] . . . pretending that they only had attained to perfection that could do what they would and not sin." Many a Ranter believed himself to be God; see Robert Barclay, *The Inner Life of the Religious Societies of the Commonwealth.* Similar heresies were not unusual in the Middle Ages. See W. Preger, *Geschichte der Deutschen Mystik.*
78. *High base! indeed.* An unnatural union of contraries.
79. *Gaius.* The name is borrowed from the New Testament. See Rom. 16:23, and St. John's Third Epistle, written to "the well beloved Gaius, whom I love in the truth." The brethren and strangers "have borne witness of thy charity"—III John 6.
80. *Dwelt first at Antioch.* "And the disciples were called Christians first in Antioch"—Acts 11:26.
81. Bunyan's information about the martyrs Ignatius, Romanus, and Polycarp comes from Foxe's *Actes and Monuments* (1563).
82. *He that was hanged up in a Basket in the Sun for the Wasps to eat.* Marcus of Arethusa.
83. *I will now speak on the behalf of Women.* Bunyan has often

paid tribute to women. Women played an important part in the Bedford church. See Note 50, *The Pilgrim's Progress,* First Part.

84. *A Heave-shoulder and a Wave-breast.* See Lev. 7:32, 34—"And the right shoulder shall ye give unto the priest for an heave offering of the sacrifices of your peace offerings. . . . For the wave breast and the heave shoulder have I taken of the children of Israel from off the sacrifices of their peace offerings." Lev. 10:14—"And the wave breast and the heave shoulder shall ye eat in a clean place."
85. *I conceited.* I thought.
86. *Mr. Mnason, a Cyprusian.* See Acts 21:16—"One Mnason of Cyprus, an old disciple, with whom we should lodge."
87. *Harbour.* Shelter.
88. *Mr. Mnason stamped with his foot.* It was thus that the servants in the kitchen below were summoned.
89. *A cumbered condition.* Encumbered; occupied obstructively.
90. *Has need of an Item.* Needs a hint.
91. *Much more moderate now,* i.e., since the Declaration of Indulgence of 1672, to which Bunyan owed his liberation.
92. *An Hospital for young children.* An institution for the education and maintenance of the young. Christ's Hospital (the Bluecoat School), founded in London, 1553, is one of the most famous of such institutions.
93. *A lesson.* A suite or sonata.
94. *The Palace door.* Bunyan's mistake. There was no palace on the Delectable Mountains when Christian was there.
95. *Washing of an Ethiopian.* A common emblem theme. See Rosemary Freeman, *English Emblem Book,* p. 216.
96. *A looking-glass.* The Bible. The image was drawn from James 1:23. See Bunyan's *Divine Emblems,* No. 39—"Unto this glass we may compare the Word."
97. *How many did Samson slay with the Jaw-bone of an Ass?* Judges 15:15.
98. *A man of his hands.* A man of action and courage.
99. *A Serpent.* Probably Apollyon, though he was not killed by Christian.
100. As Canon Venables has remarked, this charming poem reminds one of Amiens's song in *As You Like It.*
101. *Slabbiness.* Slipperiness.
102. *Beautified with Greens,* i.e., with verdure.
103. *Tinder-box.* A box in which tinder (prepared from partially charred linen or from corkwood fungus) was kept together with the flint and steel with which the spark was struck.
104. *His Book or Map.* The Bible.

105. *Blessed is the man that feareth always.* Cf. Ps. 115:13.
106. *Madam Bubble. Bubble* is used traditionally to designate something unsubstantial, empty, or worthless.
107. *Open places of Feasting. Feasting,* and not *cheating.* See note, p. 351, in R. Sharrock's edition.
108. *His name has been to me as a Civet-box.* Civet is an animal perfume. Cf. Shakespeare: "He rubs himself with civet"—*Much Ado,* Act III, Scene 2.

MERIDIAN BOOKS

published by The World Publishing Company
2231 West 110 Street, Cleveland 2, Ohio

LIVING AGE BOOKS

- LA1 AN INTERPRETATION OF CHRISTIAN ETHICS *by Reinhold Niebuhr*
- LA2 THE MIND OF THE MAKER *by Dorothy L. Sayers*
- LA3 CHRISTIAN MYSTICISM *by W. R. Inge*
- LA4 PRIMITIVE CHRISTIANITY IN ITS CONTEMPORARY SETTING *by Rudolf Bultmann*
- LA5 THE DESCENT OF THE DOVE *by Charles Williams*
- LA6 THE RELIGIOUS SITUATION *by Paul Tillich*
- LA7 WHAT MEAN THESE STONES? *by Millar Burrows*
- LA8 THE MEANING OF PAUL FOR TODAY *by C. H. Dodd*
- LA9 MARTIN LUTHER: ROAD TO REFORMATION *by Heinrich Boehmer*
- LA10 RELIGIOUS DRAMA 1: FIVE PLAYS *selected and introduced by Marvin Halverson*
- LA11 THE SOCIAL SOURCES OF DENOMINATIONALISM *by H. Richard Niebuhr*
- LA12 CHRISTIAN THOUGHT *by Ernest Troeltsch*
- LA13 LEAVES FROM THE NOTEBOOKS OF A TAMED CYNIC *by Reinhold Niebuhr*
- LA14 MYSTICISM EAST AND WEST *by Rudolf Otto*
- LA15 DOSTOEVSKY *by Nicholas Berdyaev*
- LA16 THE UNITY OF THE BIBLE *by H. H. Rowley*
- LA17 THE SERMONS OF JOHN DONNE *selected and introduced by Theodore Gill*
- LA18 A HANDBOOK OF CHRISTIAN THEOLOGY
- LA19 ETHICS AND UNITED STATES FOREIGN POLICY *by Ernest Lefever; introduced by Hans Morgenthau*
- LA20 RELIGIOUS DRAMA 2: MYSTERY AND MORALITY PLAYS *selected and introduced by E. Martin Browne*
- LA21 PETER: DISCIPLE, APOSTLE, MARTYR *by Oscar Cullmann*
- LA22 THE FAITH OF THE CHURCH *by Karl Barth*
- LA23 AN INTRODUCTION TO THE BOOKS OF THE OLD TESTAMENT *by W. O. E. Oesterley and Theodore H. Robinson*
- LA24 A SHORT HISTORY OF CHRISTIANITY *by Martin E. Marty*
- LA25 THE CULTURAL SIGNIFICANCE OF THE REFORMATION *by Karl Holl*
- LA26 ESSAYS IN APPLIED CHRISTIANITY *by Reinhold Niebuhr*
- LA27 RELIGIOUS DRAMA 3 *selected and introduced by Marvin Halverson*

LA28 RELIGION IN THE MAKING *by Alfred North Whitehead*

LA29 EXISTENCE AND FAITH: SHORTER WRITINGS OF RUDOLF BULTMANN *edited by Schubert M. Ogden*

LA30 REMBRANDT AND THE GOSPEL *by W. A. Visser 't Hooft*

LA31 GOD'S KNOTTY LOG: SELECTED WRITINGS OF JOHN BUNYAN *edited by Henri A. Talon*

LA32 THE PRIVATE DEVOTIONS OF LANCELOT ANDREWES *edited by F. E. Brightman*

MERIDIAN BOOKS

published by The World Publishing Company
2231 West 110 Street, Cleveland 2, Ohio

M1 ABINGER HARVEST *by E. M. Forster*
M3 ROUSSEAU AND ROMANTICISM *by Irving Babbitt*
M4 IMPERIALISM AND SOCIAL CLASSES *by Joseph Schumpeter*
M5 WAYWARD YOUTH *by August Aichhorn*
M6 THE PLAYWRIGHT AS THINKER *by Eric Bentley*
M7 THE PHILOSOPHY OF MODERN ART *by Herbert Read*
M8 CREATIVE INTUITION IN ART AND POETRY *by Jacques Maritain*
M9 OUTLINES OF THE HISTORY OF GREEK PHILOSOPHY *by Eduard Zeller*
M10 LANGUAGE AND THOUGHT OF THE CHILD *by Jean Piaget*
M11 SEVEN TYPES OF AMBIGUITY *by William Empson*
M12 ESSAYS ON FREEDOM AND POWER *by Lord Acton*
M13 THE MAN OF LETTERS IN THE MODERN WORLD *by Allen Tate*
M14 THE ORDEAL OF MARK TWAIN *by Van Wyck Brooks*
M15 SEX AND REPRESSION IN SAVAGE SOCIETY *by Bronislaw Malinowski*
M16 PRAGMATISM *by William James*
M17 HISTORY AS THE STORY OF LIBERTY *by Benedetto Croce*
M18 NEW DIRECTIONS 15: INTERNATIONAL ISSUE
M19 MATTHEW ARNOLD *by Lionel Trilling*
M20 SHAKESPEAREAN TRAGEDY *by A. C. Bradley*
M21 THE DEVIL'S SHARE *by Denis de Rougemont*
M22 THE HERO WITH A THOUSAND FACES *by Joseph Campbell*
M23 BYZANTINE CIVILIZATION *by Steven Runciman*
M24 ESSAYS AND SKETCHES IN BIOGRAPHY *by John Maynard Keynes*
M25 NIETZSCHE *by Walter Kaufmann*
M26 THE MIND AND HEART OF LOVE *by M. C. D'Arcy*
M27 CONGRESSIONAL GOVERNMENT *by Woodrow Wilson*
M28 TWO ESSAYS ON ANALYTICAL PSYCHOLOGY *by C. G. Jung*
M29 THE WRITINGS OF MARTIN BUBER *edited by Will Herberg*
M30 BERLIOZ AND HIS CENTURY *by Jacques Barzun*
M31 FREEDOM, EDUCATION, AND THE FUND *by Robert M. Hutchins*
M32 A PREFACE TO LOGIC *by Morris R. Cohen*
M33 VISION AND DESIGN *by Roger Fry*
M34 FREUD OR JUNG? *by Edward Glover*
M35 THE MAKING OF EUROPE *by Christopher Dawson*
M36 THE FORMS OF MUSIC *by Donald Francis Tovey*
M37 THE VARIETIES OF HISTORY *edited by Fritz Stern*
M38 THE ESSENCE OF LAUGHTER *by Charles Baudelaire*
M39 EXISTENTIALISM FROM DOSTOEVSKY TO SARTRE *edited by Walter Kaufmann*
M40 ITALIAN PAINTERS OF THE RENAISSANCE *by Bernard Berenson*
M41 SIGHTS AND SPECTACLES *by Mary McCarthy*
M42 MOHAMMED AND CHARLEMAGNE *by Henri Pirenne*

M43 THE WHEEL OF FIRE *by G. Wilson Knight*
M44 GOTHIC ARCHITECTURE AND SCHOLASTICISM *by Erwin Panofsky*
M45 FREUD AND THE 20TH CENTURY *edited by Benjamin Nelson*
M46 POLITICS AND THE NOVEL *by Irving Howe*
M47 A SHORTER HISTORY OF SCIENCE *by William Cecil Dampier*
M48 A GUIDE TO CONTEMPORARY FRENCH LITERATURE *by Wallace Fowlie*
M49 THE RENAISSANCE OF THE 12TH CENTURY *by C. H. Haskins*
M50 NEW POETS OF ENGLAND AND AMERICA *selected by Hall, Pack, and Simpson*
M51 ST. AUGUSTINE: HIS AGE, LIFE, AND THOUGHT
M52 CIVILIZATION ON TRIAL *and* THE WORLD AND THE WEST *by Arnold Toynbee*
M53 RELIGION AND CULTURE *by Christopher Dawson*
M54 PROUST: A BIOGRAPHY *by André Maurois*
M55 ST. THOMAS AQUINAS *by Jacques Maritain*
M56 MEMOIRS OF A REVOLUTIONIST *by Dwight Macdonald*
M57 DEBATES WITH HISTORIANS *by Pieter Geyl*
M58 POLITICS: WHO GETS WHAT, WHEN, HOW *by Harold Lasswell*
M59 GODS AND HEROES OF THE GREEKS *by H. J. Rose*
M60 RELIGION IN AMERICA *edited by John Cogley*
M61 MEN AND IDEAS *by Johan Huizinga*
M62 WITCHCRAFT *by Charles Williams*
M63 SCENES FROM THE DRAMA OF EUROPEAN LITERATURE *by Erich Auerbach*
M64 THE HUMAN MEANING OF THE SOCIAL SCIENCES *edited by Daniel Lerner*
M65 ARISTOTLE *by W. D. Ross*
M66 THE DISINHERITED MIND *by Erich Heller*
M67 THE BOOK OF JAZZ *by Leonard Feather*
M68 THE WORLD OF ODYSSEUS *by M. I. Finley*
M69 THE SCROLLS FROM THE DEAD SEA *by Edmund Wilson*
M70 GREY EMINENCE *by Aldous Huxley*
M71 THE LOGIC OF THE SCIENCES AND THE HUMANITIES *by F. S. C. Northrop*
M72 HISTORY 1
M73 ON MODERN POETS *by Yvor Winters*
M74 THE MAIN STREAM OF MUSIC AND OTHER ESSAYS *by Donald Francis Tovey*
M75 JONATHAN EDWARDS *by Perry Miller*
M76 THE CONFEDERACY *edited by Albert D. Kirwan*
M77 TALENTS AND GENIUSES *by Gilbert Highet*
M78 APES, ANGELS, AND VICTORIANS *by William Irvine*
M79 PAINTING AND REALITY *by Etienne Gilson*
M80 MOZART'S LIBRETTOS *translated by Robert Pack and Marjorie Lelash*
M81 PHILOSOPHY IN THE MIDDLE AGES *by Paul Vignaux*
M82 THE RECOLLECTIONS OF ALEXIS DE TOCQUEVILLE *edited by J. P. Mayer*